Human Evolution

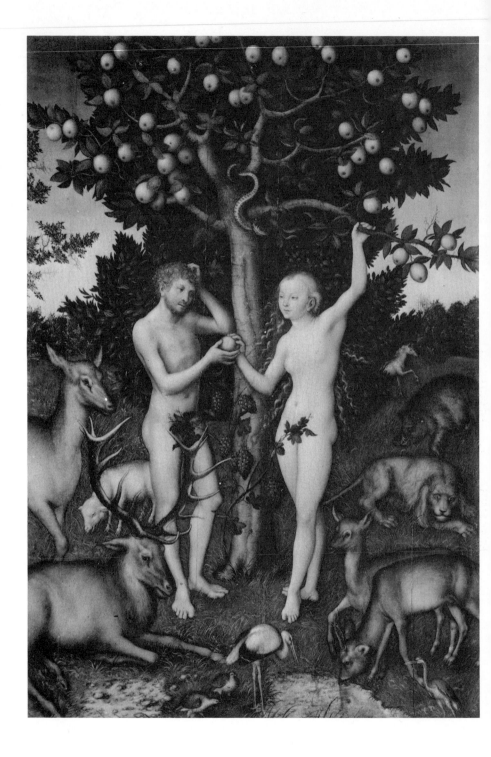

Human Evolution

AN INTRODUCTION TO MAN'S ADAPTATIONS

by Bernard G. Campbell

ALDINE PUBLISHING COMPANY / Chicago

First published 1966 by
ALDINE Publishing Company
320 West Adams Street
Chicago, Illinois 60606

Second printing, with corrections, 1967
Third printing, 1968

Library of Congress Catalog Card Number 66-15197
Designed by Bernard Schleifer
Printed in the United States of America

I hope to have convinced you that the zoological study of man, when grounded on a knowledge of his organization and functions, and enlightened by the analogies, the contrasts, and the various aids afforded by an acquaintance with the animal kingdom in general, is the only means by which a clear insight can be gained into human nature;—into the physical and moral attributes, the comparative powers, the liability to change or modification of the individual, the race or the variety, and consequently into the frame, capabilities, and destiny of the species.

W. LAWRENCE, *Lectures on Physiology, Zoology and the Natural History of Man* (London, 1819)

Preface

IN WRITING THIS BOOK I have attempted to gather under the title of *Human Evolution* a range of matter not normally included in texts of this kind. My object has been to try to expand our view of evolving man from skeletal and dental transformations to something more complete. While I have clearly fallen far short of describing the whole man, I have made a move to stretch the subject into one which requires knowledge of many different fields of biology. Though there are many gaps, I have attempted to define what I consider the proper study of human evolution.

My aim has been to make the book intelligible to readers with no previous knowledge of biology, but they will need a real interest to carry them through a text as dense as this. For those who are more advanced I have added references as well as reading lists so that they may pursue topics that may interest them. If the references appear thin in places, it is a reflection of the small number of papers that follow my own approach and interest.

My main object in quoting references has been to indicate sources of richer data than I have given; I have not attempted to justify my statements by this means or to acknowledge the sources of my ideas. The references do not therefore adequately indicate how much I owe to the work of my colleagues and predecessors: I owe them so much that to acknowledge them all would expand the book considerably. What I have written I do not claim to be original, but rather the freshly digested work of others.

Many of my colleagues have read parts of the text and to these

I record my grateful thanks: Theodosius Dobzhansky, Edmund Leach, Ernst Mayr, Kenneth Oakley, Colwyn Trevarthen, and Emile Zucker-kandl. The final typescript has been read and carefully criticized by C. R. Carpenter, F. Clark Howell, Stanley M. Garn, Gabriel W. Lasker, John Pfeiffer, David Pilbeam, Anne Roe, Elwyn Simons, and Sherwood L. Washburn. I have also received an immense amount of help with both text and figures from my publisher, Alexander J. Morin, who has made many invaluable suggestions. That is not to say, of course, that those who have helped me necessarily agree with either my intentions or my methods, but they have not hesitated to give me their own ideas and the benefit of their advice, and I am most grateful to them. Sherwood Washburn started this particular ball rolling, and I thank him, for I have enjoyed the game that ensued.

Acknowledgments

FOR THE PRIVILEGE of including quotations long enough to require special permission, grateful acknowledgment is made to the the following publishers: Aldine Publishing Company for permission to quote from A. H. Schultz, in *Social Life of Early Man,* edited by S. L. Washburn (Viking Fund Publications in Anthropology, No. 37, Chicago, 1961); Harper and Brothers for permission to quote from an article by C. J. Herrick in *Science* (1946); Longmans, Green and Company for permission to quote from W. R. Inge, *Outspoken Essays* (London, 1922); Princeton University Press for permission to quote from W. Penfield and L. Roberts, *Speech and Brain Mechanisms* (Princeton, N.J., 1959); the University of Chicago Press for permission to quote from A. I. Hallowell, in *Anthropology Today,* edited by A. L. Kroeber (Chicago, 1953); Yale University Press for permission to quote from L. Z. Freedman and A. Roe, in *Behavior and Evolution,* edited by A. Roe and G. G. Simpson (New Haven, Conn., 1958), and G. G. Simpson, *The Meaning of Evolution* (New Haven, Conn., 1949); the Zoological Society of London for permission to quote from an article by R. A. Dart in *Symposium of the Zoological Society of London* (1963).

Figures 6.16 and 6.17 have been redrawn from "The Evolution of the Hand," by John Napier, with special permission from W. H. Freeman and Company. Copyright © 1962 by Scientific American, Inc. All rights reserved.

For original drawings and for redrawings that involved original work, I have pleasure in thanking Diana Darke, Mrs. E. K. Frankl, Rosemary Powers, and Jo Reed. The frontispiece, "Adam and Eve," by Lucas Cranach the Elder, is used with the kind permission of the

Trustees of the Courtauld Institute Galleries of London. The other figures and photographs are cross referenced to the list of references, and I wish to express my appreciation to these authors and their publishers for allowing me to use their material.

Contents

INTRODUCTION: METHOD AND PLAN   1

Chapter 1. Evolution and Environment
1.1   Organic evolution   8
1.2   Natural selection and fitness   10
1.3   Genotype, phenotype, and the environment   12
1.4   Homeostasis of the individual   16
1.5   Behavior   19
1.6   Homeostasis of a deme   23
1.7   Evolution and progress   24
1.8   Environmental change and evolution rate   28
1.9   Organism and evolution—a summary   32

Chapter 2. Progress in Homeostasis
2.1   The origin and evolution of mammals   34
2.2   Homoiothermy   35
2.3   Mastication and heterodontism   40
2.4   Reproductive economy: prenatal   42
2.5   Reproductive economy: postnatal   48
2.6   Determinants of behavior   49
2.7   Man a mammal   52

Chapter 3. Primate Radiation
3.1   The origin of primates   55

3.2 The primates   57
3.3 Primate classification   59
3.4 Primate locomotion: arboreal adaptations   64
3.5 Primate locomotion: terrestrial adaptations   69
3.6 Neural correlates of arboreal locomotion   70
3.7 Neural correlates of binocular vision   74
3.8 Fossil hominids: candidates for man's ancestry   80
3.9 Summary   84

Chapter 4. Body Structure and Posture
4.1 Body structure and locomotion   86
4.2 Center of gravity   90
4.3 Evolution of the spine and thorax   92
4.4 The head and neck   97
4.5 The tail   104
4.6 Summary   106

Chapter 5. Locomotion and the Hindlimb
5.1 The generalized primate limb   108
5.2 The evolution of the pelvis   110
5.3 The hindlimb   123
5.4 The evolution of the foot   128
5.5 Summary   136

Chapter 6. Manipulation and the Forelimb
6.1 The mammalian forelimb   138
6.2 The pectoral girdle   140
6.3 The evolution of the upper arm   147
6.4 The forearm   152
6.5 The hands of primates   157
6.6 The evolution of the human hand   161
6.7 Man's ancestors as semibrachiators   166

Chapter 7. Feeding, Ecology, and Behavior
7.1 Functions of the head   168
7.2 Food-finding and diet   170
7.3 Taste and the tongue   174
7.4 The masticatory apparatus   176

7.5	The human jaw	181
7.6	Dentition: the incisors	187
7.7	Dentition: the canines	190
7.8	Dentition: the premolars	194
7.9	Dentition: the molars	196
7.10	Digestion	198
7.11	Ecology, diet, and behavior	200
7.12	Food and fire	204
7.13	Summary	207

Chapter 8. The Evolution of the Head

8.1	Factors determining head form	209
8.2	The masticatory apparatus and the head	210
8.3	The eyes	214
8.4	The nose	218
8.5	The ears	220
8.6	Changes in brain structure and function	222
8.7	The brain as a determinant of skull form	230
8.8	The face	235
8.9	The hair and skin	238
8.10	The human head	244

Chapter 9. Reproduction, the Family, and Social Structure

9.1	Reproduction and the placenta	246
9.2	Birth and infancy	249
9.3	Female sexuality	252
9.4	Male sexuality	256
9.5	Sexual behavior and copulation	257
9.6	Sexual dimorphism and secondary sexual characters	260
9.7	The life-span of man	265
9.8	Primate social life	271
9.9	The nature and evolution of the human family	276
9.10	The evolution of exogamy	281
9.11	The rise of human society	283

Chapter 10. Culture and Society

10.1	Culture	286
10.2	Percepts and concepts	292
10.3	Memory	298

10.4   Intelligence   300
10.5   Communication and speech   304
10.6   The evolution of speech   308
10.7   Social stability and social institutions   313
10.8   The evolution of ethics   318
10.9   The rise of the individual   321
10.10 Human behavior   323

Chapter 11. The Origin of Man
11.1   Ape or monkey?   326
11.2   The earliest hominids   328
11.3   Leaving the forest   331
11.4   The origin of man   335
11.5   The first men   339
11.6   The genus *Homo*   343
11.7   The rise of modern man   348
11.8   Modern man as a zoological species   351
11.9   Tools and technology—man's material culture   356
11.10 The function of modern culture   359
11.11 The dream animal   361
11.12 Human evolution   363

       APPENDIX   367

       REFERENCES   370

       GLOSSARY   384

       INDEX   411

Human Evolution

Introduction:
Method and Plan

SCIENCE DOES NOT claim to discover the final truth but only to put forward hypotheses based on the evidence that is available at the time of their presentation. Well-corroborated hypotheses are often treated as facts, and such a fact is that of organic evolution. If a hypothesis is fairly general in its presentation, it is difficult to test, but a detailed hypothesis like that of organic evolution is readily susceptible to disproof. The evidence for evolution is overwhelming, and there is no known fact that either weakens the hypothesis or disproves it.

As part of organic evolution, the phenomenon of human evolution also amounts to a fact, but as yet its detailed path is not known with much certainty. We shall not aim merely at showing that human evolution has occurred, for this has already been well demonstrated (see, for example, Le Gros Clark 1962 and 1964). My intention here is to examine what evidence we have available for the detailed path of human evolution, in an attempt to discover the origin of man. Such a detailed hypothesis as I have here presented is likely to prove a fallible achievement, but its fallibility will not altogether detract from its value. Not only does the presentation of such a hypothesis have a high heuristic value, but it is by the erection and testing of hypotheses that science progresses. They may indeed be tested and found wanting; science demands only that they should be consistent with the available evidence and as far as possible self-consistent.

With the heuristic as well as the scientific value of the exercise in mind, I have attempted to synthesize into a coherent account the evidence now available of the course of human evolution. This evidence is derived from two sources, from fossils and from living animals. When we examine the evidence carefully, however, we realize that neither source supplies directly pertinent facts, but inferences from both sources must be made as to what happened in time past. The evidence is always indirect; inference after inference must be made as to the course of the evolution of man. The whole truth will perhaps never be known, but that does not negate the value of making a hypothetical interpretation of what evidence we can lay our hands on.

Our interpretation of the evidence of human evolution rests on three kinds of inference:

1. A first inference, which lies nearest to the facts, may be obtained from a study of fossil bones and teeth. The evidence that these ancient fragments furnish is not *directly* relevant because we cannot tell whether or not any fossil actually belonged to a human ancestor. Indeed, such a coincidence would be unlikely for any particular fossil individual, but whether it be the case or not can never be known for sure. However, even if such fragments do not lie on the main stem of human evolution but are side branches, they can tell us something of the main stem from which they themselves evolved. Their relevance can of course only be understood in the light of the other evidence that we have at our disposal.

Studies of fossil bones and teeth tell us directly of the skeleton and dentition of the animals of which they were a part. We can, however, make a second inference from their structure, which will tell us more about the animal. We can make deductions about the size and form of the nerves and muscles with which they formed a single functional unit. Muscles leave marks where they are attached to bones, and from such marks we can assess the form and size of the muscles. At the same time, such parts of the skeleton as the cranium give us considerable evidence of the size and form of the brain and spinal cord.

2. Having built up a picture of at least some part of our fossilized creature, we can now make a further inference as to its whole biology and its way of life. In the first place, knowledge of its body will tell us something of its mode of locomotion (swimming, running, jumping, climbing, burrowing, etc.), from which it is not a long step to infer its environment (marine or fresh water, terrestrial or arboreal). At the same time, supporting evidence derived from a study of the geological

context of the fossil may confirm the presence in the prehistoric times when it lived of seas, lakes, plains, or forests. Another line of inference also begins with the teeth. These may suggest the diet on which the animal fed (herbage, roots, flesh, etc.), and here again we find some indication of how the animal lived. In this way, by rather extensive deductions, we can build up a picture of the whole biology of the extinct animals.

3. But these interpretations are based on one further and essential line of evidence, that of living animals. This third kind of inferred evidence, though rather remote, will prove of inestimable value. If we assume from the fact of evolution that all animals are related, it is reasonable to deduce that those most similar are most recently descended from a common stock. We must therefore compare the anatomy and physiology of living animals—and especially the monkeys and apes— with that of living man. This method can also be used to assess the closeness of relationship of different fossils. We can then assume that fossil bones most similar to any living animal are the remains of an ancestor of that animal, or a near relative of that ancestor. In turn, geological data that indicate the age of the fossil deposit will give us some idea of the succession in which the fossils lived. And we can make a further inference from the study of the comparative anatomy of living animals, for it is possible to predict within certain limits what a common ancestor was like, even in the total absence of fossils. Indeed, we can in that way infer the existence of ancient forms and from them infer their way of life.

In view of the methods of studying human evolution outlined above, it is not surprising that our concern will be mainly with bones and teeth, for they are the only parts preserved as fossils. But that is not as limiting as might be supposed, since the skeleton is the most useful single structure in the body as an indicator of general body form and function. The teeth, in turn, are very valuable in assessing the relationships of animals because their basic form is not affected by the environment during growth. It is, however, a feature of the present study to infer from the bones and teeth—by consideration of their function— the maximum possible amount about the body as a whole and the way of life of the animal. In that way we shall attempt to trace the evolution of the whole human being as a social animal. We shall move from a study of the evolving human body to consider evolving human behavior and human society.

In synthesizing evidence to discover the course of human evolution, we therefore draw on three kinds of data; we study living animals, fossil animals, and their geological age. At one point, we shall be comparing the living primates—man's nearest relatives—with man himself, to gain insight into their differences; at another we shall compare their structure with that of fossil remains of their ancestral relatives. The structure of this approach is shown in the accompanying diagram.

Human ancestors in linear sequence

The underlying argument should be clear at any stage. As we shall see in chapter 3, the living primates form a series, from the most primitive to the most advanced, which suggests a general trend of evolutionary development. We shall investigate that trend to see what light it can throw on the origin of man, who is the most advanced of all primates. On the basis of our varied evidence, we shall finally postulate how man may have evolved from his primate ancestor. Such a final inference of the origin and evolution of *Homo sapiens* will, as we have said, be valid yet hypothetical: it will always be subject to revision as new evidence becomes available.

The only way to infer the whole life history of an animal from a few fragments of bone is to investigate the function of those fragments. For example, the form of fossil shoulder and arm bones will be informative in that respect only if we try to find how the muscles were attached to the bones and compare them with those of living animals. We may thus be able to determine the difference in function of our fossil bones from that of the bones of living animals. Was this fossil shoulder joint the type associated with animals that walk quadrupedally upon the ground or with animals that hang by their forelimbs from trees? An answer to that question gives us immense insight into the whole life history of the animal, and such insight is gained from our knowledge of living animals.

This *functional* approach involves rather detailed study of the working of each part of the body—in particular the structural parts—and for that reason the method adopted in this book is to study the evolution of the different parts in turn. Such an approach presents considerable problems, however, since the body is a single complex mechanism, not a collection of discrete mechanisms. Any number of different "functional complexes" can be recognized, but every stage in the subdivision of the animal for descriptive purposes means a loss of truth. We must therefore examine a functional complex in its broadest possible interpretation.

The idea of a functional complex of characters is not new, and it is certainly the most informative and valuable way of analyzing the biology of an organism. According to that approach, therefore, the body is divided not into skull, dentition, trunk, arms, and legs but into the different parts involved in the different functions, which means, of course, that we must face a considerable overlap of subject matter in different parts of the book. It must also be stressed that the meaning of each great functional complex itself cannot be understood alone; on the contrary, even consideration of the whole physical body as a single unit is ultimately meaningless without consideration of its psychological and social correlates.

Function, in fact, which describes the structure and operations of an organism, is only half the study of biology. We must also be concerned with *behavior*, which describes how the organism interacts with the environment (which is everything other than the organism): how the organism actually receives its sensory input, and how it delivers its motor output. (The distinctions between function and behavior have been clearly made and discussed by Rosenblueth *et al.* [1943], and their short paper would make a useful introduction to this book.) The social and cultural behavior of man, which is the correlate of his complex functions, is in essence no more than an extension and development of the simple behavior of the smallest and simplest protozoa: it is the means of interaction between the organism and the environment that makes possible the function of the individual and the survival of the species.

Our study of human evolution will therefore be set forth as follows: We begin with an introductory chapter on the nature of evolution, followed by a survey of the background to human evolution—that is, mammals and man's nearest relatives, the primates (chapters 2 and 3). We then trace in detail the evolution of certain broad functional and behavioral complexes: posture, locomotion, and manipulation (chapters 4, 5, and 6); sense reception, feeding, ecology, and the head (chapters 7 and 8); reproduction and society, communication and culture (chapters 9 and 10). Finally, chapter 11 will review those different evolving complexes in a time sequence, and the last stages of the story of human evolution will there be told.

It should be said that the text does not include a complete account of primate anatomy or taxonomy at even the simplest level; such accounts should be consulted elsewhere (Le Gros Clark 1962, Napier and Napier 1966). Our consideration of anatomy will be limited to features that have evolved in such a way as to differentiate man from other primates and in so doing made man the creature he is. Our aim is at all times to build a picture that shows how primate biology was modified in the course of time into human biology. This study will show how the primate pattern of life associated with the forest was changed into a totally different pattern of life adapted to a different environment, our own.

In such a task and in an attempt to achieve consistency with recent research, an effort has been made to make this account of human evolution up to date by incorporating new ideas and data (often untested) in their appropriate places. Yet we have attempted to maintain a properly balanced picture; new research has not been included simply because it is new, and the reader may be disappointed to find scant reference to topical and controversial issues. What is of central importance is not the controversial problem of classification of fossil man but the anatomy and ecology that we can learn from fossil bones. If famous sites like Sangiran, Choukoutien, Sterkfontein, and Olduvai, from which our fossil evidence has come, receive only occasional reference, it is because we are not attempting a historical review of the science of paleoanthropology but a study of the paleontology of man. We must not, however, lose sight of our debt to the men who have discovered the relics of our ancestry, for they make possible the preparation of a book of this kind.

In spite of the contribution of archeologists, geologists, and paleontologists, our knowledge is still small. Crucial gaps in our account appear in every chapter, and we have not overlooked them. What we do not know is as exciting as what we do know, especially at a time like the present, when the subject is developing very fast. Let us hope that in ten years this account of human evolution will be thoroughly superseded.

Evolution and Environment

1.1 Organic evolution

WHEN, IN 1858, Charles Darwin and Alfred Russel Wallace published their theory of evolution by natural selection, they provided a rational and convincing explanation of the causes as well as the fact of evolution in plants and animals.

These two naturalists both traveled widely and had observed minutely the variation that clearly existed within each species. Members of species, they observed, are not identical but show variation in size, strength, health, fertility, longevity, behavior, and countless other characters. Darwin, in particular, realized that natural variation was used by man in the selective breeding of plants and animals, for, by selection, man would breed only from the particular individuals possessing the qualities desired by the breeder.

In due course, the key to how a similar kind of selection operated in nature to transform wild species of organisms came to both men, and it arose from the same source. The first edition of a book entitled *An Essay on the Principle of Population,* by an English clergyman, T. R. Malthus, appeared as early as 1798, and in that book the author showed how the reproductive potential of mankind was far in excess of the natural resources available to nourish an expanding population. Malthus showed that in practice the size of populations was limited by such lethal factors as disease, famine, and war and that such factors alone appeared to check what would otherwise be an expanding population.

Both Darwin and Wallace read Malthus' essay independently, and, remarkably enough, both men record in their diaries how they realized (in 1838 and 1858, respectively) that in that book lay the key to understanding the cause of the evolutionary process. It was clear to both that what Malthus had discovered for human populations was true for populations of plants and animals: their reproductive potential was vastly in excess of that necessary to maintain a constant population size. They realized that the individuals that in fact survived must for that reason be in some way better equipped to live in their environment than those which did not survive. Thus it followed that in a natural interbreeding population any variation would most likely be preserved that increased the organism's ability to leave fertile offspring, while the variations that decreased that ability would most likely be eliminated.

The theory that Darwin and Wallace formulated on that basis (at first, independently of each other) may be stated as four propositions and three deductions. Both propositions (P) and deductions (D) have since been well corroborated by careful observation.

P.1. Organisms produce a far greater number of reproductive cells, and, indeed, young individuals, than ever give rise to mature individuals.

P.2. The number of individuals in populations and species remains more or less constant over long periods of time.

D.1. *Therefore there must be a high rate of mortality both among reproductive cells and among immature individuals.*

P.3. The individuals in a population are not all identical but show variation in all characters, and the individuals that survive by reason of their particular sets of characters will become the parents of the next generation.

D.2. *Therefore the characters of those surviving organisms will in some way have made them better adapted to survive in the conditions of their environment.*

P.4. Offspring resemble parents closely but not exactly.

D.3. *Therefore subsequent generations will maintain and improve on the degree of adaptation realized, by gradual changes in every generation.*

As a result of the weight of evidence presented by Darwin in his famous book of 1859, *The Origin of Species by Means of Natural Se-*

lection, biologists became convinced of the value and truth of the theory of evolution that he and Wallace proposed. Since that date, scientists have closely investigated the processes involved in the different propositions and deductions, and geneticists have come to understand the mechanism that accounts for the origin of variation and the transmission of characters (see, for example, Dobzhansky 1940). Of direct interest to students of human evolution are the concepts involved in deductions 2 and 3, for, while the genetic processes of man are no different from those of the rest of the animal kingdom, the selective factors that caused human evolution were unique.

The directing force in evolution is natural selection, and we must satisfy ourselves as to exactly how selective action came to effect the evolution of mankind.

1.2 Natural selection and fitness

IT IS CLEAR that only a proportion of individuals in a population survive long enough to reach maturity and in their turn bear offspring. The environment itself determines the fate of each and, in destroying a proportion, selects the remainder. Through its effect upon each individual the environment controls to a decisive extent the direction and rate of evolution, and for that reason it may be considered to be one creative factor in the process of evolutionary change.

Although natural selection acts on individuals, it is the population that evolves, since the genetic plan of an individual is unalterable and remains constant throughout its life. A novel genetic plan arises only in the production of germ cells (*gametes*) and in the fusion of male and female germ cells in sexual reproduction. Not only are successive generations therefore necessary for the introduction of new gene combinations, but they are in fact the source of variation on which natural selection acts. This is not to deny the existence of evolution among animals and plants that reproduce asexually, but the sources of variation are more limited in them. In this book we shall consider only sexually reproducing animals.

A series of successive generations reproducing sexually relates individuals not only through the dimension of time but also in the dimension of space. Animals must find a mate among their contemporaries, and if they mate more than once in a lifetime (as most of them do), sexual relationships will be spread widely. Thus, the unit of evolution, the breeding population (the Mendelian population, or *deme*), includes all the individuals able to mate with each other. The size of the deme may vary, but it is the breeding unit, with its network of sexual relations, that evolves in the course of time.

The *fitness* of such a deme requires not only ability to cope with the existing environment and to reproduce but also the potentiality to evolve in the future in response to environmental change. This potentiality requires not only genetic stability (see 1.6), which reflects the broad stability of the environment, but also genetic variability (consequent upon sexual reproduction), which reflects the instability of the environment. That is to say, a deme cannot afford to vary greatly in a stable, competitive, and hostile environment, for random variation may be lethal; the deme must remain well adapted. At the same time, the deme must be able to change, evolve, in adaptation to environmental change. This necessary genetic stability, accompanied by flexibility in the form of adaptability, is the basis of Darwinian fitness, and the balance struck between these two factors determines how fit a population is.

The dynamic stability of all the genetic components of a population (called the *gene pool*) makes possible adaptation to the environment without losing the possibility of modifying such adaptation in the presence of environmental change in the future. The absence of such modification can result in extinction; a proper balance must be found between stability and flexibility, and it is an alteration in the form of this balance that, among other things, characterizes the evolution of man.

It is clear that every gene, every character of the individual, its anatomy, physiology, and psychology, contributes to the biological fitness of the deme, and it is in this sense and this sense only that a particular character is of evolutionary significance. There is no reason to suppose that any character can be neutral in this respect. Whatever characters evolve in a deme, it is the contribution that they make to the deme's fitness that results in their selection, in their survival. It is the deme that evolves, not the individual.

At the same time, since all parts of an organism require energy for their maintenance, any part that ceases to have a function will be rapidly lost in the process of evolution. Not only any part but any process will also be lost. As an example, color vision is believed to have been evolved by the reptiles and then lost in the very early period of mammalian evolution; it was evolved a second time in the evolution of the primates, but other mammals cannot see color because it has not been selected during their evolution. Thus we do not find characters without functions, a fact that may well apply to so-called vestigial characters; it seems probable that they have at least a reduced function.

The function of a character can therefore be understood fully only as an activity that is necessary and contributes to the overall reproductive advantage of the deme in which it has evolved. The function of any character that cannot be interpreted in that light cannot be said to be properly understood. It follows that in order to understand the evolution of man it is desirable to consider the function of each new character that was evolved and to discover how it bestowed upon the deme in which it became established a greater probability of survival in a changing environment.

How populations have survived by changing their nature is the story of evolution. The concept of fitness involves both adaptedness and adaptability, but, like evolution itself, though it may be elucidated in the past, it can only be surmised in the present.

1.3 Genotype, phenotype, and the environment

THE GENOTYPE of an individual organism is its heredity—the factors that determine the path that development may follow in different environments. The determinants are called *genes,* and they take the form of very complex chemical substances—in particular, that known as *DNA, deoxyribonucleic acid.* This substance, which forms immensely long chain-like molecules, is found in the nucleus (the controlling center) of every living cell. The DNA of the male and female gametes (the sperm and egg), together with some other genetic factors outside the nucleus, when combined in the egg cell, determine the form and structure of the new individual into which the egg cell will develop. From that time onward, as the egg cell divides many times, the DNA molecules are copied exactly, and similar copies lie within every cell of the growing individual's body. Once the genotype is determined at fertilization, therefore, it is fixed throughout the life of the individual organism. It is a highly condensed encoded bank of information, which during the development of the egg determines the kind of organism that the egg will grow into in a given environment.

The *phenotype* is the whole individual, the manifest characters of an organism, the discrete biological unit, the man himself or the worm. It is formed as a result of the living interaction of the genotype and the environment, an interaction called assimilation or growth. The phenotype is neither constant in form and structure nor permanent. Through its interaction with the environment, the genotype determines not only the phenotype's mature form (its *morphology*) but also its total growth pattern, that is, its form at all ages, together with its growth rate, its capacities, and its life-span. While the genotype is constantly copied in cell division, its form does not change, but the phenotype itself does change as it grows from an egg into old age.

Variation in the genotype occurs between generations as a result of sexual reproduction. In the process of fertilization, a single set of paternal genes is combined with a single set of maternal genes to produce a novel genotype. With the exception of identical twins, no two individuals of *Homo sapiens* are ever likely to be similar in spite of their vast numbers, so efficient is the shuffling of the pack of tens of thousands of genes that occurs in sexual reproduction. By combining different genotypes in fertilization, sexual reproduction is an essential source of genetic variation in evolution (see Dobzhansky 1940, 1962), and the process itself has been selected as a reproductive mechanism for that reason. It is through selective breeding that plant breeders can create such remarkable phenotypes as the hybrid roses we enjoy in our gardens. Created by sexual reproduction, they are in turn preserved by asexual vegetative propagation in which no further variation of the genotype can occur.

But, although sexual shuffling is of great importance, it is not the fundamental source of genetic variation. There is also the phenomenon of so-called "spontaneous" change in the genotype (*mutation*), which results from "imperfections" in its natural and ordered reduplication during cell division. This valuable and inherent "flaw" in genetic replication is most clearly seen in the production of the paternal and maternal gametes, when the paired gene sets of the normal body cells are separated. In this process of division, the DNA chains undergo stress, which very often results in chemical modifications. This kind of mutation is random and therefore is usually lethal, for no highly complex mechanism is likely to benefit from random interference.

Thus the mutations that allow survival of the gametes (let alone of the individual) and are subject to natural selection are themselves already selected by the need for internal coordination in the cell. This internal selective process therefore limits the kinds of mutations available to be selected by the environment (Whyte 1965). The nature of organic mechanisms is such that slight changes that might improve adaptedness are possible. Organic characteristics (for example, growth rate, body temperature, size, and so forth) vary continuously (not discontinuously, in jumps), so small adjustments in the mean or average form of these characters may be advantageous at any time in a changing environment. It therefore follows that spontaneous mutation, if of very slight effect on the phenotype, can be of value to an individual, and if it is, it may spread by the aid of sexual reproduction to a whole deme over a period of time. But the value of such mutations can be realized for the deme only by natural selection, the selective interfering effect of the environment upon the gene pool.

In practice, the environment can interfere with the genotype in three ways, which blend into each other:

1. Random interference from the environment is perhaps the least common. The most obvious example is the radiation that enters the earth's atmosphere from outer space and penetrates organic substance. It may be *mutagenic*; that is to say, it may cause mutations in the genotype of the cell that it penetrates. Should this cell be a gamete or newly fertilized egg cell, the radiation either may kill the cell or, by changing the chemical structure of one or more individual genes that do not lethally affect cell function, may cause an increase in variation in the gene pool. Atomic radiation is powerfully active in this way, and, although man-made and localized, its effects on the genotype are random.

2. Most of the other ways that the environment acts upon individuals are more or less selective, and they may be either lethal or sublethal. Lethal interference of a particular kind (for example, famine) may kill some kinds of individuals (for example, thin ones) more readily than others, and for this reason it will change the nature of the gene pool of the deme (individuals with reserves of fat are selected). Sublethal interference will also affect the nature of the gene pool if it

affects the reproductive capacity of any individuals as a result of a particular character they possess (for example, disease or displacement of the uterus may result in abortion). Such selective interference is enough to result in evolution, even if all the progeny survive; it is only necessary for them to vary in the rate at which they reproduce themselves.

3. Finally, the environment might interfere with a deme in a non-selective manner, though it would be hard to prove that any feature of the environment had absolutely no effect on the reproductive rate of an individual or a deme. The environment affects strongly the growth and development of individual phenotypes because they show a certain amount of developmental *plasticity* (see 1.4), yet this plasticity is itself sometimes adaptive and as such helps to insure a constant and high rate of reproduction in the face of environmental variation. The effect of the environment upon the gene pool will ultimately depend on the intensity of the interference (or "selection pressure," as it is usually called) and the degree of adaptation developed by the species in response to this pressure.

It should be noted that the individual (and, of course, the deme) will alter the environment to some small extent merely by its existence, but, while the genotype cannot change in the face of selective interference, the gene pool can and does. Such change is evolution; failure to change may result in the final extinction of the deme.

It must be recognized that as a correlate of the theory of evolution we recognize an element of competition that is invariably associated with organic life. Because organisms reproduce at a rate much higher than that necessary to maintain a stable population, there is always competition within a single deme for the available food and space. In this way, every individual changes the environment. Similarly, there is competition among demes of the same species, as well as among species. It is noteworthy, however, that members of a single species are in more immediate competition because they require the same food and habitat, and therefore they alter their own environment more than members of different species that are adapted to different ecological conditions (see Birch 1957).

Natural selection resulting from competition within species (intra-specific competition) is therefore as much a cause of evolutionary change as selection resulting from competition between species (interspecific). Intraspecific competition is a permanent feature of organic life, as is natural selection, and a noncompetitive situation cannot exist for more than an extremely short time because the reproductive potential of species is always greater than that which is required to maintain even an expanding population in times of beneficial environmental change. This intraspecific competition means in effect that the evolution of further adaptation may occur even when the overall external environment is fairly constant. And evolution within one deme will of course come to change the environment of its neighbors.

It is clear that the total interaction among individuals, demes, and their environment is intricate, and the totality of living plants and animals upon the earth's surface forms a dynamic system of great complexity. This complexity is seen to be immense when we consider further that among animals the connecting link between the environment and the phenotype is the medium of behavior, since what an animal *does,* as well as what it *is,* determines its ability to survive.

1.4 Homeostasis of the individual

BEFORE WE EXAMINE FURTHER the interaction of the deme and the environment, it is necessary to consider the interaction of the individual and the environment, in an attempt to understand how one is related to the other. An individual organism is a very delicate and complex living system and is clearly very unstable, since it can stand only limited outside interference; a momentary electric shock or shortage of oxygen may destroy the living system entirely. Its survival depends upon its property of self-regulation.

A living organism is a self-regulating dynamic system that maintains a more or less steady state or equilibrium, both within itself and between itself and its environment. Cannon (1932) has proposed the term *homeostasis* for the self-regulating property of organic systems. The particular character of an organic homeostatic system arises from the fact that it is an open system that depends for its continued existence on an energy supply obtained from the environment by chemical interchange yet at the same time must maintain itself as an integrated and discrete mechanism separate from the environment. Furthermore, the system is maintained throughout the growth and development of each individual, and during this period the whole cellular structure is being continually broken down and replaced as it matures. The same body in infancy and old age has little in common beyond its genotype and a dynamic system of a particular kind. Human personality, the continuing identifiable nature of an individual man, is an aspect of this system.

Cannon has described in his book *The Wisdom of the Body* (1932) how the homeostatic physiological mechanisms of man's body maintain what has been termed his "internal environment" at a constant level. He has described how the body maintains constant (within narrow limits) its water content, salt concentration, level of sugar, fat and protein in the blood, oxygen supply, temperature, and many other features of its organization. The efficiency of these systems is remarkable; for example, man can survive dry heat temperatures up to 128° C. without an increase in body temperature above normal (37° C.). Arctic mammals can similarly survive 35° C. below zero without a drop in body temperature. This particular homeostatic mechanism is, as we shall see, a property of mammals (and birds), and it is of the utmost importance in the story of human evolution. This kind of homeostatic mechanism enables an animal to survive changes in the external environment that otherwise would destroy its delicate chemical systems, changes it could not otherwise survive. Animals with a limited range of homeostatic mechanisms are limited to more or less constant environments; animals with a wide range of homeostatic mechanisms can occupy unstable environments and survive external conditions that in no way approximate their internal environments.

Thus marine organisms live in a relatively constant environment of water, containing salt, food, and oxygen. For deep-sea animals, changes in temperature associated with the seasons are negligible. In the course of the evolution of simple marine creatures into the terrestrial vertebrates, homeostatic mechanisms have been developed that maintain their internal environment so that it will approximate that of their marine ancestors. Every living cell of the body of mammals is bathed in a fluid called lymph. The composition of this watery matrix is kept constant by the diffusion of salt, proteins, sugars, oxygen, and other substances from the blood vessels. Thus we can survive dry heat and cold because the living cells of our bodies are preserved in a saline environment of constant temperature and unvarying composition.

The homeostatic mechanisms of mammals are numerous and complex; they may operate in such varied ways as, for example, sweating or sun tanning (the former lowers the body temperature; the latter lowers the penetration of ultraviolet light). Both these adjustments to hot, sunny weather are methods of coping with environmental change and, as such, increase the chances of survival of their possessors. Such internal adjustments, however, are not the only kind of homeostatic adjustment that is made, for the maintenance of the organism depends on chemical interchange with the environment. Thus a low water content will cause the sensation of thirst and lead to the drinking of water; a low oxygen content will cause an acceleration in the respiratory rate to increase oxygen intake from the atmosphere. Food is required to maintain sugar, fat, and protein levels. The sensations of thirst, breathlessness, and hunger are therefore aspects of the homeostatic mechanisms involved, and so in turn are the behavioral responses necessary to satisfy these needs. If there is not food, water, and oxygen in the environment surrounding the organism (as is the case for a flourishing colony of bacteria), the organism must go to them. Behavior, then, is part of the homeostatic mechanism because it is the process whereby animals satisfy their need to maintain their internal equilibria. Indeed, the maintenance of this steady state is survival, and animal behavior exists to that end (see 1.5).

Physiological homeostatic mechanisms are not the only means by which an individual maintains a steady state in its relationship with the environment. Another kind of homeostatic adjustment is discernible during individual growth and development; it is called, appropriately, *developmental homeostasis* and is a mechanism, as yet not fully understood, whereby the development of the phenotype seems to involve some self-regulating mechanism that maintains its integrity in the face of environmental variation (Mayr 1963, p. 220). Like any self-regulating mechanism, developmental homeostasis is based on a factor of stability (due to the genotype) and a factor of variability, which is the *plasticity* of the phenotype during its development. Examples of such plasticity are found among lower animals and plants more easily than among vertebrates, which have other methods of dealing with environmental change (that is, versatility of behavior). Yet the plasticity of individual vertebrate development is clear. For example, man's physique is affected by the kind of life he leads; muscles enlarge with use or atrophy as a result of disuse; fat deposition depends upon activity and climate as well as upon genes. The digestive processes can become adjusted to different diets, and jaw strength and size respond to the demands made upon the masticatory apparatus by the food. This kind of plasticity is a valuable character, which has evolved like any other and is under genetic control. The mechanisms of developmental homeostasis control the dynamic interaction between the genotype and the environment, so that the phenotype is enabled to survive changes in the environment during its growth.

1.5 Behavior

THE STUDY OF BEHAVIOR refers to what animals do in their interaction with the environment, and it is concerned to a great extent with the activity of locomotion. Broadly, it is concerned with how animals come into contact with their environment—how they breathe, how they touch and move upon the ground, how they eat the portion of the environment that constitutes food, how they escape from the portion that constitutes predators, and how they communicate with and copulate with the portion that constitutes their own species. "Behavior" describes the way that an animal is related to the environment, and much of the interaction between the phenotype and the environment occurs through the medium of behavior. Therefore, an understanding of the behavior of an animal is necessary for a full understanding of the interaction of a deme and its environment; such interaction must be studied in an analysis of the process of evolution.

How is animal behavior determined? That is a difficult subject, but some broad generalizations may be made as a basis for our discussion of the evolution of human behavior. In the first place, behavior, like morphology, arises as a result of the interaction between the genotype and the environment. The potentialities of all behavior patterns are genetically determined, but in the absence of a suitable environment a behavior pattern may not mature, just as an individual may not. Behavior that is thus determined, and in which learning plays no part, is usually called *innate,* and is well exemplified among insects. A most remarkable example of such behavior is found in the honeybee. Since it concerns a visual "language," it is of some interest to students of human evolution and will be referred to again in chapter 10. By a remarkably skillful piece of research conducted over many years, von Frisch (1950) has shown conclusively that a worker bee that has discovered a new source of food will, on returning to the hive, perform a dance on the face of the honeycomb. This dance has been shown to transmit information to other worker bees about the direction, distance, and nature of the food source and is a rare example of a descriptive language among animals. It is significant that it is found among one of the insects with a highly organized society. This descriptive information is in condensed, coded form and accurately enables other bees to find the flowers described. The bees' capacity for this very complex behavior pattern is innate, but, since it records variable information, it is determined in its details by the conditions of the external environment.

There is a great deal of variation among animals in the extent to which the environment determines behavior, but it is not so much the extent of this determination as the way in which the external stimulus is assimilated by the organism that is of interest here. In the case of dancing bees, or of any innate behavior, the environment influences each behavioral activity anew every time it occurs, obviously a necessity in the case of the bee dance in order that a correct report be given of each fresh discovery (see accompanying diagram, *left*). But among

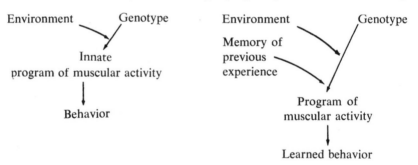

many other animals it is clear that the effect of the environment upon each action may be recorded in some way in the central nervous system so as to influence future action. In the latter case some degree of *learning* has occurred (see diagram, *right*). Behavior, then, can be either innate or, to varying extents, learned.

In practice it is difficult to draw a line between innate and learned behavior.* Even the lowly flatworms, with a much simpler internal

---

* The problem is that since innate behavior develops as a result of the interaction of internal and environmental influences, it is, like learned behavior, to some extent determined by the environment. For this reason the distinction is not clearcut, and the term *unlearned* is often preferred to the terms *innate* or *inborn*.

organization than insects, have been shown to be capable of benefiting from experience; but the more complex the animal is, the greater the part that learning appears to play in determining behavior. Among birds, for example, there is wide variation in the relative contribution of learning and inheritance in the development of the mature song repertory. Some birds develop their songs quite normally when reared away from their own species, while others develop abnormal songs when reared in this way. But, most commonly, broad characteristics are inherited and only the details are learned.

Such data have been gathered by separating birds from their kind, an experiment that cannot be performed easily with mammals, because so much behavior is learned that growth is deeply disturbed in the absence of a mother and it is impossible to isolate the effect of deprivation upon any particular behavior pattern. But, even in the absence of relevant experimental data, it is clear that in nearly all the behavior of the higher mammals there is an element of learning, and it may be very great. Genes supply the capacity for behavior of different kinds, together with some basic components that help form the full behavior pattern; learning makes possible this full pattern of activity. For example, studies of bird song suggest that genes make possible the capacity to sing and, especially, to sing certain notes and trills; the actual pattern of the song is, however, usually learned.

Clearly, both innate behavior and learned behavior have their advantages. Behavior that is innate obviates the need for learning processes that may involve danger and saves time and energy on the part of the animal. On the other hand, it is not flexible and in a fast-changing environment could be disastrous for the species, since it could be changed only by the slow processes of variation and natural selection. Learned behavior, on the other hand, is expensive in time and danger but is much more flexible and allows readaptation to occur in every generation. Just as evolution results from the interaction of factors causing variability and stability, so behavior has this dual character. Heredity makes behavior patterns more or less stable (though subject to evolution), while learning introduces a flexibility that may be of great survival value.

There are three different ways of learning: by trial and error, by imitation, and by instruction. The trial and error method is found in all

---

The term *instinct* has also been used with this meaning, but with many others as well: for this reason it is not used here.

animals that can learn and is the sole means of learning in invertebrate animals. Compared with other methods, it is lengthy and dangerous. It is the method usually referred to in discussions of learning and in experiments testing learning ability. For example, rats can learn their way through a maze by trial and error (just as humans can) so long as some reward is offered. The rate at which learning can take place by this method has been used as a rough indication of the degree of complexity evolved in the central nervous system (Rensch 1956). Learning by trial and error reaches its highest development in mammals. As a method, it is highly flexible and adaptable to environmental change, and therefore it has been evolved to a remarkable extent among some groups of mammals—particularly among the primates.

Learning by imitation is, however, a speedier and more sophisticated means of building up behavior patterns. Imitation depends in the first place on the ability of an animal to recognize and copy another member of its species, usually its mother. Such recognition is not often found among lower animals, except when necessary for purposes of copulation. Imitation is a short cut to learned behavior, but it introduces a certain inflexibility in the behavior pattern that is not found in trial and error learning and is therefore more valuable when behavior is concerned with the more constant features of the environment. Rats can learn to pass through mazes more quickly than by trial and error alone if they are allowed into the maze, during a learning period, with other rats already trained in the art. Many birds learn their song repertories almost entirely by imitation. Monkeys and apes also learn a great deal in that way, and children learn still more (and faster). During the early stages of human development, imitation is the most important factor in developing behavior patterns.

Instruction is, of course, a uniquely human way of creating behavior patterns, for it involves conscious thought and intent. It is the means of learning that is essential to the development of culture yet is dependent upon culture for its existence (see chapter 10).

There is another and very different determinant of behavior that has not yet been mentioned; it may be termed "intelligent thought." It is in all probability a uniquely human characteristic and so is a novelty of great importance in man's evolution. Action determined by intelligent thought may draw on learning but is itself not the result of a learned behavior pattern; it is original. It is discussed in more detail in section 10.4.

With its three determinants—heredity, learning, and intelligence—the study of behavior is highly relevant to the study of human evolution, for the evolution of behavior itself has played a vital role in the evolution of man. In the following sections we shall see more clearly the importance of the less easily detected changes in learning and behavior; we must study them as well as the more obvious changes in anatomy and physiology that characterize our evolution.

1.6 Homeostasis of a deme

JUST AS THE physiological and behavioral mechanisms that we have discussed maintain a steady state in each individual organism during its lifetime, so there are mechanisms that maintain the steady state of the whole deme over long periods of time, keeping an equilibrium between it and the environment.

The environment is always changing, and, at the same time, natural variation in individuals from generation to generation will tend to cause random changes in the average characteristics of a deme. Living populations are homeostatic in the face of both these kinds of variation insofar as they remain in a relatively steady state in spite of constant environmental and genetic change. This phenomenon has been termed *genetic homeostasis* (Lerner 1954). Such a mechanism will maintain an equilibrium between the deme and the environment and will thus tend to insure the survival of the deme. Gross and long-term environmental change will result in a homeostatic readjustment on the part of successive generations of the population.

For example, the fittest mean weight and size of a species in a more or less constant environment will be maintained in the face of individual variation. Natural selection will cut down the reproductive rate of the more extreme variants and will thus operate to maintain this character constant. On the other hand, a gross change in external conditions (such as increased food supply resulting from climatic change) may affect what is the fittest weight, and so a homeostatic adjustment will be made to a new mean weight (probably larger) that is homeostatic, in this case not for individuals but for the deme. Such an adjustment constitutes evolution and fulfills Dobzhansky's definition (1940) of evolution as a systematic change in the genetic structure of the deme.

Such a change is termed an *adaptation*—an adaptation to changed environmental conditions. This, then, is evolution by natural selection: shifts in the mean of existing variable characters, called adaptations, yet entirely passive as far as the population is concerned. For example, even one unusual season (an extreme drought or a very hard frost) can, by killing animals and plants, almost instantly cause shifts in the mean of the physiological characters of the populations to which they belonged. New mutations are not necessary for such changes, but variability is essential both for change and for survival.

We see, then, that at the level of both the individual and the deme, homeostatic mechanisms are operating to maintain a steady state. This steady state is the means of survival, and the maintenance by evolution of a means of survival is the property of living organisms. From this point of view, the phenotype is relevant only insofar as it secures the survival of the genotype.

Many different kinds of phenotype have in fact survived, and it is of interest to consider whether any one form of survival mechanism is in any way better than another.

1.7 Evolution and progress

THE NATURE OF EVOLUTION has been indicated by the foregoing discussion. *Evolution* is an adjustment on the part of a deme to maintain itself in the face of a change in its environment. There is no force operating within individuals that causes evolution, nor are systematic changes in the genetic structure of a deme necessarily "advances" on the *status quo*; they are attempts to maintain that status. Some changes may prove retrospectively to result in more success than others, depending entirely on the definition of success in a particular context.

The idea of progress and the idea of evolution are, however, not unrelated. The idea of progress was hardly in existence three hundred years ago, for, like evolution, it was, above all, a nineteenth-century concept. Evolution has formed mankind from the primeval ooze, so it is clearly in one sense progressive—progressive from man's viewpoint. But the view *sub specie aeternitatis* is very different. Here is a process, operating in time, which has produced a whole range of living organisms, from bacteria to men. While there has been, on the one hand, a trend toward size and complexity, the smaller and simpler forms of life have at the same time survived and evolved in great variety and numbers. The plant kingdom as a whole has achieved a dominant position without the evolution of a nervous system or musculature. Man's greatest competitors in the world today are not other mammals but minute and relatively simple viruses, bacteria and protozoa. As Inge has written:

> The progressive species have in many cases flourished for a while and then paid the supreme penalty. The living dreadnoughts of the Saurian age [the ruling reptiles] have left us their bones, but no progeny. But the microbes, one of which had the honour of killing Alexander the Great at the age of thirty-two, and so changing the whole course of history, survive and flourish [1922, p. 166].

Evolution, as a process, can hardly be described as progressive in the usual sense of that word; it is characterized by change (not necessarily involving improvement), the sole function of which is survival. It is in that case reasonable and much more valuable to examine the process from man's viewpoint in order to discover whether man is in any sense progressive compared with the rest of the animal world. In what sense is man an improvement upon other animals?

The success of a species can be measured in terms of its numbers, or the gross weight of its *biomass* (the total mass of all its individual members); it can be judged in terms of its stability in time, its variety of adaptations, or its geographical range. Man is in fact actually increasing his total biomass, at present, faster than any other organism, yet that can hardly be called a sign of real progress, since we know it to be both undesirable and dangerous. Other species have had population explosions, so even if man excels in such characters, they do not explain his special evolutionary position. If we look at man himself, we see, for example, that he is very complex (especially his nervous system) and self-conscious (which is probably unique in the organic world). He has also intentionally altered his environment. But again we cannot be sure that it is necessarily progressive to be complex, or to be self-conscious, or to alter the environment. Any of those characters could prove disastrous to their possessor, and they may do so to mankind. But their combination does reflect one single evolutionary trend in which man appears to be progressive: man has an improved homeostatic response to environmental change, or, as Herrick (1946) puts it, progressive evolution is "change in the direction of increase in the range and variety of adjustments of the organism to its environment." (See Simpson [1949] for further discussion of evolutionary progress.)

Let us examine the mechanism of homeostasis further in order to discover how such an improvement may have come about. A homeostatic mechanism consists basically of three parts: (1) the receptor, which measures the status of the environmental character that the mechanism controls (for example, the hypothalamus at the base of the brain senses the temperature of the blood, as described in chapter 2); (2) the controller (or mediating mechanism), which acts when the signal from the receptor indicates a need for an adjustment (again, in our example, it is the hypothalamus); and (3) the effector, which the controller causes to correct the deficiency or excess (in our example, the effectors are various and cause shivering, sweating, etc., as described in chapter 2). Their interaction can be summarized as shown in the accompanying diagram.

Receptors that sense the status of the internal environment are of course internal, and they usually are to be found in the brain itself. The survival value of response to changes in the external environment (for example, absence of food) has resulted in the evolution of the sense organs or sense receptors (which in our example can detect food chemically or visually). The evolution of such receptors makes possible response to the external environment, but by themselves the sense organs are not sufficiently accurate as generators of input to allow very precise homeostatic adjustment. For example, the very simple eyespot of certain single-celled animals is able to detect the direction of light sources, but it required not just the eye but the vertebrate visual system as a whole to recognize distinct shapes within the overall visual pattern of the environment. Thus the evolution of the sense organs must be accompanied by the evolution of analytic mechanisms in the brain that can differentiate between different intensities and patterns of stimulus. The evolution of such a refined input mechanism has been accompanied by the evolution of appropriate controllers and effectors.

With the early mammals we find not only the full range of sense organs that we ourselves have, which respond to changes in the external environment, but also the full range of internal homeostatic mechanisms already mentioned (see 1.4) and described by Cannon (1932). But during the more recent stages of human evolution, during the primate stage, we find the development of a more or less new kind of general-purpose controller—the cerebral cortex of the brain—and a rather general-purpose effector—the versatile trunk and limbs, which made possible a wide range of behavior. In this study of human evolution we shall place great emphasis on this new kind of homeostatic mechanism, which is not specific but is generalized and versatile. It takes the outward form of learned and intelligent behavior.

Thus we see in human evolution that increased homeostatic response is based on (1) broad sense reception with very detailed analysis of input, (2) a general-purpose controller, the cerebral cortex, and (3) much increased versatility of the behavior effector, the muscles and bones by which the limbs and body move.

It is in this respect that man can claim to be an improvement over other animals: his sensory input supplies far more data about the environment than does that of other animals, and his effector organs make possible a greater range and greater versatility of behavioral activity. The evolution of the large brain is the necessary concomitant of this extended interaction with the environment.

How do we reconcile the recognition of improvement in human evolution with the definition given at the beginning of this section? The answer is that evolution involves two kinds of adaptation. The first and simplest is an adjustment by existing homeostatic mechanisms (different mean weight, different salt concentration, different coloration). The second and the more complex is an alteration in the functional homeostatic systems themselves. For example, in the evolution of many internal parasites, such as the tapeworm, various functional homeostatic mechanisms have been lost because the present external environment (the body of another animal) is more constant than that in which the tapeworm originally evolved as a free-living organism. On the other hand, the evolution of the temperature-regulating mechanism in primitive mammals was something altogether new and certainly progressive, since it gave mammals improved homeostasis and so a greater independence from environmental change. Since the appearance of mammals, further improvement in homeostasis has arisen from behavioral rather than physiological mechanisms. Man's body in its structure and function is very similar to that of other mammals; his difference from them lies in his behavior and the mechanisms determining it. Such differences are far-reaching because the environment in which man evolved has itself changed drastically.

1.8 Environmental change and evolution rate

ENVIRONMENTAL CHANGE is the prime determinant of homeostatic adjustment in the gene pool of organic populations. Environmental change may take a great variety of different forms, but its ultimate cause is change in the earth's climate. Not only will a long-term climatic change in a geographical region directly affect every single living organism within that region, but every organism will be indirectly affected by the change in every other organism that the change in climate causes. For example, a lowering of rainfall in a particular region will have the effect of changing the vegetation from plants adapted to a relatively high rainfall to plants adapted to a relatively low rainfall. Such a change will immediately affect all herbivorous animals, which may be unable to find enough of their usual food plants. If they survive, such animals will have adapted their behavior and digestive processes to the new food plants that become dominant; alternatively, they may become extinct. In turn, their carnivorous predators will be affected. Change in rainfall may also, for example, affect the transmission and occurrence of parasites, for they may depend on damp conditions to survive the period of transmission between their host animals or plants. Drinking water will perhaps become scarce, and animals may survive only by an adaptation in their water-storage capacity requiring only one visit to a water hole per day.

It is clear that a single change in one feature of climate may have very complex and far-reaching effects on the whole nature of the environment. Homeostatic adjustment among the different populations of plants and animals may be a lengthy process, for every change in one species will affect the environment and in turn effect change in every other. In stating therefore that the ultimate cause of environmental change is a change in climate, we refer to the whole causal chain of adjustments that result from a change in the prime features of the earth's environment; the level of solar radiation, the nature of the earth's crust and atmosphere, and the earth's rotation, for these features determine climatic change.

Evolution, which is the resultant of genetic variation and environmental change, can therefore occur in the following ways.

1. In a more or less constant environment, a population may evolve better adaptation to it. Such evolution may, however, be limited in extent and will presumably follow a change in the environment.

2. From such a more or less constant environment, a population (usually part of an existing population) may move into a neighboring and different environment to which it may prove to be already to some extent adapted. New adaptations may then follow.

3. The environment may change, and the population may adapt to the change. That is of course the most common situation; it results in situation 1 and very often causes the kind of animal migrations that result in situation 2. It is, however, worth noting that environmental change may not necessarily result in evolution, since, if the change takes the form of movement of climatic belts on the earth's surface, the fauna may move with the belts, so no new adaptation is necessary. Such a situation would be particularly likely in animals like monkeys or the herbivores of the plains, which are highly mobile and would move within shifting climatic belts without any modification in their way of life.*

The rate of evolution must in turn be related to its two causative factors, genetic variation and environmental change. Environmental change is the prime determinant of the evolution rate, but in times of fast change the maximum rate will depend upon the amount of genetic variation available from mutation and the sexual shuffling of genes. How is the mutation rate itself determined? It varies considerably among different animals and plants, and it seems most probable that

* It has been claimed that a change in gene frequency resulting not from selection by the environment but from random genetic variation in small populations (known as *genetic drift*) can result in significant evolutionary change. Evidence for that claim is, however, slight, and the matter does not require further discussion here (Mayr, 1963, p. 214). This does not mean, however, that we understand the selective factors that have caused the evolution of every character of living species.

the rate is selected in evolution like any other character. A fast rate will allow fast evolution yet will give a higher ratio of ill-adapted members in a stable population. A low rate will allow well-adapted conformity in a deme, yet in times of environmental change a slow rate might inhibit sufficiently fast adaptation to permit survival. Like every other character, the mutation rate of a deme is adapted to the environment, and in particular to its overall rate of change. Genetic stability and variability, as we have seen, are important features of biological fitness (1.2).

It is possible that both climatic change and genetic variability may be simultaneously affected by one and the same factor, the level of cosmic radiation. An increase in such radiation could possibly speed up the rate both of climatic change and of genetic mutation. The significance of this suggestion is hard to assess at present, but its importance may well become clear when we understand better the causes of the remarkable climatic changes that have occurred during the earth's history, and in particular those which rapidly changed the climate during the most recent geological period, the Pleistocene, when *Homo sapiens* finally evolved from his more primitive ancestors.

The extent to which a deme is adapted to a particular environment is termed its degree of *specialization*. As we shall see, some primates are more highly adapted to arboreal life, are more specialized in this respect, than others. Their degree of specialization can be seen as their degree of commitment to their environment: highly specialized species may not survive environmental changes that less specialized species might survive. Specialization in fact seems to cut down the possibility of further evolution, and, in the long view, highly specialized groups can be seen to have been all too often doomed to ultimate extinction when gross changes in the earth's environment have occurred. From the point of view of survival, therefore, a species must remain fairly generalized in its overall character; specialization may ultimately involve extinction—and indeed it has usually done so.

There is, however, one remarkable way out of the dilemma, and from our position of hindsight we can see that it has been followed on a number of occasions. It is a process that effects despecialization and is called *neoteny* or *pedomorphosis*. The process operates somewhat as follows: we can suppose that the adult form of an individual is determined by two sets of genes; the first determines the adult characters, and the second determines the rate of growth and time of onset of sexual maturity. Since specializations must be present in the adult stage, they usually appear during growth and are determined by the first set of genes. The second set of genes establishes the permanent adult form by its power to time the onset of sexual maturity. By speeding up the onset of sexual maturity, the adult form may become established before all the specializations can be fully developed. The animal becomes sexually mature when in the young stage; the result is a very remarkable evolutionary change, which is due to a very simple alteration in growth pattern. The phenomenon, discussed by De Beer (1954), has been an important factor in evolution, and perhaps the most famous instance is the evolution of the chordates (the ancestral group of the vertebrates) from the echinoderms (the sea urchins). We have evidence that the primitive chordate evolved from a creature like the larva of a sea urchin that had become sexually mature. There is no doubt that the adult echinoderms are a very unusual and specialized group, which could not possibly evolve into chordates, yet by the process of neoteny that specialization is believed to have been cast off, with the result that there appeared what amounted to an altogether different kind of animal of unspecialized form—the sexually mature echinoderm larva.

Thus neoteny gives evolving groups a way out of the dead end of overspecialization, and, with limited mutations affecting mainly growth rate and time of maturity, it can result in a saving generalization of form. As might be expected, there is evidence that such a development is a frequent evolutionary phenomenon and that it has played some part in the evolution of man himself. While the process in no sense accounts for the evolution of man, nor does it account for all his characters, there is no doubt that a great many characters considered typically human are present in the early stages of the development of primates and that they have been retained in man by retardation in the growth rate of certain parts of the body. Two examples will suffice: the limited body hair of *Homo sapiens* and the fair skin of certain races may be the result of the arrested development of the hair follicles and the melanin cells, respectively. A list of man's neotenous characters is given by Montagu (1962), who discusses this interesting phenomenon.

If we do not again refer to this phenomenon, it is because it does not relate to human adaptations themselves but only to the developmental and genetic means by which certain changes have occurred. All evolution is due to developmental and genetic changes, and the character of neoteny is of particular interest only because it is a shortcut to drastic change through change in growth rate, without change in form-determining genes. It is also likely that mutations affecting growth rate and the timing of the onset of sexual maturity are less likely to encounter the effects of internal selection (see 1.3; Whyte 1965) than are those affecting structure, because the former threaten less fundamentally the harmony of the whole organism. Though the phenomenon of neoteny gives evolving species a way out of the trap of overspecialization, it does not require us to change our ideas about the action of natural selection and the process of evolution.

1.9 Organism and evolution—a summary

THE ORGANISM can be described as a self-regulating, self-reproducing open system that passes vital information (coded in DNA molecules) to copies of itself. It can be considered to be of two parts: the genotype, which consists of the informational nuclear molecules of DNA within each cell of the individual, and the phenotype, which is the whole individual formed by the genotype through its interaction with the environment.

The genotype interacts with the environment through a causal chain of which the phenotype and its behavior are the connecting links. This interaction maintains the genetic homeostatic equilibrium of the individual and deme that is necessary for its survival. The individual phenotype system maintains the physiological and developmental equilibrium of the internal environment for the preservation of the genotype.

Reproduction by the fusion of gametes from different individuals creates in time a network of sexual relations between individuals that constitutes the interbreeding population or deme. In the formation of the gametes, variation arises in the information store of the DNA, and thus gives variability to the deme and makes possible changes in it. Both the extent of variation at a given moment (which is ultimately related to the mutation rate) and the long-term alterations in the gene pool (which constitute evolution) are controlled by natural selection, which is the process whereby the reproductive capacity of individuals not well adapted to the environment is depleted by environmental interference. The change in the deme brought about by changes in the environment (which constitute selection pressure) can be described as adjustments made in the deme that serve to maintain a homeostatic equilibrium between it and the environment. Because living processes are so unstable and delicate, such equilibria must be maintained at all times for the survival of life.

Progress in human evolution is seen as the appearance of new homeostatic mechanisms that make possible survival in the face of ever greater environmental variation. The mechanisms themselves increase in turn the complexity of the genotype and phenotype. Progressive evolution in any but an anthropocentric sense cannot be recognized. Evolution is merely a homeostatic adjustment in the mean or average characters of a living system in response to environmental change and can be the outcome only of such adjustment and nothing more. By a study of the anatomy, physiology, behavior, and environment of living organisms related to man, it is possible to learn how human nature was formed and to attempt to understand how each character of our species serves its survival.

SUGGESTIONS FOR FURTHER READING

There is a vast literature on all aspects of evolution, although the concept of homeostasis has not been greatly stressed until recently. For general reading see G. G. Simpson, *The Meaning of Evolution* (New Haven, Conn.: Yale University Press, 1949). For a more technical treatment see E. Mayr, *Animal Species and Evolution* (Cambridge, Mass.: Harvard University Press; London: Oxford University Press, 1963). For a treatment of genetics and the general biology of human evolution see T. Dobzhansky, *Evolution, Genetics and Man* (New York: John Wiley & Sons; London: Chapman & Hall, 1955), and *Mankind Evolving* (New Haven, Conn., and London: Yale University Press, 1962). For studies of the relationship of behavior and evolution see A. Roe and G. G. Simpson, *Behavior and Evolution* (New Haven, Conn., and London: Yale University Press, 1958).

Progress in Homeostasis

2.1 The origin and evolution of mammals

IN TRACING THE origin of man it is not our concern here to describe in detail the part of his evolutionary history that he shares with other mammals. Our interest lies rather in the most recent stage of his evolution, in which his own particular nature was evolved. It would, however, be a serious omission to neglect to mention the features that, although shared with other mammals, are the absolutely necessary basis for the evolution of an organism as complex as a human being. The evolution of man cannot be fully understood without some consideration of the main features of his class, the Mammalia.

Mammals are separated by zoologists into three subclasses, the monotremes (such as the platypus), the marsupials (such as the kangaroo and opossum), and the placentals. The first two groups are limited today both in species and in range, and, although they may have had a period of temporary dominance in the past, they were very soon superseded by the placental mammals—the group to which man belongs. Although what follows applies in part to the two primitive subclasses, we shall concern ourselves from now on with the great *radiation* —the evolutionary divergence and dispersal—of the placental mammals.

While the characters of mammals are poorly recorded in the fossil record, consisting as they do for the most part of soft tissues, the fact that certain characters are common to such a large and varied group of organisms suggests that they were evolved by a common ancestral lineage. Paleontologists see the origin of the mammals from reptiles of the Triassic period, and by Cretaceous times the main orders of the placental mammals were established (Table 2.1 and Fig. 2.1).

Mammals are characterized by evolutionary novelties of the utmost importance to the story of human evolution. The characters that relate mammals to each other and separate them from other groups, such as birds and reptiles, are very numerous indeed, yet they arise from the evolution of only four great complexes, all of a homeostatic nature. These four complexes can be seen in turn to contribute to a single adaptive development, which made it possible for this most remarkable class of animals to succeed the mighty reptiles that had previously dominated the earth, yet which shared with the mammals a common origin. This all-important adaptation was the ability for constant and lively activity: the maintenance of a steady level of activity in the face of basic changes in the external environment. From being dependent, like reptiles, upon the external temperature with its daily and seasonal rhythms, mammals were enabled by the evolution of new homeostatic mechanisms to remain active at any time.

The four adaptive complexes that made this constant activity possible will be considered in turn: homoiothermy, mastication, improved reproductive economy, and new ways of determining behavior.

2.2 Homoiothermy

THE CHEMICAL REACTIONS that underlie homeostasis and constitute the process of living, like any other chemical reactions, can generally occur more quickly at a higher than a lower temperature, but such a temperature should not be so high as to cause breakdown in the relatively unstable organic molecules. At the same time, a constant body temperature makes possible the regularity of the highly complex chemical reactions that underlie the activity of higher organisms, together with the highly elaborate patterns of activity in the brain, which make possible the very rapid and precise control of motor activity and the storage of an extensive memory. The evolution, perhaps dating from 150 million years ago, of *homoiothermy—*

the phenomenon of constant and appropriate body temperature—enabled the early mammals to maintain a high level of activity at times when reptiles and amphibians became sluggish (at night and in cold weather). During the Cretaceous period an animal had for the first time gained a tactical advantage over the great ruling reptiles of that age (such as the dinosaurs). At the same time, this animal could move north from the tropical regions to which terrestial life was then more or less limited and could exploit the vast forests of the temperate zones.

The maintenance of body temperature, at first approximate but later exact, involved a complex regulating mechanism under control of the *hypothalamus,* a small structure at the base of the brain (see Fig. 8.11, p. 229). As has been explained (see 1.4), the hypothalamus is the thermostat of the mammalian body, and it brings into action the

TABLE 2.1 EVENTS IN HUMAN EVOLUTION APPROXIMATELY DATED

MILLIONS OF YEARS

Stratigraphical Phases of the Earth's History		*Extent*	*Beginning Before Present (B.P.)*	*Event*
Quaternary	Pleistocene	3	3	Rise of man
Tertiary	Pliocene	10	13	Rise of hominids
	Miocene	12	25	
	Oligocene	11	36	Rise of monkeys
	Eocene	22	58	and apes
	Paleocene	5	63	Rise of placental mammals including primates
Mesozoic	Cretaceous	72	135	First placental mammals; extinction of ruling reptiles
Paleozoic	Jurassic	46	181	First mammals, the pantotheres
	Triassic	49	230	
	Permian	50	280	
	Carboniferous	65	345	First reptiles
	Devonian	60	405	First amphibians
	Silurian	20	425	
	Ordovician	75	500	
	Cambrian	?100	?600	First fossilized animals

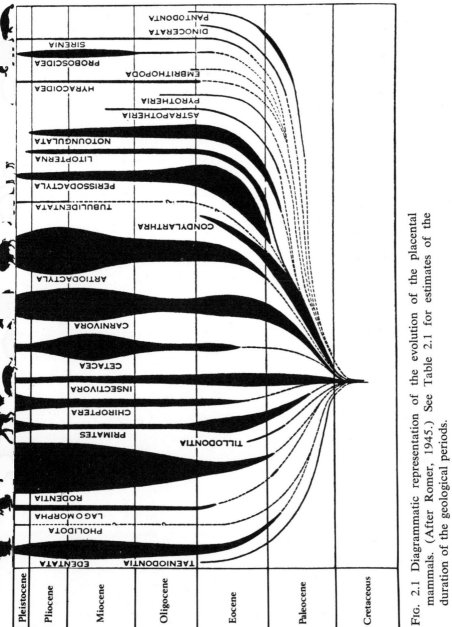

FIG. 2.1 Diagrammatic representation of the evolution of the placental mammals. (After Romer, 1945.) See Table 2.1 for estimates of the duration of the geological periods.

effectors of temperature regulation when the blood departs from that set point to which the species has become adapted. Temperature regulation involves physiological and behavioral adjustments of many different kinds, some of which are listed below.

To lower the temperature of the body, during hot weather or great exertion, the usual rate of heat loss is increased as follows.

1. An increase in effective surface area is effected by spreading the limbs (and the ears in some mammals); increasing the ratio of surface area to volume increases heat loss.

2. Fur or hair, which has been evolved to form an insulating layer, is laid flat upon the skin, to reduce its effective thickness.

3. Respiration rate increases to allow the loss of heat by the vaporization of water in the lungs, throat, and mouth. Panting is most commonly seen in dogs, though it is a human character as well in times of great overheating.

4. The *capillaries* (small blood vessels) under the skin dilate and so increase the circulation of the blood near the surface; blood supply to the internal organs is reduced. Heat loss through the skin is thus increased.

5. Sweat glands produce water on the skin, which vaporizes and so lowers skin temperature. Blood temperature is in turn lowered.

To raise the body temperature, the usual level of heat loss is decreased as follows.

1. A reduction is made in effective surface area by curling up into a ball; a sphere is the shape with the minimum ratio of area to volume.

2. The fur is raised to form a thick insulating layer.

3. The capillaries in the skin are constricted and reduce circulation near the surface of the body.

There are two positive reactions to a lowered body temperature: The generation of body heat is increased by an increased rate of metabolic oxidation of foodstuffs and involuntary muscular activity in the form of shivering.

The maintenance of constant body temperature can thus be seen to be made possible by the evolution of certain new organs, common to mammals. The most important are the fur or hair and its *follicles*, with their erector muscles, which raise and lower the animal's coat, together with the sweat glands in the skin. Mammals are also the bearers of a layer of subcutaneous fat below their outer layer of skin, which helps to insulate them from the external environment and acts as a food store. The whole thermostatic adjustment is effected by the novel functioning of the hypothalamus as a heat receptor: both it and the eye (the light receptor) develop from the same tissues at the base of the brain. Finally, mammals have a behavioral response to temperature change in the skin, for they will seek out a warm place during cold weather and a cool, shady spot in the heat of the day. The effectiveness of the whole mechanism has increased during the evolution of mammals, and in Figure 2.2 we can get some idea of this progress by

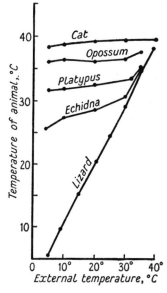

FIG. 2.2. The evolution of homoiothermy is demonstrated in this diagram. Shown are changes in body temperature of different animals during changes in the external temperature. The body temperature of the lizard varies with the environment; the three primitive mammals are some way toward a controlled body temperature, which is almost constant in the cat. (After Martin, 1902.)

noting the response of different animals to change in the external temperature. Although in some mammals and a few primates the regulation of body temperature is subject to activity rhythms (see DeVore 1965, p. 293), this pattern is superimposed on the homoiothermic mechanism.

2.3 *Mastication and heterodontism*

THE MAINTENANCE of a constant body temperature requires a reliable source of food—as fuel—to develop not only muscular power but also heat, which is carried round the body by both the deep and the superficial blood vessels. Mammals therefore needed a readily available food supply not altogether dependent on season. The need for such a food supply involved the evolution of a new kind of jaw function and tooth structure (*dentition*) to make possible a more complete exploitation of the environment.

The mammal's *heterodont* dentition, in which different teeth have different shapes and functions, arose from the reptilian *homodont* dentition, in which the teeth were similar in shape and function (Fig. 2.3).

FIG. 2.3. Skull of python (a reptile) (*A*) and lower jawbone of primitive Jurassic mammal (*Amphitherium*) (*B*) drawn the same size. Note that in the python all teeth are identical in shape and function, whereas in the mammal the teeth are differentiated into incisors, canines, premolars, and molars. (Python after Romer, 1956; *Amphitherium* after Simpson, 1935.)

The reptile jaw and homodont dentition acted mainly as a trap, and food was swallowed whole, as is commonly seen in snakes and alligators. The teeth were often incurved and served only to grasp the prey or, in the case of herbivores, to tear the foliage. In contrast, the mammal jaw and heterodont dentition achieved much more. The jaw was strengthened and different teeth evolved specially for chewing, grinding, and cutting, with the result that the entrance to the alimentary canal served a more valuable purpose than the mere trapping of food. In particular, more kinds of food could be exploited, and the effectiveness of the digestive juices were increased by mastication (as well as by the higher body temperature). A new digestive enzyme (*ptyalin*) was introduced to the food in the mouth as saliva, so that starch digestion could begin during mastication, even before the food was swallowed. The heterodont dentition has evolved within the different orders of mammals in a remarkable variety of ways, and not least in the primates, though in that group the more extreme specializations (such as tusks) have been avoided. A reversal to a homodont condition can be seen in toothed whales, while in other members of the Cetacea, such as the whalebone whales, the teeth have been altogether lost.

The evolution of mastication and the resulting heterodontism (to be considered again in chapter 7) is of great importance to mammalian evolution. By it, they were enabled to exploit food resources that were not available to their reptile predecessors. The teeth of mammals were able to release nutriment from food that the digestive juices alone could not penetrate. Just as the gizzard performed this function among birds, the heterodont dentition released to mammals the full food value locked up within the hard outer skeleton of insects and in plant-food storage organs (such as nuts and other seeds). The densely packed carbohydrates and fats of seeds, the sugars and starches of underground tubers and roots, and all the plant proteins locked up in tough vegetation were released to mammals by the chewing and grinding action of their teeth, thus making possible the maintenance of constant body temperature and more or less continuous activity.

Another development, of less importance, that affected the dentition was the loss of continuous tooth replacement and its evolution into a sequence of only two successive series of teeth during the growth of the individual: the so-called "milk" teeth and the later permanent dentition. Changes in diet and tooth action probably reduced tooth loss, which in turn removed the need for perpetual tooth replacement. The milk teeth or deciduous dentition make possible mastication when the jaws are still small and unable to carry the permanent dentition. The permanent dentition erupts during the second half of the growth period and forms an extremely strong and powerful masticatory apparatus.

2.4 *Reproductive economy: prenatal*

THE EARLY REPTILES had become fully adapted land animals by the evolution of internal fertilization by copulation, thus removing dependence on fresh or salt water for the external fertilization of their eggs. The reptiles had also evolved the *amniote* egg—an egg for dry land, sealed against dehydration by a shell and membranes, which allowed the growing embryo to develop in its own little aqueous environment. Reptiles, however, maintained their numbers, like more primitive animals, by the mass production of eggs rather than by the successful establishment of small numbers of offspring. Their numerous eggs were usually hidden and left to hatch alone, and the young animals had to fend for themselves from that moment. Both eggs and young were easy prey to small carnivores, especially the little mammals that were then evolving.

These evolving mammals developed a quite new kind of reproductive system, which, by cutting down losses of eggs and young, improved their overall reproductive economy. It consisted of two basic developments, each involving a whole range of new physiological and anatomical characters. The first was *viviparity* (which has occurred as a parallel adaptation in some other classes)—the retention and nourishment of the fertilized egg within the mother until a quite advanced stage of growth. The second, to be considered in the following section, was the evolution of parental care of the young after birth, for their nourishment and protection.

While such behavior as feeding affects the future of every individual separately, the reproductive activity of animals affects in particular the future generations rather than the fate of the individuals involved. In this sense, reproductive mechanisms are above all the property of the species rather than the individual. As a result, reproductive behavior tends to be innate and stereotyped and much less subject to versatility, for too much variation in reproductive behavior might endanger the survival of the species. The first requirement of biological fitness is the maintenance of the reproductive rate by regular and successful reproductive activity.

Partly for historical biological reasons and partly for the reasons discussed above, we find that the reproductive processes of mammals are primarily under control of the *endocrine* system rather than the nervous system. The endocrine system was early evolved as a method of communication between the cells and organs of an animal's body. It operates by means, not of nerves, but of *hormones*, sometimes described as "chemical messengers," which are chemical substances emitted by one group of cells and carried in the blood stream and by diffusion around the body. According to their chemical structure, they evoke a specific response in another group of cells, tuned, as it were, to receive them. In mammals the endocrine system operates in co-operation with the nervous system: the former tends to effect response in long-term life processes, such as the rate of basic metabolism and the seasonal activity of the reproductive system; the latter effects more immediate changes in the body, such as behavioral responses in general.

The part of the endocrine system that controls seasonal egg-laying and copulation in reptiles and amphibians has in mammals been expanded to control a regular cycle of sexual activity throughout the mating season and, in some species, throughout the whole year. The cycle, known as the *estrous cycle*, arises with the evolution of viviparity, and is part of the mammal's reproductive adaptations. It results from the need to follow up the growth and production of the egg or eggs (*ovulation*) within the *follicles* (egg-producing bodies) of one or both *ovaries*, by changes in the walls of the ducts through which they pass (the *oviducts,* which in higher mammals become the *fallopian tubes* and *uterus* [Fig. 2.4]). These changes are such as to allow the *implantation* of the egg or eggs after their fertilization. Implantation is the means by which the developing egg becomes attached to the specially modified wall of the uterus (*endometrium*); the egg derives nourishment for its growth from the maternal blood vessels within the endometrium. If fertilization occurs, it is followed by implantation and *gestation* (pregnancy). If not, the changes in the wall of the uterus are arrested, and new eggs develop in the ovary, later to be shed into the uterus. The complete estrous cycle can be observed only in the absence of fertilization, for implantation arrests the cycle. The complete cycle is as follows.

1. Egg develops in the ovarian follicle.
2. Egg is shed into fallopian tube and passes to uterus.
3. Endometrial lining of uterus is prepared for implantation.

4. If no implantation occurs, endometrial lining of uterus returns to normal condition.

1^2. New egg develops in ovary.

Since the egg remains in the female for only about three days after ovulation in most mammals, fertilization, if it is to occur, must take place during this period. Sexual interest of the male, culminating in copulation, is induced at this time by the particular physiological changes in the female known as *estrus*, commonly called "heat." (The word "estrus" comes from the Greek word for "sting," which sends an individual into a frenzied condition). By means of scent signals (and occasionally visual signals) the female attracts the male to copulate. It is characteristic of mammals generally that only during the period of estrus and at no other time in the estrous cycle is the female receptive or the male sexually stimulated.

In order to understand the changes that have occurred in the evolution of man's reproductive system, it is desirable to understand how

Fig. 2.4. The oviducts in the female mammal have been modified to supply nourishment to the developing embryo. The arrangement of the reproductive organs of a woman is shown in relation to the pelvic girdle; the front of the pelvis (the pubic region) is shown cut away where it would obscure the cervix. The arrangement is not strikingly different in other higher primates.

the estrous cycle is controlled by a system of hormones produced by the *pituitary body*, a small endocrine gland that lies close under the base of the brain (see Fig. 8.11, p. 229). In spite of intensive research, it is still not fully understood how the whole system of the estrous cycle is maintained, but at least part of the mechanism is known. Probably under the control of the hypothalamus (Fig. 8.11), the pituitary, during each estrous cycle, produces two hormones successively, which have been termed the *follicle-stimulating hormone* (*FSH*) and the *luteinizing hormone* (*LH*). Their production is shown graphically in Figure 2.5, *A*. Shed into the blood stream, the two hormones stimulate, respectively, the growth and production of one or more eggs in the follicles of one or both ovaries (FSH) and what has been called the "yellow

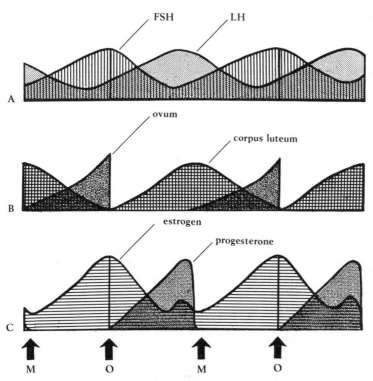

FIG. 2.5. Some of the phenomena associated with the estrous cycle: *A*, pituitary hormone levels; *B*, development of ovarian products; *C*, ovarian sex hormones; *M*, menstruation; *O*, ovulation and termination of estrus. *FSH*, follicle-stimulating hormone, *LH*, luteinizing hormone. (Adapted from Mason, 1960.)

body" or *corpus luteum* (LH), which develops in the ovary in place of the egg after it has been shed (Fig. 2.5, *B*). But the developing ovarian follicle and the corpus luteum themselves both produce hormones when they are activated by the pituitary: the well-known female sex hormones called *estrogen* and *progesterone* (Fig. 2.5, *C*). The estrogen brings on estrus or "heat" by causing activity of the scent glands and enlargement of the external female genitalia; the progesterone initiates the special changes in the endometrium that prepare it for implantation.

If fertilization and implantation take place, a hormone produced by the developing egg arrests the cyclic activity of the pituitary; the production of progesterone continues and in turn brings about all the accessory changes associated with pregnancy. If fertilization and implantation do not occur, the pituitary produces a new secretion of FSH, which causes the development of new ovarian follicles and new eggs. The corpus luteum in this case degenerates, and the progesterone level falls. *Menstruation* is the loss of blood seen in certain mammals when the preparatory changes in the endometrium are reversed at the end of the cycle, and the spongy, blood-filled tissues that have been induced by the progesterone are shed. The estrous cycle of mammals and humans has been described by Eckstein and Zuckerman (1956) and Mason (1960). It is shown diagrammatically in Figure 2.6.

This remarkable series of changes in the ovary and uterus is effected by the pituitary hormones. While egg production in lower vertebrates is also under simple endocrine control, mammals have evolved the additional functions of the luteinizing hormone, the corpus luteum, and the endometrium, together with all the other changes brought about in pregnancy. But mammalian viviparity involves other changes in the mother too, some of which are also under the endocrine control of the pituitary gland. For example, the hormone *pitocin* contracts the muscular wall of the uterus at the end of pregnancy, and *prolactin* promotes milk secretion after birth. We see, then, that the evolution of mammalian viviparity involves the evolution of new endocrine activity, as well as anatomical modifications, such as those we see in the oviduct.

Correlates of these evolutionary developments are the adaptations of the membranes of the *fetus* (the developing young in the womb) to form a *placenta*, the organ that penetrates the endometrium and, by diffusion, receives nourishment for the growing fetus from the maternal blood stream. Waste products also pass from the fetus by this route.

The intimate association of mother and fetus, which is typical of placental mammals, means that the egg is fully protected during its development and that the young stand a far greater chance of survival than do the young of reptiles, which are left to the mercy of predators —especially the egg-eating mammals. But the prenatal relationship between mother and fetus is not more important as a means of reproductive economy than is the postnatal relationship between mother and young.

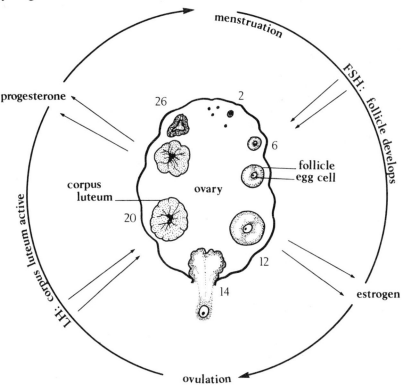

FIG. 2.6.   Diagram showing the changes in the ovary that take place during the estrous cycle. The cycle in higher primates lasts approximately 28 days, and the numbers shown round the ovary give some indication of the timing of the events, counting from the first day of menstruation, when the follicle starts to grow. Menstruation has been recorded as characteristic only of the Old World monkeys, apes, and man, though it is known in a few other primates.

2.5 *Reproductive economy: postnatal*

CARE OF THE NEWBORN by one or both parents is not peculiar to mammals but has been extensively evolved among birds and is found occasionally among reptiles and in a few invertebrates. What is unique to mammals is that the "parasitic" mode of life of the offspring is continued after birth, in that they are fed by the special milk glands (*mammae*) of the mother, subcutaneous in origin and probably evolved from the sweat glands (another mammalian novelty). Milk contains all the substances necessary for the growth and development of the young (including antibodies) and may continue to be taken for long periods (the record for all mammals is probably four to five years among Alaskan Eskimos). The relative safety of the postnatal environment, in which the young remain close to the mother, is also important in the reduction of mammal mortality and in allowing, secondarily, a slower growth rate in some orders. As a correlate of this lowered mortality rate, we may note a reduction in the number of eggs fertilized annually from some millions in fishes to dozens in reptiles and to no more than one per year in man.

We shall see (in 9.7) that the exceptionally slow growth rate typical of man is a character of great importance in human evolution, and it is interesting that the quantity of protein in the mother's milk (the food most essential for growth) is quite precisely related to the growth rate of the infant. Table 2.2, which indicates the early growth rate of different mammals, also shows how the protein content of the milk is correlated with this feature.

The intimate relationship between generations resulting from suckling and caring for the young makes possible the transmission of

TABLE 2.2 GROWTH RATE AND MILK PROTEIN (AFTER SIVERTSEN, 1941, P. 97)

Animal	Days to Double Birth Weight	Protein in Milk Parts per 100
Rabbit	6	10.4
Dog	8	8.3
Sheep	10	7.0
Pig	18	6.9
Cow	47	4.0
Horse	60	2.3
Man	180	1.9

learned behavior by imitation. Behavior patterns learned by trial and error have been recognized among lower vertebrates and invertebrates, but the simplicity and origin of such behavior puts it into a different class from that of mammals. It is the transmission of complex learned behavior by imitation that makes it unnecessary to learn solely from direct experience—a dangerous process (see 1.5). Instead, the experience of generations can be assimilated in a short time with reduced danger to the young. Thus the mammals have the great advantage (shared to some extent by birds) of being able, as it were, to "inherit" (by imitative learning from parents) "acquired" (i.e., learned) behavioral characters. The inheritance of acquired characters makes possible a high rate of evolution of those characters, and thus the behavior patterns of mammals have evolved fast and increased in complexity in such a way as to put them in that respect at a different level from all other living organisms. Their learned behavior repertory is immense, complex, and flexible (because it is still subject to trial and error learning). It makes possible the maintenance of the deme in face of even very extensive and demanding environmental changes.

2.6 *Determinants of behavior*

BEHAVIOR HAS BEEN DESCRIBED as both innate and learned (see 1.5), and we have seen that learned behavior assumes great importance among mammals. The intimate relationship between different generations brings the possibility of building up quite complex behavior patterns by imitation, without the need to learn by trial and error in each generation. Such learning is confined to animals (birds and mammals) in which parental care has evolved.

But mammals also depend on learning by trial and error, which must always be the original source of learned behavior. While in most animals activity and learning result from the need to satisfy the primary drives of hunger, sex, and self-preservation, a new determinant of behavior is found among mammals that does not satisfy these immediate needs. This new factor is a drive to investigate and explore the environment without the immediate object of satisfying one of the three prime biological needs mentioned above, and has been termed *effectance motivation* (R. W. White 1959).

Effectance motivation is seen in the playful and exploratory activity of young mammals with the parts of the environment that provide changing and interesting feedback in connection with effort expended. Such activity leads individuals to discover how the environment can be changed and what consequences flow from the changes. Such moderate but persistent activity is possible only under the protection of parents, because its value to the individual and the species is not immediate, as are the primary drives, but is of a long-term nature. This type of behavior forms part of the process whereby the young animal learns to interact effectively with the environment and builds up its perception of its surroundings (see 10.2).

The value of a computer in the solution of a very complex problem depends not only on the computer's size and complexity but also on the amount of data that is fed into it. For reliable results, a large input is a prerequisite. It is equally necessary in the evolution of the brain as a mechanism for prediction and problem-solving, for complex problem-solving depends on sufficient input data, and this need explains the evolution of effectance motivation. The motor exploratory activity that results in the satisfaction of the primary drives of hunger, sex, and self-preservation was supplemented by the increased input that was derived from effectance activity and is an essential correlate of the evolution of mammals into organisms with brains much larger (in relation to body size), much more complicated, and much more efficient than had been known before in the organic world.

There were two developments within the brain itself concomitant with the increased input. The first was the evolution of a greatly expanded memory store (that is, an unconscious record of experience); the second was the evolution of an expanded "computer," that is, the part of the brain that actually makes predictions and solves problems.

When we compare the mammalian brain with that of lower vertebrates, we see that it is typified by the relatively great development of what has been termed the *cerebral hemispheres*, compared with other parts (Fig. 2.7). It is in the cerebral hemispheres, and particularly in their surface layers or *cortex*, that we believe the memory store and most complex computing activities are to be found. We know the function of some of the lower parts of the brain, and they seem to be of a simpler order. For example, we have recorded how the hypothalamus controls body temperature and the estrous cycle, and it has other relatively simple functions, such as the control of sugar metabolism, heart

FIG. 2.7. Sections (not to scale) through the longitudinal axis (termed "medial" or "sagittal") of the brain of a fish, reptile, rabbit, and man, showing the difference in size of the cerebral hemispheres in relation to the older parts of the brain. For names of the different parts see Figs. 8.8 and 8.11. (From Magoun, 1960.)

rate, blood pressure, salt and water balance, and sleep. The *brainstem* and *cerebellum* (see 8.6) control many innate reflexes relating to balance and muscular control. It is the cerebral hemispheres, however, that are concerned not so much with executing a program of bodily activity and maintaining it as with initiating such activity with a "decision" (unconscious, except occasionally in man) as to what activity should be undertaken next, on the basis of the sensory input and accumulated experience that is memorized.

Just which parts of the cerebral hemispheres are mainly concerned with memory will be discussed later (see 8.6). Investigations into which parts of the hemispheres are concerned with decision have achieved poor results, which has led to the theory that it is the activity of the cerebral hemispheres as a whole, rather than that of any part, that determines most mammalian behavior (the so-called "law of mass action"). Quite extensive damage to the human brain may be sustained in many parts without any serious impairment of function, leading us to deduce that the problem-solving and predicting activities of the brain are not truly comparable to those of a computer, which cannot function after the mutilation of any part.

In summary, we see the evolution of the cerebral hemispheres of mammals into a mechanism somewhat similar in function to a large computer with an extensive memory store. Unlike a computer, the brain operates with nonlocalized systems of activity; like a computer, its value to its user in complex prediction is directly related to the information content of the input. The mammalian brain functions therefore not only to control the mechanisms that maintain the steady state of the body but also to store the memory of an enormous range of experiences. Input is maintained by the highly evolved sense organs and by effectance motivation, which brings to the animal an enlargement of experience. On the basis of such experience the brain is able to make predictions about the likely course of external events and on this basis to initiate novel patterns of adaptive behavior.

2.7 *Man a mammal*

WE HAVE DISCUSSED four evolutionary novelties that characterize the placental mammals, each one a whole complex of characters. Two of them, homoiothermy and heterodontism, contribute in an obvious way to make possible the constant metabolic level of the organism in the face of environmental change. Following our discussion of evolutionary progress (see 1.7), we see that insofar as they are improvements in the internal homeostatic state of the organism, they are progressive in the direction of man and in the sense defined by Herrick (1946). We have already indicated their importance to the early mammals, in the advantages that these new character complexes gave to their bearers in the reptile-dominated environment of the cretaceous period.

Clearly, any such advances in internal homeostatic mechanisms increase the chances of survival not only of the individual but of the whole species, because each individual is more likely to survive and reproduce itself. But the advantages to the species of the second two characters are perhaps more obvious. The improvements in reproductive economy that result in a much lower wastage of eggs and young mean an increase in biological efficiency as a whole for the species: fewer eggs need to be produced, and less energy and living substance is devoted to that end. The trend of a lowered rate of fertilized egg production reaches its apogee in *Homo sapiens*.

Our fourth evolutionary novelty, effectance motivation, is a behavioral development, concomitant with the evolution of a larger brain, which by making possible a better knowledge of the environment increases the chances of survival of the individual and so of the species. The ability to assimilate and utilize this knowledge is selected in the genotype, but its transmission between generations is made possible by imitation within the close mother-infant relationship. This transmission of behavior patterns in an extra-genetic manner is the seed from which culture was eventually to grow (see chapter 10).

It is not necessary to stress the importance to man of these complexes and all their structural correlates. Man, with his remarkable ability to survive every sort of climate (1.4), to live off almost every sort of food (7.2), has a wonderfully efficient reproductive system (9.1 and 9.2) and a body of transmitted behavior (10.1) that is far beyond anything known in the rest of the animal kingdom. This vast body of transmitted behavior of different kinds he owes mostly to the extraordinary knowledge of the environment that he has gained by experience. His perception of the environment, which gives him that enriched experience, he owes to the exploratory nature which he shares with other mammals. Improved homeostatic mechanisms and a new behavioral relationship with the environment made mammals the potential ancestors of *Homo sapiens*. Man is a mammal and could belong to no other class of vertebrates.

SUGGESTIONS FOR FURTHER READING

For an outstanding text on the biology of mammals see J. Z. Young, *The Life of Mammals* (Oxford: Oxford University Press, 1957). For a simple taxonomic survey of the Mammalia see M. Burton, *Systematic Dictionary of Mammals of the World* (London: Museum Press, 1962).

১৩

Primate Radiation

3.1 The origin of primates

A GLANCE at Figure 2.1 (p. 37) will show that the mammals that gave rise to the primates (and indeed to all other placental mammals) are believed to have been of a kind that would now be classified as Insectivora. The central position of the order Insectivora in the figure is intended to indicate that they have diverged least from the ancestral mammalian stock that gave rise to the whole radiation of mammals.

Some of the fossil insectivores from the Paleocene period are very similar to some living genera of this order, and in particular to the genus *Sorex*, the little shrew (Fig. 3.1). Though many of the Cretaceous and Paleocene insectivores were rat-sized, the shrew and its relatives are very small animals, and the one illustrated is only 4.5 inches long, including tail. The insectivores are insect-eaters, as their name implies, but, like the shrew, the majority supplement their diet with other small animals, seeds, buds, and so on; they are in fact omnivorous. The shrew is an active, nervous, nocturnal animal and eats its own weight in food daily. A large food supply is apparently necessary to maintain a creature so active and so small, since small animals have a much larger surface area in relation to their weight, through which heat may be lost, than do larger animals.

The shrews and other ground-living genera have exploited the dense environment of the forest floor, where, living almost exclusively upon the ground, they are able to find the practically continuous food supply

FIG. 3.1. Common European shrew (*Sorex araneus*), with a body about 3 inches in length, is very similar to the North American species *S. cinerens.* (From Burton, 1962.)

that they require. As can be seen from Figure 3.1, the shrew has a long snout and sensitive tactile *rhinarium* (the sensitive area of naked skin at the end of the muzzle, familiar in dogs). They snuffle through the grass after seeds and minute animals. To their small size and dense habitat they owe their obscurity, which has certainly contributed to their survival by protecting them from the larger carnivorous reptiles and mammals. The adaptations of small size and nocturnal activity have obviously given these lively and omnivorous creatures an immense advantage over their reptile competitors. Yet their adaptations did more than this, for not all of them remained in obscurity. The moles went underground; the African otter shrews and American marsh shrews (among others) have become aquatic; other insectivores took to the trees and evolved into tree shrews, now recognized to be closely related to the earliest and most primitive primates. From some of these arboreal shrews evolved the bats (Chiroptera). Still other ground-living forms evolved at the same time into the whole range of great terrestrial mammals (Fig. 3.2).

Our special interest will lie in the tree shrews, a group that invaded the trees, climbing with their sharp claws and using their long tails to balance them. From animals not unlike them the order Primates is believed to have evolved, and finally man himself.

3.2 The primates

THE DIAGNOSTIC CHARACTERS of the order Primates, whose origins it is claimed can be traced to the Late Cretaceous (Van Valen and Sloan 1965), are not easy to define and describe in a simple list. But their characters, though numerous, are easily understood as adaptations to the arboreal environment in which the primates lived. Rather than present a list of characters at once, it is better to consider first the primate adaptations as a whole and then the characters that evolved as their basis.

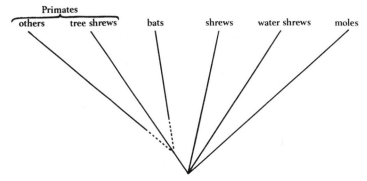

FIG. 3.2. Simplified diagram showing part of the radiation of the primitive ground-living shrew-like placental mammals.

In the face of competition from other forest-living creatures, the primates evolved the ability to climb trees. Tree-climbing was necessary to exploit the environment to the full, to gather fruit and insects, as well as to escape from predators on the ground. The forest environment was a difficult one, densely filled with objects of different kinds and demanding accurate and swift mobility and keen sensory awareness. Since scents were unreliable in identifying the exact direction of food or enemies and were of little help in negotiating trees and undergrowth, efficient vision became the great need of these forest dwellers. Primates therefore became characterized (1) by the evolution of limbs adapted for tree-climbing and (2) by eyes adapted for much-improved vision. Almost every character we normally associate with primates is part of one or the other of these two functional complexes, and from this point of view they fall into place very neatly. Let us consider each complex in turn.

1. Tree-climbing involved the following adaptations:
    a) Retention of a generalized limb structure and *pentadactyly* (five fingers) with free mobility of limbs and digits, giving support to the body in any direction, and with limb movement not restricted to one plane.
    b) Development of mobile digits capable of grasping, with sensitive pads supported by nails (which replaced claws in primate evolution) and hairless toughened palms.
    c) Retention of a tail as an organ of balance (or as a "fifth limb" in some New World monkeys).
    d) Much improved sense of balance.
    e) Improved motor control.
    f) Retention of fairly small body size, compared with ground-living mammals.
2. An improved visual sense involved the following changes:
    a) Enlargement of the eyes, which increased the amount of light and detail received.
    b) Evolution of an improved retina with increased sensitivity to low levels of illumination and to different frequencies (that is, to color).
    c) Eyes that look forward, with an overlapping visual field that gives three-dimensional visual assimilation of the environment, accompanied by the mechanisms associated with interpretation and analysis of input to the brain.
    d) Development of a bony protection for the large eyes.
    e) Reduction (as a corollary of enhanced visual sense) of the apparatus involved in the sense of smell, the olfactory lobes and protective bony snout or muzzle.

The foregoing two functional complexes reflect only part of the whole pattern of primate biology, but the most important part. One complex, the developed visual sense, is concerned with receiving information about the environment; the other is concerned with its active exploitation. The brain processes information from the first and instructs the second. Their interaction is an example of the intensification of total metabolic and nervous activity typical of the primates. The brain, the mechanism for analysis and prediction, is the necessary correlate of the evolution of either sensory or motor activity. Development of both these functions goes hand in hand with development of the brain.

The sight of gibbons moving through a forest canopy is a beautiful instance of precise motor action under delicate visual control. The unique speed and accuracy of their movement depends on a brain that can assimilate many factors of weight, distance, and wind and process them to give immediate and precise motor instruction. It is to the exploitation of this dense, complex, and demanding environment that we owe the development of a brain that is unique in the extent of its memory bank, in the quantity of the data it processes, and in the speed of its operation. It is accompanied by nervous and muscular mechanisms that are precise and flexible in operation.

The structural characters listed here will be referred to again in the following chapters when we consider how they have contributed to man's own form. We shall in this chapter consider first the classification of the order Primates and then how the different groups within the order have developed different locomotory adaptations. Finally, we shall consider some aspects of the evolution of the nervous system that have accompanied these important adaptations.

3.3 Primate classification

AMONG LIVING PRIMATES we find a wide range of fifty-one genera of different appearance, size, and habitat. This varied order, which extends from the little tree shrews to man himself, forms a series that suggests a trend in evolutionary development—a suggestion that is in some parts supported by the fossil remains available for study. Groups perhaps not very dissimilar to different ancestral stages in human evolution appear to have survived surprisingly unchanged from early times, since they can certainly be identified as close in morphology to their ancestral forms. The situation has been diagrammatically presented by Le Gros Clark (1962), and his figure is reproduced here as Figure 3.3. Five main terminal kinds of living primate, the tree shrew, lemur, tarsier, monkey, ape, and man, are shown in Figure 3.4. These particular kinds have presumably survived because they became successfully adapted to particular ecological niches; intermediate forms have been lost.

It is a remarkable, rare, and happy fact that we have this series of forms still living, for they can help us visualize certain stages of human

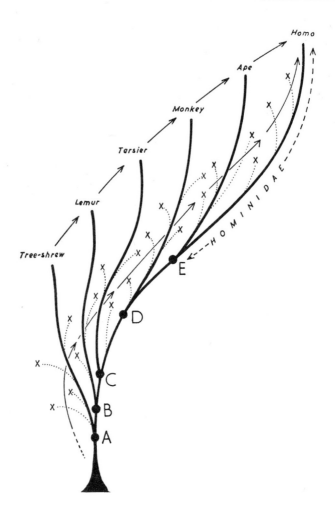

FIG. 3.3. Diagram showing that the living primates form a series from tree shrew to *Homo,* a series that suggests a general trend of evolutionary development. From comparative studies of such types it is possible to postulate the probable linear sequence of human ancestry. This sequence leads from the basal primate stock through hypothetical transitional stages, *A–E,* at which the different ramifications of the primates are presumed to have branched off. Fossil primates approximating to the postulated ancestral stages are represented by crosses. (From Le Gros Clark, 1962.)

FIG. 3.4. Some living members of the order Primates, representing a series that, broadly speaking, links man anatomically with some of the most primitive of placental mammals: *1*, tree shrew; *2*, lemur; *3*, tarsier; *4*, Old World monkey; *5*, chimpanzee; *6*, Australian aboriginal. (From Le Gros Clark, 1962.)

evolution. Of course, we can never be certain of the interrelationships of living forms in past time, but, *on the basis of the evidence available at present*, a working hypothesis of the kind shown in Figure 3.3 forms a popular interpretation of the evidence. It seems unlikely, however, that human ancestry passed through a stage that would be identified as a lemur or a tarsier, though the evidence from that remote period is still very limited. The actual character of the forms marked *E* and "Hominidae" in the figure and how they evolved are the subject of this book.

A formal classification of the order Primates is given in Table 3.1.

TABLE 3.1 CLASSIFICATION OF THE PRIMATES SHOWING NUMBERS OF LIVING GENERA (AFTER LE GROS CLARK AND SIMPSON)

Order: Primates
  Suborder: Prosimii
    Infraorder: Lemuriformes
      Superfamily: Tupaioidea   Tree shrews (4 genera)
                   Lemuroidea   Lemurs (8 genera)
                   Daubentonioidea Aye-ayes (1 genus)
    Infraorder: Lorisiformes
      Superfamily: Lorisioidea   Lorises (5 genera)
    Infraorder: Tarsiiformes
      Superfamily: Tarsioidea   Tarsiers (1 genus)
  Suborder: Anthropoidea
      Superfamily: Ceboidea   New World monkeys
                                     (13 genera)
                   Cercopithecoidea Old World monkeys
                                     (13 genera)
                   Hominoidea   Apes and men
                                     (6 genera)

Six of the superfamilies listed have been illustrated in Figure 3.4, the other two are not important to this study. We shall be concerned mainly with the so-called "higher" primates or Anthropoidea, the monkeys, apes, and man, which are most closely related to ourselves (see Tables 3.2 and 3.3). The lower primates (Prosimii) are of less immediate relevance.

We see from the classification that there are two groups of monkeys: the Ceboidea, or New World monkeys, confined to Central and South America, and the Cercopithecoidea, or Old World Monkeys, which are spread throughout the tropical regions of the Old World, in Africa and Asia. (These two groups, which have striking and important differences, are also sometimes termed the *platyrrhine* and *catarrhine* monkeys, re-

TABLE 3.2 GENERA OF LIVING MONKEYS

CEBOIDEA: NEW WORLD MONKEYS

Callithrix	Marmoset	*Alouatta*	Howler
Leontocebus	Tamarin	*Cebus*	Capuchin
Callimico	Geoldi's "marmoset"	*Saimiri*	Squirrel monkey
Aotus	Douroucouli	*Ateles*	Spider monkey
Callicebus	Titi	*Brachyteles*	Woolly spider monkey
Pithecia	Saki	*Lagothrix*	Woolly monkey
Cacajao	Uakari		

CERCOPITHECOIDEA: OLD WORLD MONKEYS

Macaca	Macaque	*Presbytis*	Common langur
Cynopithecus	Black ape	*Pygathrix*	Douc langur
Cercocebus	Mangabey	*Rhinopithecus*	Snub nosed langur
Papio	Baboon	*Simias*	Pagi Island langur
Theropithecus	Gelada	*Nasalis*	Proboscis monkey
Cercopithecus	Guenon	*Colobus*	Gueraza
Erythrocebus	Patas monkey		

TABLE 3.3 CLASSIFICATION OF THE HOMINOIDEA AND HOMINIDAE

HOMINOIDEA

Family	Pongidae	Apes
Subfamily	Hylobatinae	Gibbons
	Dryopithecinae	Fossil apes
	Ponginae	Great apes*
Family	Hominidae	Men
Family	Oreopithecidae	Swamp apes

HOMINIDAE

Genus	*Ramapithecus*	Early man-apes
Species	*R. punjabicus*	
Genus	*Australopithecus*	Man-apes
Species	*A. robustus*	Robust man-apes
	A. africanus	Gracile man-apes
Genus	*Homo*	Man
Species	*H. erectus*	Early man
	H. sapiens	Modern man

For a more detailed classification of the Hominidae, see Campbell (1963).

* The great apes include three genera, *Gorilla, Pan,* and *Pongo.* The latter is quite distinct from the former two genera, which have much in common and are sometimes placed in the single genus *Pan.*

spectively.) The third superfamily of the Anthropoidea, the Hominoidea (apes and men), was also confined to the Old World until man entered the American and Australasian continents in geologically recent time. The Hominoidea are clearly much more closely related to the Old World monkeys than to the New World monkeys, as both geographical and anatomical evidence make clear. The New World monkeys became isolated at an early stage in primate evolution, and they probably have had a separate prosimian ancestry. Therefore, we shall refer very little in this book to the New World monkeys. Though they are a successful and fascinating group, we must confine our attention here to the Old World forms, which may lie near to man's ancestral lineage.

Of all the characters deserving consideration in any study of primate evolution, one of the most important, as we have seen, is their locomotor adaptations to tree-living. We shall now discuss the different ways that the order has become adapted to locomotion in the forest.

3.4 Primate locomotion: arboreal adaptations

THE MODE OF LOCOMOTION of a group of animals is necessarily closely adapted to the ecological niche they occupy. Among primates we find variations in the exact environment they occupy, variations in size, and so variations in their locomotor behavior and structural adaptations. While a few primate genera have become secondarily terrestrial, most have remained arboreal, so we shall consider the arboreal adaptations first.

1. *Quadrupedalism*. Since the primates evolved from ground-living forms, we can be sure that the earliest form of locomotion in the group was running up the trunks of trees and along the branches on "all fours." This mode of locomotion requires minimum arboreal specialization and is found in other groups of arboreal mammals, such as squirrels. The essential structural features are as follows.

a) A means of gripping the tree, such as claws or long, flexible fingers (*phalanges*)

b) Hindlimbs that are more powerful and often longer than the forelimbs

c) A shift backward of the center of gravity, so that a sitting position is common (Fig. 3.4, *1* and *2*)

d) Development in the size of the tail to improve balance

As might be expected, this method of locomotion is common to many of the prosimians, such as the lemurs, as well as many monkeys, especially the Old World forms, such as *Macaca*. It does not prevent the animals from leaving the trees and crossing open ground from time to time.

A modified kind of quadrupedalism, however, has evolved among certain small prosimians. While the large groups, such as most lemurs and lorises, tend to move through the trees slowly and steadily, walking up the trunks and along the branches, the smaller genera tend to leap and cling. The small loris, *Galago* (the bush baby), leaps like a little kangaroo, pushing off with its strong hind legs, and tarsiers leap and cling similarly. This kind of locomotion enables these small animals to jump from tree to tree as well as between branches and was probably evolved very early by the most primitive primates. One of its most important correlates was a change in the resting position from one in which the trunk is horizontal to a position in which the trunk is held vertically. We have here the early and original evolution of erect posture in the primates, which was to be a necessary prerequisite for man's erect and bipedal stance (see the tarsier in Fig. 3.4). It is possible that the semibrachiating monkeys, to be considered next, evolved from some of these little leaping prosimians.

2. *Semibrachiation.* Monkeys, which are generally larger than the prosimians, can often reach the branches above their heads by stretching their forelimbs upward. Larger size makes possible the use of the forelimbs in a novel way. In *semibrachiation,* the forelimbs, fully extended above the head, are often used to suspend the body and propel it through space. The limbs are stretched out to grasp the branches as the monkey jumps from tree to tree. Such locomotor behavior is common among some New World monkeys, which also use the tail as a grasping organ (Erikson 1963). It has, however, also been recognized in certain Old World genera, including *Nasalis, Rhinopithecus, Presbytis,* and *Colobus* (Napier 1963b).

The anatomical adaptations to this locomotor pattern are superimposed upon those already listed above.

a) We find the complete absence of claws in all Old World higher primates and some New World genera; claws catch in the bark and are quite unsuitable for fast arboreal locomotion. Anyone who has observed a cat trying to descend a tree will understand the disadvantages of claws. Long phalanges are far better, with the pads at the ends of the fingers stiffened by nails, as in man.

b) The forelimbs are lengthened in semibrachiators, an adaptation that clearly brings more branches into range, as well as giving greater leverage to the arm and shoulder muscles.

c) The phalanges are lengthened for gripping the branches as a hook, and the thumb is used rather less than among the prosimians, for it is not opposed to the finger so as to allow gripping of the opposite side of the branch but more often lies alongside the fingers. This adaptation is for quick movement: it is easier to release a hook quickly by simply releasing the finger muscles and opening the hook, than to pull the thumb and fingers apart when they are gripping in opposition.

d) Detailed changes have been identified in the form of the shoulder and arm bones and muscles. These changes are associated with increasing the lifting power of the forearm from above, as distinct from its supporting power from below. The arm is also enabled by these adaptations to move more freely above the head than it is in the quadrupedal forms.

3. *Modified brachiation.* A rather more developed form of *brachiation* is found among the great apes *Pongo* (the orang), *Pan* (the chimpanzee), and *Gorilla* (Napier 1963b). Owing to the great size of these animals, their movement through the trees is more sedate. Their hindlimbs supply partial support for the heavy body from below, and they are limited to the stronger branches. *Gorilla* and *Pan* are frequently quadrupedal on the ground as well as in trees, but they use their phalangeal knuckles to support their weight on their front limbs, rather than using the palms of their hands (Fig. 3.5); their hands have so completely evolved as hooks that they cannot be flattened. In the slow brachiating movements of the heavy body, jumping is minimal, so in the course of evolution the tail, no longer required for balance, has been lost. The orang, limited to southeast Asia (Borneo and Sumatra) is somewhat different from the two African forms. There is reason to believe that it has a long independent but parallel evolutionary history, and it is certainly a more evolved brachiator than *Pan* and *Gorilla*. In this locomotor classification it falls near to the true brachiators.

FIG. 3.5. The baboon (*above*) is a quadrupedal monkey that has become terrestrial. The gorilla *(below)* is a brachiator, and when he walks quadrupedally he is unable to use the flat surfaces of his hands and feet but takes his weight on his knuckles. Note that the gorilla's arms are much longer than his legs (Not drawn to scale.) (By permission of the trustees of the British Museum [Natural History].)

4. *True brachiation.* In this form of locomotion, the forelimbs alone, fully extended above the head, are used to suspend the body and propel it through space. In the Old World, it is found only in the gibbons and siamangs, the two genera of the subfamily Hylobatinae (Fig. 3.6). Among New World primates, the spider monkey *Ateles* is considered to have evolved in a parallel manner (Erickson 1963). In the two Old World genera the feet usually support the body only when resting. We find here that the structural adaptations of the semibrachiators are further evolved.

a) Fingers now very long and hook-like, with thumbs greatly reduced
b) Forelimbs greatly lengthened so that they are now one-quarter again as long as the hindlimbs
e) Structural modifications in the shoulder and arm, giving even greater power and flexibility
d) No tail

As a result of the extreme adaptation of the gibbon hand, we find that it cannot be straightened, so, when the gibbon walks on the ground quadrupedally, he uses his metatarsal knuckles to take his weight. It is also noteworthy that, of all the nonhuman primates, it is said the gibbon most readily adopts a bipedal run when he wishes to cross open ground at speed, which is probably due to the very erect posture that is typical of brachiating primates.

These locomotor adaptations need detailed consideration in our study of human evolution, since it is of some importance to discover

FIG. 3.6. The gibbon *(Hylobates)* is a skilled brachiator. When he is traveling fast from tree to tree, he carries his legs fully retracted; under these circumstances they have no locomotor function. Note the very long arms and long hands.

what kind of locomotor pattern might have evolved into man's own unique bipedal locomotion. This subject we shall discuss in chapters 5 (hindlimbs) and 6 (forelimbs).

3.5 Primate locomotion: terrestrial adaptations

IT IS OF GREAT INTEREST that man is not the only primate that has left the forest and become adapted to life on the open plains. Baboons and patas monkeys have also moved out into open country and in some parts of Africa have become adapted to life in a totally treeless environment.

We must ask why these ground-living monkeys have not evolved into men, and why men are today so much more than ground-living monkeys. There are many similarities in what we know of their history. It will be one of our purposes in this book to distinguish the different determinants of their very different evolutionary histories. Each group, men and baboons (better known than the patas monkeys), has carried the primate complex of characters into an environment to which it was quite unsuited, yet one group has evolved out of all recognition, while the other has remained a monkey. One central factor in this complex problem will become clear in this book—that the baboon, a terrestrial quadruped, was evolved from a quadrupedal monkey, while man, a terrestrial biped, was probably evolved from a higher primate already some way on the road to brachiation, comparable perhaps to the living semibrachiators that we have considered. The evidence for such a supposition is considered in chapter 6. For the present we shall merely record two further primate locomotor adaptations:

1. *Terrestrial quadrupedalism.* The baboons (*Papio*) and the patas monkeys (*Erythrocebus*) are ground-living quadrupeds. The savanna baboon (Fig. 3.5) is a very common and well-known African monkey that lives in open country and normally climbs into trees only to sleep. The patas monkey, less well known, occupies a similar environment. Two other genera contain species that are sometimes arboreal and sometimes terrestrial: *Cercopithecus* and *Theropithecus,* the guenon and gelada. These quadrupedal monkeys all walk on the ground on their palms, in contrast to the great apes that use the knuckles of their forelimbs. Their transfer to a terrestrial environment has involved no major struc-

tural modifications in their locomotor adaptations different from those of fully arboreal quadrupedal monkeys. They brought with them the two highly evolved primate characters of flexible and precise mobility and highly efficient sight, together with an enlarged cerebral cortex. These advantages, not obvious or necessary adaptations to plains life, perhaps enabled them to overcome such disadvantages on the ground as a lack of adaptations for running far and fast. Their establishment as a unique and stable element in the terrestrial fauna of the Old World is probably due mainly, however, to their large primate cerebral cortex and primate social structure, which we shall consider in chapters 9 and 10.

2. *Terrestrial bipedalism.* Although birds are bipedal, no mammals but man have evolved his peculiar kind of alternating bipedal gait. Many mammals move on two legs but, like the kangaroo, by hopping. Probably man alone shares with the dinosaurs the symmetrical alternating walk, but both dinosaurs and kangaroos have brought the tail into use as a prop or propulsive organ, and neither group shows any equivalence to man's erect posture. Among the whole animal kingdom, man is unique in his combination of an erect spine and a bipedal walk. In this respect, his evolution, which involved fundamental changes in structure and function, is perhaps nearly as remarkable as the evolution of marine mammals. The two hominid genera *Australopithecus* and *Homo* we know to be plains-living and bipedal. (Having only cranial fragments of the third genus, *Ramapithecus,* we can say nothing about its locomotor adaptations). In the first two genera quite fundamental changes must have taken place during their evolution from a tree-living form. It will be our purpose in chapter 5 to trace these changes so far as it is possible.

3.6 Neural correlates of arboreal locomotion

IN THE FUNCTIONAL ANALYSIS of the evolution of the human body, it has not yet proved possible, except in a very few instances, to determine in detail the neural correlates of a functional change. Studies of the descending motor nerve pathways from the brain to the muscles do, however, show that some important changes have occurred in the evolution of primates that may be correlated with the evolution of fast primate arboreal locomotion. Some significant differences between primates and other mammals, on the one hand, and between the lower and higher primates, on the other, have been demonstrated in these descending nerve tracts.

Among mammals generally we find a relatively direct system of nerve fibers running from the enlarged cerebral cortex of the brain to the motor *neurons* (nerve cells) of the spine, which supply nerves to the muscles and effect their contraction. These *corticospinal fibers* (also called the *pyramidal system*) are exclusive to mammals and reach their greatest development in the higher primates. This phylogenetically new system (that is, one relatively recently evolved) is complementary to the phylogenetically ancient and indirect *extrapyramidal* tracts, the fibers of which arise in the brainstem rather than the cortex and reach the motor neurons via a sequence of relay neurons. The evolution of the corticospinal tracts is correlated with the evolution of the cerebral cortex (see 2.6, 8.6); recent experiments have shown that they are responsible for precise motor control and that they add to muscular activity both speed and a capacity for very precise movement. This capacity of refinement is superimposed upon that of the indirect brainstem systems of the extrapyramidal tracts that direct movement in a more general way. Figure 3.7 shows in diagrammatic form the difference between the arrangement of these two kinds of nerve tracts.

In all mammals the contraction of the muscles is brought about by nerves that find their origin in the motor neurons within the spinal cord. As has been said, these motor neurons are activated by connections from the descending nerve fibers from either the brainstem or the cortex. The connection is made by a relay neuron, the so-called *internuncial neuron*. However, it has been shown through studies on monkeys, chimpanzees, and man, that in primate evolution an increasing number of corticospinal fibers make direct connection with the motor neurons and bypass the internuncial cells (Kuypers 1964). This is a most important primate evolutionary development, and it is especially interesting that the motor neurons of *distal* muscles (farthest from the trunk) receive more direct cortical fibers than do those of *proximal* muscles (nearest to the trunk). This finding (reviewed in Kuypers 1964) correlates nicely with the evolution of the primate hand and foot, and especially with the evolution of the human hand. Kuypers has shown that these direct connections from the cortex to the motor neurons are not established at birth but develop during early life with the coming of precise motor activity.

In the evolution of man's motor-nerve pathways, we see therefore (1) a large increase in the number of direct connections between the cortex and the spine that are shown to effect muscular speed and precision and (2) the appearance during primate evolution of a direct connection between these fibers and the motor neurons, especially in connections to the distal musculature of the hand and foot. Here we have a clear-cut neurological correlate of the evolution of the human hand, a striking and significant organizational improvement in motor control.

FIG. 3.7. Diagram of motor (descending) nerve fibers. *CS* labels a cortico-spinal fiber that in higher primates forms a direct link between the motor cortex *(MC)* and the motor neuron *(MN)* of the spinal cord. *EP* labels two of the extrapyramidal fibers that connect the cerebral cortex through a complex sequence of relay neurons in the brainstem to the motor neurons of the spinal cord. (Internuncial neurons omitted.) (Redrawn after Noback and Moskowitz, 1963.)

Precise muscular control is not, however, achieved merely by fast muscular contraction. The extent of such contraction is controlled by information returned to the brain by special sensory nerve endings within every muscle, the *proprioceptors*. The proprioceptors feed back to the brain information as to the extent of the effected contraction and cause adjustment in the frequency of the motor-nerve impulses. The precise control of muscular contraction by proprioceptors is believed to be carried out in the cerebellum (Fig. 3.8, *C*) as well as in the cerebral cortex.

Ascending fibers from the proprioceptors as well as from the sen-

Fig. 3.8. Diagram of sensory (ascending) nerve fibers. *LS* labels a fiber of the lemniscal system, which forms a relatively direct link between the sensory neuron *(SN)* (from proprioceptors in the muscle shown here, but also from the skin) and the somatic sensory cortex *(SC)* via relay neurons *(RN)* in the brainstem near the cerebellum *(C)* and in the thalamus *(T)*. *RS* labels a reticular fiber that constitutes a relatively indirect link between the sensory neuron and the cortex (Redrawn after Noback and Moskowitz, 1963.)

sory nerve endings in the skin (the somatic sensory nerve tracts) are therefore of almost equal importance with the descending fibers in the evolution of primate locomotion. While studies of these ascending tracts in mammals have not yet revealed such a striking novelty as that which we have recorded in the descending pathways, we do have evidence of two equivalent and complementary systems of nerve paths like those described above. The *lemniscal system* is prominent in mammals and reaches its highest development in the primates and especially in man. It is a relatively direct system of fibers linking the peripheral sensory nerve cells with the cerebral cortex. The phylogenetically older *reticular system* is, as its name implies, more indirect and diffuse and is the more primitive of the two. Nerve tracts of the two systems are shown diagrammatically in Figure 3.8. Here the sensory neuron, which lies in a small knot (*ganglion*) of nervous tissue near the spinal cord, can transmit an impulse from the proprioceptors in the muscle of the forearm to both the lemniscal and reticular systems. According to Herrick (1956), the lemniscal system is fast, specific, and analytical, the reticular system nonspecific and integrative. The latter has been shown experimentally to be responsible for arousal and wakefulness and effects a general condition of alertness. Both systems are well developed in primates, and particularly in man.

When we look, therefore, at the ascending and descending nerve pathways in primate evolution, we see a general increase in relatively fast direct connections between the cerebral cortex, the sense receptors, and the muscles. The precision of primate muscular activity is due not only to the evolution of these direct systems of nerve fibers, however, but also to a very complex feedback control mechanism, which depends on both descending and ascending nerve tracts as well as upon an increasingly complex organization in the brain.

3.7 Neural correlates of binocular vision

IN ORDER TO UNDERSTAND the evolution of primate vision, it is necessary to understand in some detail the structure and operation of the visual system as a whole.

The brain is a spatially organized and oriented organ in which the two sides are connected by nerve tracts to the opposite sides of the body.

Through these motor and sensory connections, the two sides of the brain are, as it were, concerned with the opposite two halves of the environment, the left hemisphere with the right half and the right hemisphere with the left half. The optic nerves, which carry the input to the brain from the eyes, therefore cross before they reach the brain, at a structure called the *optic chiasma*. The evolution of stereoscopic vision has, however, involved an overlap in the field of view of each eye, so the light from a single object can enter both eyes at the same time (Table 3.4). There is some overlap—some binocular vision—in many mammals, especially cats (whose eyes face forward), but in the primates this feature reaches its full development.

TABLE 3.4 APPROXIMATE EXTENT OF VISUAL FIELDS OF CERTAIN MAMMALS (WITHOUT HEAD MOVEMENT)

Mammal	Angle between Optical Axis of Eye and Midline of Head	Total Visual Field*	Greatest Width of Binocular Field
Horse	40°	360°	57°
Dog	20°	250°	116°
Cat	8°	287°	130°
Monkey, ape, and man	0°	180°	120°

* Note that, since in the primates the eyes come to point straight ahead, the total visual field is reduced; this reduction is compensated for by free movement of the head. Data from Walls 1963.

In primate evolution the eyes have moved toward each other in the face, so in many lower and all higher primates the two fields of view overlap almost entirely. As sense organs, the eyes are no longer concerned individually and exclusively with the two halves of the environment; instead, they are each receiving information from both halves of the environment, which involves a new distribution of the optic nerve tracts. We find that in animals with stereoscopic sight the nerve fibers are so arranged at the chiasma that those from the left side of *both* eyes pass to the left side of the brain and similarly for the right side (Fig. 3.9). That is to say, a portion of the nerve fibers do not cross at the chiasma, and, as the extent of the binocular field increases over that of the monocular field, the noncrossed fibers increase over the crossed fibers until in man nearly 50 per cent of the fibers from each eye pass to the same side of the brain. Information from each eye is thus equally distributed to the two sides of the brain, which receives a double image of the environment.

It is on the basis of the slight differences in this double image that the brain is enabled to assess the relative and, with experience, the absolute distance of different objects. Visual knowledge of the relative distance from the animal of different parts of the environment makes

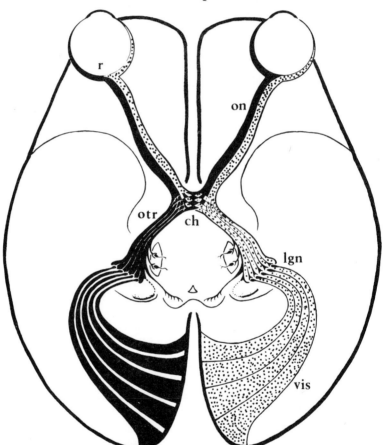

FIG. 3.9. Diagram of the human visual system: *r,* retina; *on,* optic nerve; *ch,* optic chiasma; *otr,* optic tracts; *lgn,* lateral geniculate body; and *vis,* tract to visual cortex. Fibers originating in the inner or nasal halves of the retinae cross at the chiasma so the visual cortex of each side receives signals from the same half of the field of view—that is, the opposite half. The signals, however, represent two slightly different images, and on the basis of these differences depth and distance are perceived. (After Polyak, 1957.)

possible three-dimensional perception. Depth is added to breadth and height.

The estimation of distance on the basis of a difference in the analysis of form (that is, a slightly different view of an object) involves a comparison of the images of the two eyes. The difference in the two images of a near object will be much greater than that in the images of a distant object. It follows that to interpret depth at a distance involves greater visual discrimination than such interpretation at a close range. This fact no doubt goes some way to explain the degree of visual discrimination available to primates, for a high level of discrimination is essential to an accurate analysis of the difference between the two images received by the brain. The eyes, it appears, have evolved as precision range-finders; the ability of man to read fine print looks like a byproduct of this adaptation.

We are only beginning to get some understanding of the process of visual analysis in the brain. Experiments with the cat (Hubel 1963) have shown that analysis begins in the *retina* and continues in the *lateral geniculate body* and then in the *visual cortex* (Fig. 3.9). Hubel has shown that the pattern of impulses from the retina is analyzed by banks of neurons for individual components of pattern, color, and movement. We must assume that the result of the analysis is then compared in some way with visual patterns stored within the brain and that such comparison may result in "recognition" of certain environmental phenomena.

In animals with stereoscopic vision the analysis must also include a simultaneous comparison of images, and the differences between them are interpreted as distance and depth in accordance with memory traces of previous visual experience. Though the complexity of this process is immense, it seems quite clear that to turn an image into a view of the environment (that is, perception), it is essential to compare the image with recorded memory of other images with their context of sensory and motor experience. Perception involves memory, and perception of the detailed kind available to higher primates (and eventually man) involves increasingly extensive analysis and increasingly extensive memory banks. As we shall see (8.6) the parts of the brain believed to function as memory banks (in particular, the *temporal lobes*) have expanded rapidly in primate evolution. Recent investigations by Kuypers *et al.* (1965) show the tremendous extent to which nerve tracts from the visual cortex pass to other areas of the cerebral cortex. These intercortical connections are very typical of advanced mammals and the higher primates, and they are surely correlates of the immense importance of vision in almost every aspect of the animal's life history (Fig. 3.10).

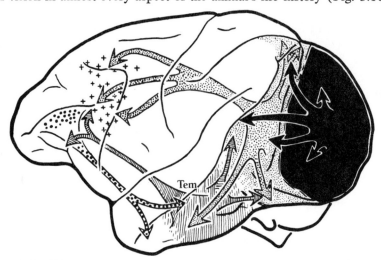

FIG. 3.10. Diagram of some of the intracortical connections in the brain of the monkey *Macaca* recently revealed by Kuypers. Note the dense connections between the visual cortex *(black)*, its neighboring association cortex *(shadad)*, and the temporal lobe *(Tem)*. (After Kuypers, 1965.) See also sec. 8.6.

We are visual animals. Three-dimensional vision gives a wide range of precise information about the environment that cannot be obtained by any other means. Because light travels in straight lines and because the nature of reflected light is determined by the chemical and physical structure of objects, very precise data about the nature of objects can be obtained at a distance. Stereoscopic vision and competent motor investigation (in particular, manipulation) make the world view of the higher primates unique both in quality and in kind. Primates alone have come to know the structure of the environment in terms of both pattern and composition. They see the environment as a collection of objects rather than merely as a pattern, and the recognition of objects is, as we shall see (9.2), the beginning of conceptual thought. With the coming of stereoscopic vision, the primate can begin to perceive non-spatial abstractions, and this advanced perception finds its foundation in combining the analytic functions of the two sides of the brain. The evolution of vision is one essential basis for the evolution of an animal that came to understand its environment so well that it could control it for its direct benefit.

Fig. 3.11. Diagrammatic representation of lineages suggesting the course of the evolution of the Old World Anthropoidea. The origin of the different groups is not known with certainty and may date from the Oligocene or earlier. Important genera are labeled as follows: *Homo* (*H*) *Australopithecus* (*A*), *Ramapithecus* (*R*), *Proconsul* (*P*), *Gorilla* (*G*), *Pan* (*C*), *Pongo* (*O*), and the gibbons *Hylobates* and *Symphalangus* (*S*). *T1–T5* are possible hypothetical origins of the Hominidae.

3.8 Fossil hominids: candidates for man's ancestry

WE HAVE already seen that, while the greatest amount of evidence for the nature of man's ancestors comes from the study of living primates, the most direct evidence is to be found among fossil forms that bear close resemblance to him. Man's relationship to both fossil and living primates is illustrated very approximately in Figure 3.11. The diagram represents no finally accepted fact of evolution but rather a hypothesis that is supported by the present evidence. In the figure, we see the monkeys evolving with little morphological change from Oligocene times, and, from near their origin, we see lineages leading to the great apes and the gibbons (the subfamilies Ponginae and Hylobatinae). Between these two groups (drawn here for convenience rather than to show the degree of morphological divergence) is shown the aberrant human family, the Hominidae, which left the forest and evolved so differently.

Some important fossil groups are shown in their approximate relationships in Figure 3.11: the Dryopithecinae, a subfamily of fossil apes, with one subgenus of fossil apes, *Proconsul* (*P*); and the three genera of the Hominidae, *Homo* (*H*), *Australopithecus* (*A*) and *Ramapithecus* (*R*). The figure also shows five different possible routes for the evolutionary lineage of the Hominidae (*T1–T5*). There are of course an infinite number of possible routes; for example, it has been suggested that man's evolution from a prosimian was independent from that of any other anthropoid primate. The evidence to be considered in the following chapters will show, however, that any other lineage basically different from those suggested here is highly improbable.

Let us consider the genera of the human lineage in turn. Beginning at the present we have man's own genus, *Homo*. There is a wide range of fossils of this genus, known from many parts of the Old World, which take us back nearly one million years. The genus is usually divided into two species, *Homo sapiens* (Fig. 3.12) and an earlier form, *Homo erectus* (Fig. 3.13, *A*). The known and supposed chronological ranges of these forms are shown in Table 3.5. This genus includes the famous fossil "men" that have made news in the last fifty years, such as Java man, Peking man, and Neandertal man. The most important fossils of the genus *Homo* are listed in the Appendix under the sites from which they were recovered. We can never know whether the populations represented by any of these fossils were actually ancestral to modern man, but their similarity to him makes it seem probable that at least some of them differed little from such ancestral groups. As might be expected, the more ancient fossils of this genus, especially those be-

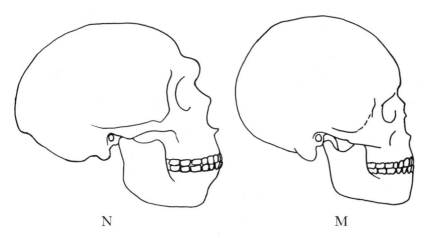

N   M

FIG. 3.12. Skulls of two subspecies of *Homo sapiens*: The large-jawed form from La Chapelle (*N*) and a more modern form from Cro-Magnon in France (*M*). Note the differences in size and shape of the jaws, facial bones, and browridges. The heavy jaws are associated with a long head, the small jaws with a round head.

A   B

FIG. 3.13. Skulls of *Homo erectus* (*A*) and *Australopithecus africanus* (*B*); both are reconstructions from imperfect fossil remains. The noticeable difference in the size of the jaws is accompanied by an equally striking difference in cranial capacity.

longing to the species *Homo erectus,* differ strikingly from modern man; but because no more man-like creatures are known from this or any more ancient geological level they fit well into the lineage of evolving man: the morphology of the fossils from earlier to later specimens makes a convincing evolutionary series (see 11.7).

From a lower level, the Lower Pleistocene, we have a group of African hominids classified as the genus *Australopithecus* (Fig. 3.13, *B*) The forms are much more typically anthropoid in head shape than *Homo,* yet they were bipedal like *Homo.* Again we cannot be sure that any of the known populations of *Australopithecus* were ancestral to the genus *Homo;* yet, on the basis of comparative morphology and chronological sequence, it seems highly probable that one species, *Australopithecus africanus,* was a link in the human lineage. Again the best preserved fossils are listed in the Appendix, the earliest known of which date from about 1.8 million years.

Before this time, we have no other known hominid fossils for at least 10 million years. In the Lower Pliocene or late Miocene, there are fossil remains of a genus termed *Ramapithecus.* Unfortunately, the remains are limited to the jaws and teeth, and even they are not complete, yet on the basis of the similarities that these fragments bear to *Australopithecus* and to *Homo* it is not unreasonable to place this genus near the origin of man's lineage, at least until further evidence

TABLE 3.5 APPROXIMATE CHRONOLOGICAL RANGE OF HOMINID SPECIES

		CHRONOLOGY IN THOUSANDS OF YEARS	
		Known Range of Fossils	*Assumed Range of Species*
Period	*Species*		
Present day	*Homo sapiens*	150–0	200–0
	Homo erectus	1000–490	1000–200
Pleistocene (3 million years' duration)	*Australopithecus africanus* *Australopithecus robustus*	1900–600?	4000–600
Pliocene (10 million years' duration)	[no Pliocene fossils known]		
Miocene (12 million years' duration)	*Ramapithecus punjabicus*	14,000	15,000–4,000

becomes available (Fig. 3.14, *R*). Because any fossil specimen less human than *Ramapithecus* would be indistinguishable from the fossil monkeys and apes, we can safely put this specimen near the origin of man's distinct lineage from his anthropoid ancestry.

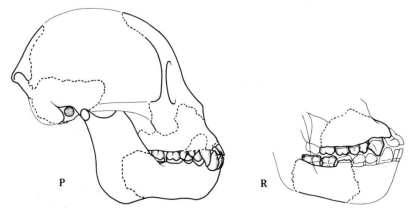

FIG. 3.14. Fragmentary skull of *Proconsul* (*P*) and jaws of *Ramapithecus* (*R*). Dotted lines indicate the edges of the bone fragments; fine lines indicate the reconstructed shape of the missing parts. Note the relative size of the canines. (Drawn to the same molar-premolar length [M2-P3].)

For example, a fossil that lies morphologically very close to *Ramapithecus* belongs to the subgenus *Proconsul,* known from East African Miocene deposits (Fig. 3.14, *P*). However, in many features of its morphology, *Proconsul* shows definite ape-like characters and therefore is placed in the subfamily of fossil apes, the Dryopithecinae. Yet it is also less specialized than the modern apes and is morphologically not very far from the point at which apes and monkeys diverged. From our considerations of *Ramapithecus,* as well as on the basis of other evidence (see chapter 11), it seems quite probable that the Hominidae became distinct from either monkeys or apes at about the time those two great groups themselves diverged (*T2* in Figure 3.11). It is possible, however, that *Ramapithecus* will prove to be more ape-like or more monkey-like than it appears on the basis of the known fragments. This possibility might suggest hypothesis *T3* or that designated by the line *T4*. On the other hand, if *Ramapithecus* should prove to be very divergent from *Australopithecus,* we may be thrown back on other possibilities, such as *T1* or *T5*. The structure and significance of *Ramapithecus* will be discussed further in chapters 7 and 11.

3.9 Summary

WE OURSELVES are primates, and the origin of our nature may be traced quite precisely to the adaptations of the primates that evolved in response to the forest environment. The special problems associated with that environment demand sensory awareness, swift mobility, and a brain able to make accurate and immediate prediction. We owe our nature primarily to the challenge of that environment. In the following chapters of this book, an attempt will be made to show how each aspect of man's physiology and behavior evolved in response to the challenge either of the forest or of the totally different open environment of the plains, in which he later achieved his manhood. The majority of mammals have evolved for tens of millions of years in one environment alone, deer and antelopes in the plains, whales in the sea, primates in the forests; man's move from the forest to the plain made us finally into what we are and is the story of our own evolution.

As we have proposed, the story of our evolution can best be told by studying in turn the evolution of each functional complex of characters according to its changing function. In treating each functional complex, we shall compare man with some of the living monkeys and apes in order to establish his relationship to them. Where fossils are available, we shall then consider the evidence from that source in order to establish in more detail the morphology and chronology of the Hominidae—the family of man's ancestors.

In that framework we shall study the special adaptations that distinguish man from other primates—adaptations to life on the plains. The movement from forest to plain was a remarkable and rather mysterious event. Some authors see it as the direct result of a lowered rainfall, which restricted the extent of the tropical forests and caused increased population pressures. Others see it simply as resulting from the normal competitive pressures of organic life, which favor the exploitation of all exploitable environments. The point to note, however, is that if a population is to exploit an environment different from that of its ancestors, it must to some extent be adapted to the new environment already, or, to use a common term, it must be *preadapted*. Of course, many animals are preadapted in varying degrees to environments not their own, and that is what is meant by a generalized species.

All quadrupedal monkeys are in their locomotor character preadapted to terrestrial life in a way that jumping prosimians and full brachiators are not. It is certain that man himself must have been preadapted to plains life, otherwise he could not have evolved into a fully terrestrial animal. The extent of preadaptation and the kinds of selection pressure involved will be discussed in chapter 11. Our purpose in the next and following chapters is to examine man's adaptations in some detail and in a historical setting so that it may be possible at a later stage to make an extrapolation to his origin.

SUGGESTIONS FOR FURTHER READING

The most convenient reference book on the living primates is J. R. and P. H. Napier, *Handbook of Living Primates* (New York and London: Academic Press, 1967). For a full account of primate anatomy in process of publication, consult W. C. Osman Hill, *Primates* (Edinburgh: University of Edinburgh Press, 1953–). The most compact text on fossil primates is W. E. le Gros Clark, *The Antecedents of man* (Edinburgh: University of Edinburgh Press, 1962). Some of the most important fossil Hominidae are briefly described in M. Day, *Guide to Fossil Man* (London: Cassell, 1965). For a complete catalog of Hominid fossils refer to a work at present in course of publication: K. P. Oakley and B. G. Campbell, *Catalogue of Fossil Hominids* (3 vols.; London: British Museum [Nat. Hist.]). On the general features of the nervous systems of mammals consult J. Z. Young, *The Life of Mammals* (Oxford: Oxford University Press, 1957). For the evolution of the vertebrate visual system consult S. Polyak, *The Vertebrate Visual System* (Chicago: University of Chicago Press, 1957).

$\mathscr{L}4$

Body Structure
and Posture

4.1 Body structure and locomotion

A VAST MAJORITY of the visible and gross features of the vertebrate body are related to the function of locomotion. Primitive locomotion in fish was achieved by a wave-like movement of the vertebral column in a lateral plane. The trout moves its tail from side to side, and the waves of muscular contraction pass forward up the animal's body. In primitive fish the fins are used mainly as stabilizers and for steering, but in later forms they may be used to propel the fish, especially the paired fins—the *pectoral* fins behind the head, the *pelvic* fins nearer the tail.

The first fish to climb from the water used their pectoral and pelvic fins as props for their bodies, and from that moment the locomotor function was transferred from the vertebral column to what became the limbs. The paired pectoral and pelvic fins were attached to the spine by three paired bones of the same name, later to become the shoulder and pelvic girdles. The lateral muscles at the sides of the vertebral column (the *myotomes,* which effected the wave motion of the body) were then greatly reduced, and the limb musculature developed in their place. An intermediate stage can be seen in the newt (Figs. 4.1 and 4.2), which uses both its myotome muscles and its limbs for propulsion.

FIG. 4.1. Locomotion in the fish and newt. Note that the same wave motion is used by both animals, but in the newt it is reinforced by the action of the pectoral and pelvic limbs, which evolved from the paired fins in the fish.

As the limbs took over the locomotor function in terrestrial vertebrates, the vertebral column assumed a quite new function—that of supporting the body above the limbs. The flexibility so necessary for swimming was replaced by a stiffness necessary to carry the head and body. The soft parts already *ventral* to (on the underside of) the vertebral column in fish became suspended from it in vertebrates, and the head

FIG. 4.2. The locomotion of the newt on land still combines features of fish and quadruped locomotion. Note that the limbs are splayed sideways; they cannot support the body, which is dragged along. The musculature is still lateral, not dorsal and ventral as in evolved quadrapeds.

became supported by a cantilever. The resulting structure was compared by D'Arcy Thompson (1942) to that of a cantilevered bridge
(Fig. 4.3) and can be understood as a weight-bearing compound girder.
The important muscles are now ventral and *dorsal* to (that is, below
and above) the vertebral column, no longer lateral. This change in the
evolution of vertebrates is most important and is clearly demonstrated
in the secondarily aquatic whales, which evolved from terrestial quad-

Fig. 4.3.   The bison and the cantilever bridge are constructed according
to the same mechanical principles. The nuchal muscles (*dotted line*)
in the bison, and the upper horizontal member of the steel bridge, take
the tension due to gravity; the centra of the vertebrae and the lower
horizontal member of the bridge withstand the compression. The vertical
and diagonal struts separate the horizontal members and form the webbing. The nerve cord and road are suspended within this webbed compound girder. (After D'Arcy Thompson, 1942.)

rupeds and which propel themselves in the sea by moving their tails up and down rather than laterally as do the fish.

In the terrestrial quadruped, therefore, the vertebral column is under compression—the *centrum* of each vertebra (and the *intervertebral discs*) carry the load, and the *supraspinous* ligaments are under tension, while the *nuchal muscles* of the neck support the head (see Fig. 4.4). The bending moment (that is, the force tending to cause bending) in the spine owing to the weight of the body and head is reflected in the length of the *spinous processes,* which, together with the oblique *interspinous ligaments* and muscles, constitute the web of the compound girder. The spinous processes are rarely so greatly developed over the pelvic girdle as over the pectoral because in most vertebrates the weight of the tail is less than that of the head, though exceptions to this are known (dinosaur, kangaroo). Further stressing over the center section of the girder between the limbs is achieved by an inverted parabolic girder of which the *sternum* and abdominal muscles form the ventral tension member (see Fig. 4.4).

Bridges, however, are designed for rigidity, and the anatomy of bridges is only comparable to that of animals, insofar as animals require rigidity in their skeletons. Flexible structures are of a different order

FIG. 4.4. Architecture of a quadrupedal monkey (*Cercopithecus*). Note that the nuchal muscles (*dotted*) are still important but that the head is much lighter than in the bison so the cervical spines are much shorter. The trunk is supported by an inverted parabolic structure under tension—the sternum and abdominal muscles (*interrupted line*). (From Le Gros Clark, 1962.)

of complexity and do not so clearly follow the simple mechanical principles of the bridge-builder. That is why the cantilever structure is seen more clearly in the large slow-moving animals than in the small, active forms. Flexibility means that the bony members must be jointed to allow movement, and the spinous processes of the vertebrae must be short enough not to touch each other when the body is flexed. In this case, the girder is supported by ligaments under very high stress; it has gained flexibility at the cost of strength.

The second factor to be recalled when studying skeletal architecture is that when the loads due to gravity are very slight, as in small animals, the structures associated with locomotion will mask those designed to withstand the force of gravity.

In this chapter we shall trace the evolution of posture from the quadrupedal to the erect, which, as we have mentioned, is found among prosimians as well as in man. The spine, which began in fish as a flexible rod under intermittent compression (when the myotomes contract) is, in quadrupeds, the compression member in a weight-bearing compound girder. In man it becomes a vertical weight-bearing flexible rod, stiffened a little by rigging, like the mast of a yacht. We shall see that this change of function is accompanied by change in form.

4.2 *Center of gravity*

DIFFERENCES in the form of the vertebral column among quadrupedal animals are due primarily to differences in the center of weight of the animal, better known as the center of gravity. This center will move forward or backward along the spine depending on whether there is more body weight in the head and shoulder region or in the hind quarters and tail region. In the bison, judging by the skeleton shown in Figure 4.3, the majority of weight lies over the forelimbs, and that is where the center of gravity lies. In contrast, the dinosaur and kangaroo, for example, both have far more weight over the hindlimbs, and that is the feature which allows them semierect posture with tail support, so that they can collect vegetation with their forelimbs (Fig. 4.5). A parallel trend can be seen in the evolution of the primates. Here the center of gravity has moved back for two reasons.

The first is that the musculature and length of the hindlimbs has increased, especially in the leaping and grasping prosimians, to give extra locomotive power. The second reason is that the tail has enlarged into an organ to maintain balance when jumping. It is also necessary that, when an animal is propelled forward, the force of propulsion should pass through the center of gravity; otherwise the animal would revolve in the air. It therefore follows that a center of gravity near the organ of propulsion, the back legs, will add to the stability of the jumping prosimian.

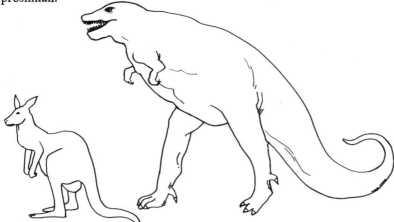

FIG. 4.5. The marsupial kangaroo and the 20-foot reptile *Tyrannosaurus* from the Upper Cretaceous are both bipedal but gain support from a heavy and powerful tail. In each, the spinous processes of the vertebrae reach their greatest development over the hindlimbs. Note the greatly reduced forelimbs. (Not drawn to scale.)

It is for these reasons that in the early stages of primate evolution we see the center of gravity well back over the hindlimbs. This development makes practical the sitting position (Fig. 4.6) and frees the forelimbs for manipulation, just as we see in the squirrel and kangaroo. It also makes possible the later stages of human evolution, when man became able to stand and run on his hindlimbs. The forest adaptation of a low center of gravity was a necessary prerequisite for this final evolutionary development. In man, while the tail was lost, the low position of the center of gravity was enhanced by still further development of the hindlimbs, somewhat reduced musculature in the forelimbs, and some changes in the form and position of the trunk and abdomen.

FIG. 4.6. The ring-tailed lemur (*Lemur catta*) achieves a comfortable sitting position, but the forearms help the balance. Note the immense tail, with heavy fur. (From Le Gros Clark, 1962.)

4.3 Evolution of the spine and thorax

THE ANTHROPOIDEA generally, adapted as they are for speedy arboreal locomotion, have evolved very flexible spines, compared with most quadrupedal plains mammals. Flexion of the spine has been added to that of the legs to give extra propulsive power in jumping, as well as to absorb the shock of impact. Flexibility was achieved by some small modifications of the spine, which are most clearly seen in the quadrupedal forms:

1. There are well-developed intervertebral discs that act as elastic buffers and allow tipping movement of the vertebrae.

2. The spinous processes are relatively short with the result that flexibility is not restricted by their proximity.

3. The *thorax* (the rib cage and its musculature), which gives the kind of support to the trunk that is achieved by a parabolic girder, stiffens the spine along the thoracic region. In quadrupedal primates (such as macaca) the *cervical* (neck) and *lumbar* (waist) regions of the spine are relatively long, and these regions in particular allow bending movements of the body (see Fig. 4.7, *A*).

FIG. 4.7. Trunk skeletons of the macaque (*Macaca*) (*A*), the gibbon (*Hylobates*) (*B*), modern man (*C*), and the chimpanzee (*Pan*) (*D*) drawn the same size. Note the different forms of the thorax (*t*) and pelvis (*p*) in these species and the different relative lengths of the lumbar region (*l*) (From Schultz, 1950.)

In semibrachiating and particularly in brachiating forms, however, this flexibility is somewhat lost, since the spine plays a far smaller part in locomotion. We find, for example, that three of the nine lumbar vertebrae found in quadrupedal monkeys become thoracic in gibbons (Washburn 1963b) (Fig. 4.7, *B*). The numbers of such vertebrae are shown in Table 4.1, where it can be seen that in this respect man is stiff-backed and is morphologically near to the brachiators and semi-brachiators. It is, however, interesting that the stiffening has proceeded further among the great apes than it has in man. As a whole, these data suggest quite strongly that man evolved from a brachiating primate. But other fundamental changes have occurred in the spine and thorax during human evolution that were adaptations to man's fully erect posture.

TABLE 4.1 AVERAGE NUMBERS OF THORACIC AND LUMBAR VERTEBRAE

	THORACIC VERTEBRAE		LUMBAR VERTEBRAE	
PRIMATE	Mean	Range	Mean	Range
Papio	10	9–11	9	9
Hylobates	13	12–14	6	5–7
Apes	13		4	
Man	12	11–12	5	5–6

1. The size of the centrum increases at the pelvic end of the spine (Fig. 4.8) because the forces of compression are no longer constant along the trunk as they are in a quadruped with a horizontal spine. As the force of compression increases from head to pelvis because of the weight of the animal, so the cross-section of the centrum, which bears it, must also increase (Schultz 1953). The proportions of the

FIG. 4.8. Medial sections through a chimpanzee (A) and a man (B) showing the curvature of the spine and form of the vertebrae. fm, base of skull; s, sacrum; ps, pubic symphysis. (After Weidenreich, 1941.)

centrum also change (Schultz 1960), and the weight distribution of the vertebrae themselves changes in order to carry the vertical forces of compression.

2. The spinous processes are more or less equally developed along the spine because the bending moment—the tendency to bend—is no longer restricted to the points of support, the limb girdles, but is now more evenly distributed. For example, the gorilla has well-developed cervical spines to support the very heavy head, but they are reduced in man, since the head is more or less balanced on top of the spine (Fig. 4.9).

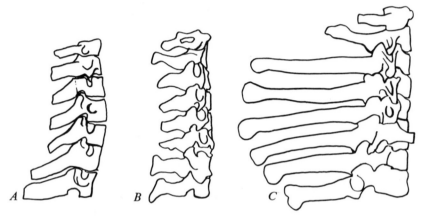

FIG. 4.9. Cervical vertebrae of modern man (*A*), *Hylobates* (*B*), and *Gorilla* (*C*). The length of the spinous processes of the vertebrae is proportional, not to the amount of weight transmitted down the spine, but to that carried by the nuchal muscles. (Not drawn to scale.)

3. The inverted parabolic girder effect of the sternum and abdominal muscles to stiffen the spine becomes less important. The sternum tends to lie nearer to the vertebral column, its segments become fused (Schultz 1930) and broaden, and the form of the thorax is wider and less deep (Fig. 4.10), bringing the center of gravity nearer the vertebral column. Schultz (1960) has studied the angle between the "neck" and "body" of the ribs and finds that among the monkeys the angle varied from 89 to 100 degrees, while among the more erect apes and men it varied from 50 to 65 degrees (Fig. 4.11).

4. Increased weight transmission through the pelvis and legs has resulted in an enlargement of the *sacrum,* that is, the "sacralization" of more vertebrae at the base of the spine. Among the lower primates

2–4 vertebrae are sacralized, while among the great apes and man they average 5.5 and 5.2, respectively (Schultz 1930). The sacrum is also relatively wider and on the internal surface more convex (Figs. 4.7 and 4.8)

We see from these data that man has a relatively stiff spine, which suggests his origin among semibrachiators or brachiators, and he no doubt benefited by this preadaptation in the evolution of his fully erect bipedal posture. In achieving that posture, the spine evolved to form a vertical weight-bearing rod in place of a compound girder, which

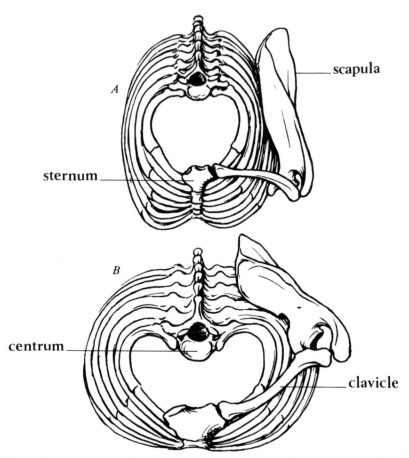

FIG. 4.10. View from above of the thorax and shoulder girdle of *Macaca* (*A*) and modern man (*B*) drawn to the same anterior-posterior depth. Note the very different shapes of the thorax and the different positions of the shoulder girdle. (From Schultz, 1950.)

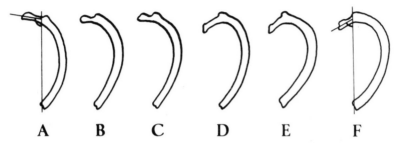

A   B   C   D   E   F

FIG. 4.11. Drawings of the second rib of three Old World monkeys (*Macaca* [*A*], *Papio* [*B*], *Presbytis* [*C*]) and two Pongidae (*Hylobates* [*D*] and *Pan* [*E*]), together with *Homo* (*F*), reduced to the same length. Note that the different form of the ribs reflects the different form of the thorax in these groups. The angle between the "neck" and "body" of the rib is shown for *Macaca* and *Homo* and is quoted in the text. (Redrawn after Schultz, 1960.)

means that the centra, which transmit the weight to the pelvic girdle, have increased in size downward, and the spinous processes, which supported the webbing of the girder, have become much reduced. The thorax has flattened to allow the center of gravity to move back toward the spine, and the centrum effectively lies within the thoracic area (Fig. 4.10). The weight of the body is transmitted to the legs via the pelvic girdle, and the changes here will be discussed in chapter 5.

The evidence of man's ancestry, derived from the vertebral column, is important and may in time prove to be supported by investigation of the fossilized vertebrae of *Australopithecus* (Robinson 1956). Known fossils of early *Homo sapiens* populations have vertebrae similar to modern man (Straus and Cave 1957), and, as we shall see, there is much evidence that erect posture was the first necessary preadaptation to be evolved before man moved from the forest to the plains.

4.4 The head and neck

WE SHALL CONSIDER the functions of the head itself in chapters 7 and 8. Our purpose in this section is to consider the head not for itself but rather in its relation to the rest of the body. Just as semierect and erect postures have affected the form of the cervical vertebrae, so they have also affected the position of the head in relation to the spine and the connecting musculature.

We have seen how in such quadrupedal forms as the bison or
monkey the head is supported by a webbed girder consisting of the
cervical vertebrae under compression and the nuchal muscles and ligaments under tension (Figs. 4.3 and 4.4). It is clear that as a more
erect posture was evolved, the strength required in the nuchal muscles
was reduced, since more of the weight was carried directly by the spine.

At the same time, we have already mentioned that in primate
evolution generally the muzzle was reduced and the brain enlarged.
This development resulted in the center of gravity of the head itself
moving more nearly over the point of pivot of the head upon the spine.

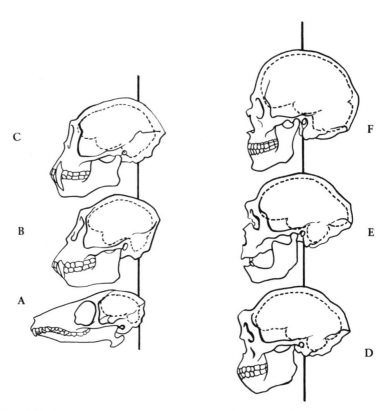

FIG. 4.12. Skulls of various primates aligned upon the point on which they
pivot on the spine, the occipital condyles. Note that in passing from
the lower to the higher primates, the center of gravity moves back;
the brain expands, the jaws recede. *Tupaia (A), Cercopithecus (B),
Hylobates (C), Homo erectus (D), Homo sapiens neanderthalensis
(E),* modern man (F). (Not drawn to scale.) (After DuBrul and Sicher
1954.)

This evolutionary trend is shown in Figure 4.12, where different skulls are aligned by their *occipital condyles,* the convex bone surfaces with which the skull pivots upon the first cervical vertebra. Here we clearly see the center of gravity moving back until it is almost exactly over the occipital condyles. It has not yet achieved a perfect balance, and probably will not do so, because there are no ventral muscles present to support the skull from the front and stop it from tipping backward. The condition of modern man is seen in Figure 4.13, where the weight of the head, ventral to the occipital condyles, is balanced by the nuchal muscles, dorsal to this pivot.

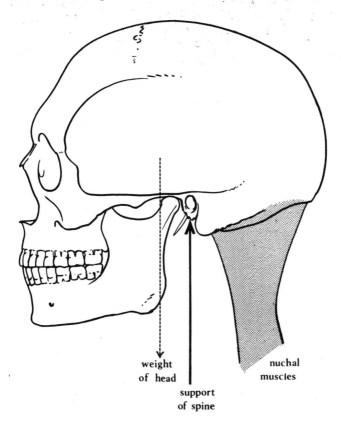

weight
of head

support
of spine

nuchal
muscles

FIG. 4.13. In the course of human evolution the center of gravity of the head has moved nearer to the point of pivot upon the spine—the occipital condyles. In modern man it approaches this point but is still slightly anterior to it. The weight is still balanced by the now rather reduced nuchal neck muscles.

Le Gros Clark has proposed a most useful means of assessing the extent to which this movement of the center of gravity has occurred in different primates, by measuring the position of the occipital condyles in relation to the rest of the skull. The *condylar position index* is calculated according to the simple geometrical basis described in Figure 8.13 (p. 235), and some figures for this index are recorded in Table 4.2.

TABLE 4.2 THE POSITION OF THE OCCIPITAL CONDYLES

Primate	Mean Condylar Position Index
Proconsul africanus	30
Gorilla	24
Pan	23
Pongo	26
Australopithecus africanus	40
Modern man	77–81

Condylar position index measured in Frankfurt plane; $\frac{CD}{CE}$ (see Fig. 8.13). Data from Le Gros Clark (1950), Ashton and Zuckerman (1951), and Davis and Napier (1963).

Note that the increase of the index has begun in *Australopithecus* but has not at this stage progressed very far in the human direction. The index numbers may be compared with the drawings in Figure 4.12. We shall return to this trend in chapter 8.

This double change, in posture and in the head's center of gravity, has had the effect of removing work from the nuchal muscles, which have in turn been reduced. Schultz (1942) has shown that six times as much power is needed in the nuchal muscles of monkeys and apes than is needed to support the head in man. This reduction in musculature has been reflected in the area of insertion of the nuchal muscles upon the back of the skull (termed the *nuchal area*) (Fig. 4.14). When we compare, for example, the gorilla and modern man, the difference is very striking. The fossil skull of *Homo erectus* (Figs. 4.12, *D,* and 4.14, *B*) is intermediate in this respect.

The reduction of the nuchal musculature has affected the form of the skull, for not only is the area of attachment in man much reduced but it is no longer bordered by a clearly defined nuchal crest. The back of the skull is relatively smooth and follows more closely the outline of the brain, for in man the outer layer of bone of the skull (the outer "table") responds very little to the nuchal muscles during growth (Figs. 4.12 and 4.14).

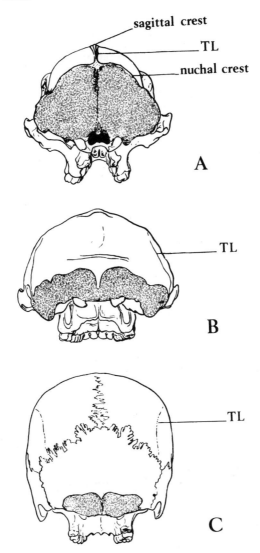

FIG. 4.14. Posterior view of skulls of *Gorilla (A)*, *Homo erectus (B)*, and modern man *(C)*. Note the decrease in size of the nuchal area *(shaded)*. *TL*, temporal line. (After Weidenreich, 1941.)

It has been mentioned that there are no ventral muscles in the neck to keep the head from tipping back—a problem probably unique to man. He can tip his head back beyond the point of balance, and he must be able to pull it forward again. The forward movement of the head is made possible by the *sternomastoid muscles*, which, lying on each side of the neck and inserted upon the *mastoid process* of the skull, and the sternum and clavical at the top of the thorax, are individually able to rotate the head upon the spine (Fig. 4.15). Their importance to the primates is very great, since this group is dependent

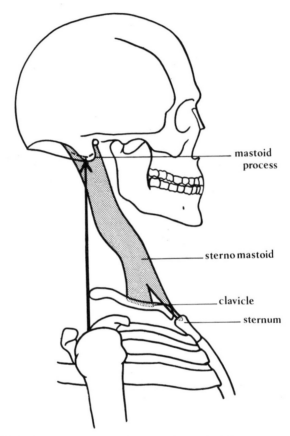

FIG. 4.15. Owing to the way the head is carried by quadrupeds, there is sufficient support for it in the nuchal muscles, and there are no muscles that attach the front of the skull to the thorax or spine. To pull the head forward after it has been thrown back, modern man relies on two rotator muscles, the sternomastoids, which are contracted together. Sufficient leverage is obtained to pull the head forward only by a slight elongation in the human mastoid process, which comes to project forward of the point of pivot (shown here [dotted] behind the mastoid process).

on rotary head movement to maintain effective all-round vision. When in man the center of gravity of the head moves back so near to the occipital condyles (the pivot of the head), the sternomastoid muscles come to counteract any backward forces upon the head by contracting together. In Figure 4.15 we see that, viewed from the side, their insertion is more or less in line with the occipital condyles.

Krantz (1963) has shown that the sternomastoid muscles obtain effective leverage to pull the head forward only because in the evolution of man an enlargement and lengthening of the mastoid processes has occurred. This lengthening alone makes it possible for the sternomastoids to raise the head after it has tipped back, because only by this lengthening is the insertion point of the muscles brought forward beyond the point of pivot when the head is thrown back (Fig. 4.16). As it is, the leverage is very poor indeed, a fact that the reader may check by throwing his head well back over the back of his chair and

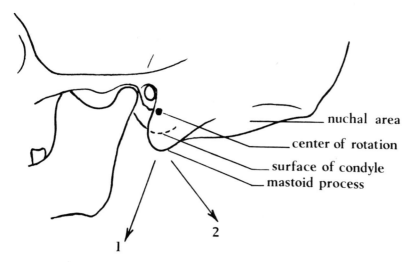

FIG. 4.16. The mechanical advantage bestowed by the mastoid process is apparent only when the head is moved from its normal position (when the sternomastoid muscle lies in direction *1*) and is tilted back, when the sternomastoid pulls in the direction indicated as *2*. Under these circumstances the mastoid can be seen to give some leverage about the center of rotation of the skull upon the spine. A smaller mastoid would reduce to nil the leverage available. The weakness of this mechanical system can be experienced if you lean well back in your chair and tilt your head all the way back; an effort is then required to raise the head. (After Krantz, 1963.)

slowly raising it again, with his hands on the sternomastoids. The enlargement of the mastoids in human evolution is thus a direct result of man's erect posture and of the forward movement of the occipital condyles in relation to the skull as a whole.

In this section we have seen how man comes to have a reduced nuchal musculature, a reduced nuchal area, and elongated mastoid processes. All these developments are facets of a double adaptive complex involving changes in the olfactory region and brain, which caused a movement in the head's center of gravity and so in the relative position of the occipital condyles. The fully erect spine of evolving man tended to tip the balance still farther, with the result that the center of gravity came to be very little forward of the occipital condyles themselves.

4.5 The tail

As WE HAVE SEEN, the tail is used by the primates for balance in jumping, and it has evolved in such a way as to bring the center of gravity back over the hindlimbs. It is also used in many groups as a rudder and elevator, in the same way as the tail of a bird or airplane, to adjust the position of the body as it passes through the air so that the animal will arrive with its limbs in a position to grasp on impact. This function accounts for the thick hair that the tail sometimes carries, which increases its aerodynamic effect (Fig. 4.6). We have also noted that in the New World monkeys the tail has evolved as a grasping organ— a fifth limb—so it adds to their mobility as well as to their stability.

As we have seen, the Hominoidea have lost their tails. Reduction has gone furthest in the gibbons, the most evolved brachiators. From perhaps twenty or thirty caudal vertebrae in the monkey, the gibbon is left with only one or two. The reason appears to be that, in this brachiating form, propulsion by the front legs rather than the back legs involves a totally different kind of motion, a different kind of flight. The aerodynamics are fundamentally changed. The gibbon moves through the air sideways, and the tail is no longer in a position to act as rudder and elevator (Fig. 3.6, p. 68). It serves no function and so has been reduced in the course of evolution.

Whether the heavier great apes were ever such lively brachiators seems doubtful, although their ancestors were certainly smaller than present forms. But, in any case, as sedate and heavyweight brachiators, they had no use for a tail and, though it is not quite so far reduced as in the gibbon, all visible signs have been lost.

In man the tail is reduced to from three to five small vertebrae known as the *coccyx*. This reduction may be due to fast brachiation, sedate brachiation, or simply to man's bipedal locomotion. We do not know when the tail was reduced, and at present no coccygeal vertebrae are known from *Australopithecus*. Reduction of the tail in modern man has not gone so far as in the gibbon, which may well be because it has assumed a totally new function arising from man's erect posture. The tail vertebrae, the coccyx, are now curved ventrally and help form the basin-shaped structure that carries the viscera. Ligaments run from the forward-pointing coccyx to the *ischium*—the lower part of the pelvis.

Figure 4.17 shows how the viscera in man are carried in a sack-shaped cavity: the spine at the back and the *rectus abdominis* muscles in front. At the base, the sack is rounded off by the curved bones of

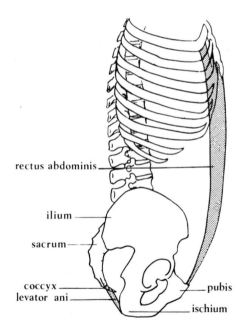

FIG. 4.17. Diagrammatic side view of the pelvis and associated musculature, which form a basin and support the viscera in man. Note that the coccyx, the remains of the tail, has an important function as a supporting structure—a totally new use for a tail.

the pelvis, the sacrum, and the coccyx and the *levator ani* muscles. This viscera-carrying function of the pelvis is again something new and is associated with bipedal locomotion. We shall consider the complex evolutionary changes in these bones in the next chapter.

4.6 Summary

IN THIS CHAPTER we have seen how the arboreal life of the lower primates has influenced the evolution of the spine in a number of ways:

1. The center of gravity moves to the back legs.
2. The tail assumes special functions, as a balancing rudder and elevator in Old World monkeys and as a fifth limb in New World forms.
3. Semierect posture develops.
4. The spine maintains considerable flexibility.

This process leads to the form of many modern arboreal monkeys without important modification, but a number of new trends have appeared in the descendent groups of higher primates:

1. A reversion to terrestrial quadrupedalism: all trends are reversed (e.g., *Papio*).
2. The evolution of brachiating locomotion: the tail is lost and the flexibility of the spine is reduced, the thorax is flattened and the posture is rather more erect (*Hylobates*).
3. The evolution of terrestial bipedalism: the posture is fully erect, the function of the spine is greatly modified as a vertical weight-bearer, the thorax is flattened to bring the center of gravity over the pelvis, the tail is modified to form a floor to the pelvis, and the relation of the head to the neck approaches balance (*Australopithecus, Homo*).

We have seen in this chapter how the different locomotor adaptations discussed in section 3.4 have fundamentally affected the form of the spine, the ribs, and the neck. We have also seen how man's unusually large brain and small muzzle have brought his head nearly into balance, and we have noted the modifications in the nuchal muscles and mastoid process that have resulted. All these changes, however, are relatively slight compared with those that have affected the locomotor apparatus.

SUGGESTIONS FOR FURTHER READING

Most of this chapter is based on the extensive investigations of Professor Adolf Schultz. Unfortunately his results have not been collected but are scattered throughout the literature. The following two papers summarize some of his research, and they both contain extensive lists of references to his work on other aspects of primate anatomy: A. H. Schultz, "The Specializations of Man and His Place among the Catarrhine Primates," *Cold Spring Harbor Symp. Quant. Biol.* 15 (1950): 37–53; "Age Changes, Sex Differences, and Variability as Factors in the Classification of Primates," *in* S. L. Washburn (ed.), *Classification and Human Evolution,* pp. 85–115 (Viking Fund Publs. Anthrop., No. 37 [Chicago: Aldine Publishing Co., 1963]).

$\mathcal{\sim}5$
Locomotion and
the Hindlimb

5.1 The generalized primate limb

IT IS THE LIMBS rather than any other part of the primate body that can be described as "generalized," that is, as having varied functions and thus capable of evolution in a number of different directions. Primate limbs are not used merely to support the body on a horizontal surface like props, as in most quadrupedal vertebrates. Among the primates, limbs have evolved to grasp the branches of trees and to support the body at various angles in relation to the branch. They have evolved to support the weight of the animal not only standing but also clinging and hanging. They have evolved as food-gathering organs, for cleaning the body, and as sense organs. The primates are characterized therefore by an efficient "universal" ball and socket joint, allowing movement in any direction, at the point of the attachment of the limbs at the shoulder and hip. The musculature has evolved accordingly, allowing the proximal limb bones (those nearest the trunk) to be moved in almost any direction and to support the body from a wide range of angles.

Flexibly mounted limbs are not so much unique to the primates as they are a primitive mammalian character that has been lost in other orders of mammals. Most terrestrial mammals, such as the ungulates, have undergone limb modifications in evolution that give greater stability at the expense of flexibility. Among horses, for example, not only is the direction of movement of the proximal limb bones limited to one plane, but the power of rotation of the distal bones (those farthest from the trunk) is lost too, and the digits are reduced in number, having no longer any grasping function. In the primates, however, we find the mammal limb developed without losing its generalized form, in response to the three-dimensional forest environment.

With a very flexible universal proximal joint to the limbs, the elbow and knee joints evolved not so much to give flexibility as to provide stability. Stability was achieved by retaining the primitive hinge joint with its more limited musculature, an arrangement that has the advantage of retaining the main mass of muscles near the trunk and keeping the limbs slender—an essential mechanical arrangement for a stable center of gravity in a fast-moving animal.

The relative length of the fore- and hindlimbs is closely related to the pattern of locomotion of primates. These lengths have been studied extensively by Schultz (1937) and others and are usually expressed by the *intermembral index*. From the data reproduced here (Fig. 5.1), it can be seen that man and the Old World quadrupedal *Macaca* have hindlimbs longer than forelimbs, while the other Hominoidea have forelimbs longer than hindlimbs. Longer limbs give greater speed of movement because they affect greater leverage: limbs primarily responsible for propulsion tend to lengthen in evolution, while those used least may tend to shorten. In this character man is closer to the Old World monkeys than to any of the other living Hominoidea; indeed, he has exceeded even the macaques in the relative length of his legs. All the forms with relatively longer arms are modified brachiators or true brachiators (Fig. 5.2).

The intermembral index of man has been considered suggestive of the stage of primate evolution at which he left the forest, but the considerable development of the hindlimb for bipedalism, which has almost certainly occurred since that event, together with a possible reduction of the forelimbs, has surely obscured the original limb proportions. For more reliable data we must await the discovery of fossil limb bones in a good state of preservation so that the limb proportions of ancestral groups may be calculated with some accuracy.

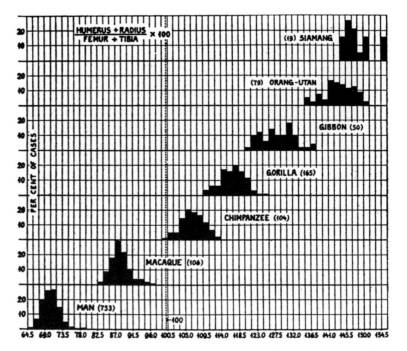

FIG. 5.1. Frequency polygons showing the distribution of variations in the intermembral index of different primates. Figures at the bottom indicate the intermembral index, those in brackets the sample size. The longer the hindlimbs in relation to the forelimbs, the lower the index; an index of 100 indicates limbs of equal length. (From Schultz, 1937.)

5.2 The evolution of the pelvis

THE PELVIS links the hindlimbs to the spine. It is a structure of complex shape, curved in all three planes of space, and together with the base of the spine (the sacrum) it forms a rigid hollow bony structure. The pelves of three primates are illustrated in Figure 5.3, and in Figure 5.4 the relationship between spine, pelvis, and legs is shown. The pelvis consists of two parts, the left and right sides (the *ossa coxae* or innominate bones), which meet in the midline ventrally and are fixed to the sacrum dorsally, as is shown in the upper row of Figure 5.3. Each side of the pelvis consists of three bones, the *ilium, ischium,* and *pubis,* and from about the time of sexual maturity these bones become completely fixed together (though there is never any movement between them). The ventral fusion of the pubic bones

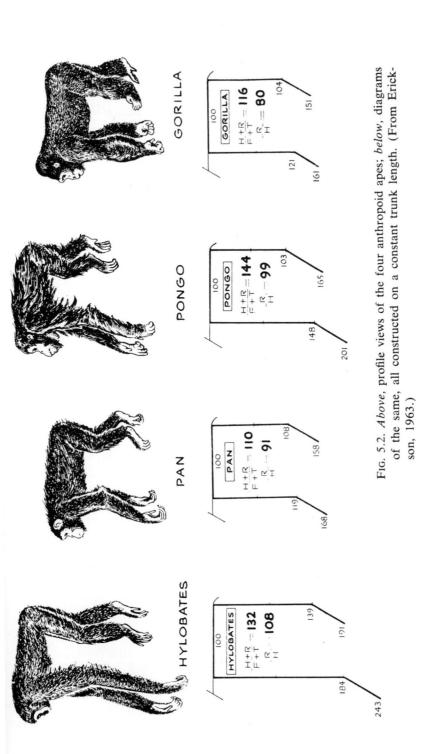

HYLOBATES

PAN

PONGO

GORILLA

HYLOBATES
$\dfrac{H+R}{F+T} = 132$
$\dfrac{R}{H} = 108$

PAN
$\dfrac{H+R}{F+T} = 110$
$\dfrac{R}{H} = 91$

PONGO
$\dfrac{H+R}{F+T} = 144$
$\dfrac{R}{H} = 99$

GORILLA
$\dfrac{H+R}{F+T} = 116$
$\dfrac{R}{H} = 80$

Fig. 5.2. *Above,* profile views of the four anthropoid apes; *below,* diagrams of the same, all constructed on a constant trunk length. (From Erickson, 1963.)

A B C

FIG. 5.3. Views from above and behind of pelves of *Macaca* (*A*), *Gorilla* (*B*) and modern man (*C*), *p.s*, pubic symphysis. All drawn the same size. (From Schultz, 1963b.)

FIG. 5.4. The pelvis in chimpanzee (*A*) and man (*B*). Note the difference in shape and size and the relationship between the pelvis, spine and femur. (After Schultz, 1963b).

(the *pubic symphysis*) is finally completed in man between the ages of seventeen and twenty-five and in other primates at an equivalent stage of development. The human pelvis is shown in Figure 5.5; the three bones and their most important landmarks are labeled.

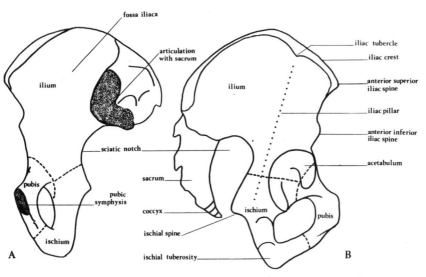

Fig. 5.5. The human right innominate bone. An internal view (*A*) and an external view from the right (*B*) showing the sacrum in position. The dashes indicate the boundaries of the fused bones; the dots indicate that thickening of the ilium which is called the "iliac pillar." The shaded areas are articular surfaces.

The ilium—which becomes fused to the sacrum—is a broad flattened bone with a blade-like extension spreading in a curve to each side of the sacrum. At its lower end it fuses with both the ischium and the pubis, and at this point of fusion is formed the cup-shaped socket into which fits the head of the thighbone (the femur). This socket is called the *acetabulum,* and through the pair of acetabula is transmitted the whole weight of the body in bipedal primates. From this central point, the ischium extends backward (dorsally) and downward (to the base of the buttock in man). In some primates it is thickened where it approaches the skin in the form of two *ischial tuberosities,* which give rigid support in the sitting position. Each *pubis* extends forward (ventrally) to meet its fellow in the midline, where it holds the two sides of thé pelvis together at the pubic symphysis (see Fig. 5.3).

When we examine typical primate pelves, however, we note some striking differences. Although the general function and relation of the bones is similar, a number of obvious differences are apparent in the monkey and ape pelves drawn in Figure 5.3, and these differences are even more striking in the lower primates. In the pelvis of the little tree shrew *Ptilocerus* (Fig. 5.6), it is possible to see the arrangement of the pelvic bones typical of primitive mammals and lower primates. The most strikingly different character here is the long, narrow blade of the ilium, which extends forward on each side of the sacrum. The most notable trend in the evolution of the human pelvis has been the shortening and widening of this blade from the condition seen in Figure 5.4 through Figure 5.3, *A,* to that in Figure 5.3, *C.* It is this structural change that we shall attempt to follow and understand.

If we compare the larger Old World monkeys with the lower primates, we find some enlargement of the blade of the ilium upon which originate the important groups of muscles that effect movement of

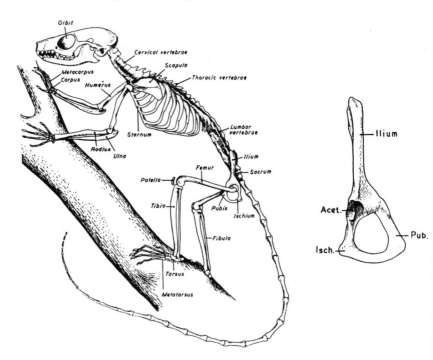

Fig. 5.6. Skeleton of *Ptilocerus,* a tree shrew, drawn about ⅔ natural size, and an enlarged drawing of right *os coxae.* (From Le Gros Clark 1962.)

the femur (Fig. 4.4, p. 89). This enlargement of the insertion areas results from the enlargement of the muscles as a whole in the larger animals caused by the increased power developed in the hindlimbs for jumping. The two ischial tuberosities are also farther apart to give a more stable sitting position, and they form a foundation for the *ischial callosities*—the especially hardened areas of skin characteristic of the Old World monkeys, which commonly not only sit, but sleep sitting, often with their feet drawn up (Figs. 9.2, p. 254, and 9.9, p. 279).

Among the nonhuman Hominoid primates we see that the larger animals have still heavier musculature to support a larger body, and as a result the blade of the ilium expands still farther (Fig. 5.3). The crest (the top ridge of the ilium) itself assumes more importance, since the abdominal muscles inserted upon it have a heavy load of viscera to carry and it must act as part of the stress member of the parabolic girder supporting the spine. But the generally elongated form of the pelvis survives, especially in the gibbon, where considerations of weight on the hindlimbs are less important.

The human pelvis shows remarkable differences compared with the pelves of other primates, differences which need detailed considera- tion. The Latin word *pelvis* means basin, and the basin-like shape that it assumes in man gives it that name. In the human family, the attainment of bipedal locomotion has fundamentally changed the stresses set up in the pelvis resulting in a change in shape (Fig. 5.3). Both Le Gros Clark (1962) and Schultz (1963b) have analyzed this change in shape into a number of components.

1. The muscles of the thigh move the leg forward and backward and provide the power for both quadrupedal and bipedal locomotion. The muscles that move the leg forward are called the *flexors* because they bend the leg at the hip; those that move the leg backward are called the *extensors* because they extend the leg at the hip joint. The development of these muscles is relatively greater in man than in any other primate because man alone depends entirely upon them for his locomotion, and his leg is proportionally larger and heavier. At the same time, there are changes in man's bone structure that tend to in- crease the leverage of the muscles. These changes involve as a whole the movement of the insertion areas of the muscles outward from the point of pivot: a small horizontal extension here greatly increases effective muscular power (Fig. 5.7).

Probably the most important flexor muscles are the *ilio psoas* and *rectus femoris*; the insertion areas of the latter are indicated in Figure 5.8. The human pelvis has a much more pronounced *anterior inferior iliac spine* (where a portion of the muscle is inserted) than has the non-human pelvis.

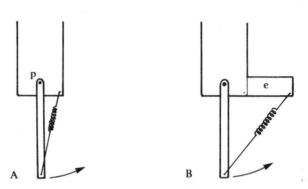

FIG. 5.7. In this diagram the effective power of the spring to move the lever to the right (*A*) is increased by moving the fixed end of the spring farther away from the pivot (*p*) as in *B*. The structural extension (*e*) is a model of the increased horizontal dimension that is typical of the human pelvis as compared with nonhuman pelvis and that increases the effective power of all muscles used in locomotion as well as of those required to maintain the balance of the trunk above the legs.

The most important extensor muscles among higher primates are parts of the *adductor magnus* and *biceps femoris* (the hamstring muscles in man), which have their origin on the ischial tuberosity and their insertion on the femur and fibula respectively. The origin and position of the biceps is shown in Figure 5.8. However, in man the extensor action of these muscles, so important in locomotion, comes to be reinforced by the action of another muscle, the *gluteus maximus,* which is an *abductor* muscle in other primates (see p. 121). This change in function has been brought about by a very complex change in the form of the ilium and in particular in the proportion and curvature of its blade, which has brought the muscle to lie behind the acetabulum rather than to one side.

The most obvious difference between the nonhuman and the human ilium is that the bone has shortened and widened so that the articular surface where the bone is connected to the base of the spine (the sacrum) has been brought nearer to the acetabulum, the socket of the femur. This change gives greater stability, since the weight of the

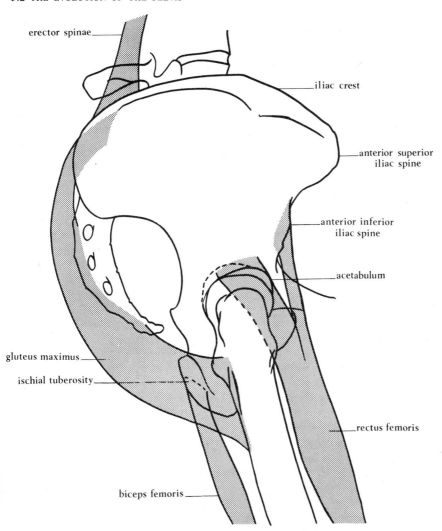

erector spinae

iliac crest

anterior superior
iliac spine

anterior inferior
iliac spine

acetabulum

gluteus maximus

ischial tuberosity

rectus femoris

biceps femoris

FIG. 5.8. Diagram of flexor and extensor muscles of the thigh in man.

trunk is transmitted more directly to the leg. As Schultz (1963b) has shown, the ilium occupies only 24 per cent of trunk length in man, whereas it occupies 36–38 per cent in the great apes.

Washburn (1950) has also pointed out that, as in evolution the ilium becomes shorter, its axis—from sacrum to acetabulum—must have a greater angle with the ischium in order to keep the same diameter in the pelvic birth canal (Fig. 5.9). Shortening of the bone must therefore go with outward displacement, and this "bending" causes the change in the position of the origin of the gluteus maximus (which arises on the iliac crest) in relation to the acetabulum and femur. As Figure 5.8 shows, the gluteus maximus in man acts as a very powerful extensor of the thigh but can get an effectively straight pull only when the thigh has already been moved back some way by the extensors. The gluteus maximus makes it possible to transmit great power through the leg at the end of the stride. The extensors move the thigh back at the beginning of the stride; the gluteus maximus gives the final drive (Washburn 1950). It is the existence of this muscle as an extensor rather than as an abductor that differentiates the human stride from the weak bent-knee gait of the apes and that gives man his buttocks.

From Figure 5.7 and 5.8 it can be seen that the greater the extension of the pelvis bones in a ventral or dorsal direction, the greater

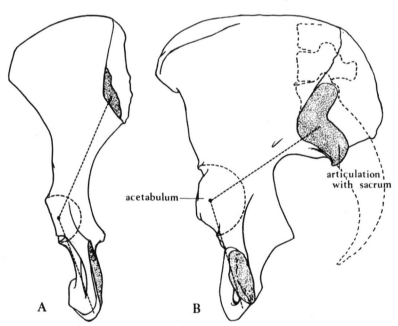

FIG. 5.9. Pelves of *Pan* (*A*) and modern man (*B*) drawn the same size to show that as the articulation with the sacrum (*shaded*) moves down toward the ground, it must also move away from the acetabulum so that the size of the pelvic canal will be maintained. The dotted line shows the change in structure of the pelvis that results in its "bent" appearance.

leverage a given muscle will exert on the leg for locomotion. Although Figure 5.8 is a great oversimplification of the musculature, the mechanics of the muscle action are straightforward. The leverage of the muscles is increased by the changes that have occurred in the pelvis during the evolution of man. The ischial tuberosity has moved outward and upward to give more leverage to the biceps muscle about the acetabulum—the pivot of the femur (Fig. 5.8). As we shall see, this evolutionary trend is found to be at an intermediate stage in *Australopithecus*. Another advantage of the increasing extension of the pelvis dorsally is the greater leverage given to the *erector spinae* muscles, which are inserted on the ilium and maintain the upright posture of the spine (Fig. 5.8).

2. The "bending" of the ilium mentioned above has resulted in the formation of a relatively deep sciatic notch, which is associated with an accentuation of the ischial spine, the point upon which important muscles forming the floor of the pelvic basin are inserted (Fig. 5.5; see also Fig. 4.17, p. 105).

Since we have seen that the "bending" of the ilium affects the diameter of the pelvic birth canal, we find here a sexual character. The "bending" has proceeded further in males than in females; the canal is smaller in males, and this difference in size is correlated with a more acute angle of the *sciatic notch*. The size of the canal in a woman is functionally related to the size of a baby's head, which must pass through it at birth; in man the size of the canal is controlled mainly by locomotor, not reproductive, factors. These differences in the pelvis cause the difference in locomotion and posture between man and woman. The canal in the human female only just accommodates the head at birth and is relatively larger than in lower forms. The cross-sectional area of the canal may well be one limiting factor in the length of the period of gestation in man, although the cranial bones of a human baby exhibit remarkable flexibility at this stage of development. Figure 5.10 demonstrates that this limiting factor is not unique to *Homo*. The figure is taken from Schultz (1963b), who states that the canal is proportionally larger in adult females than in males of the same species in all primates except the great apes. This is, therefore, clearly a secondary sexual character.

3. The "bending" of the ilium and man's erect posture bring about a reorientation of the sacrum in relation to the ilium, with the result that the axis of the pelvic canal lies almost at a right angle to the

vertebral column; the pubic symphysis and sacrum have become more nearly the floor and roof of the pelvic cavity rather than the ventral and dorsal walls (Fig. 5.4; see also Fig. 4.8, p. 94). At the same time, because greater weight is transmitted through the area of contact between sacrum and ilium, this area has increased relative to that of the ilium as a whole (Fig. 5.9). For the same reason, the acetabulum and the head of the femur have also increased in relative size during the course of human evolution.

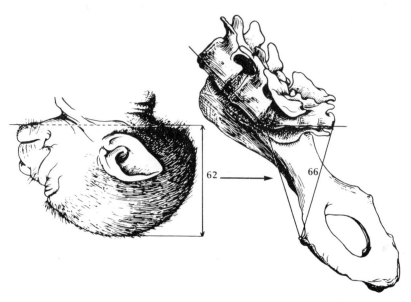

FIG. 5.10. The pelvis of the adult baboon and the head of its full-term fetus, drawn to the same scale. Mother and young died immediately after the difficult birth. (From Schultz, 1963b).

4. The *adductor* and *abductor* muscles, which move the limb from side to side in an arboreal primate according to the position of a branch or the demands of the terrain, have great importance for a bipedal creature (compare the extensors and flexors, which move the limb backward and forward). They become essential in maintaining the lateral balance of the trunk upon the legs.

During bipedal walking all the weight of the body is borne by one leg at a time, and it is the abductor muscles (together with the oblique muscles which run from thorax to ilium) which at each step raise the trunk and pull it vertically over the thigh, so that the center of gravity lies over the triangle of the foot and the weight is transmitted directly down the leg through the knee. The adductors, on the other side of the thigh, help to hold the balance (Fig. 5.11).

In the ape, all three *gluteus* muscles (*maximus, medius,* and *minimus*) lie to the side of the hip joint and act as abductors. The gluteus medius is the largest, the gluteus maximus merely half as big. In man, the two smaller gluteus muscles (the medius and minimus) alone act as abductors. It has been shown (Mednick 1955) that the *iliac pillar* and *iliac tubercle,* a thickening of the ilium unique to man among living primates (see Fig. 5.5), take the compression exerted by the gluteus medius when it lifts the whole trunk over the leg. Clearly the leverage of these muscles will be enhanced by lateral extension of the iliac bone and the lengthening of the neck of the femur (again see Fig. 5.7). Since they support the weight of the whole body, they are muscles of prime importance in maintaining erect posture.

The adductors are of somewhat less importance; they help to balance the body and are again larger in man than in apes. Clearly, a broader pelvis will further increase their leverage.

Associated as most of these changes are with erect posture and bipedal locomotion, they constitute one important set of adaptations that man's ancestors underwent in the face of an open, plains environment, and by general consent they are accepted as the most important diagnostic complex of characters of the human family, the Hominidae. Evidence from *Ramapithecus* is not yet available but will be of the greatest interest; but these characters are already present in *Australopithecus* in an evolved condition. One of the most important of the fossil discoveries that have helped to elucidate the course of human evolution is that of the pelvis of *Australopithecus.* Remains of five fragmentary ossa coxae have been reported from South Africa, as follows:

A. Africanus	(Makapansgat	2 immature ossa coxae (Dart 1949, 1958)
	(Sterkfontein	2 mature ossa coxae (Broom *et al.* 1950)
A. robustus	Swartkrans	1 mature os coxae (Broom and Robinson 1952)

These specimens are remarkably similar to those of modern man, and nearly all the characters of the human pelvis listed above are present. The differences between the *Australopithecus africanus* pelvis and that of modern man are slight and include the following features (Le Gros Clark 1955, Napier 1964):

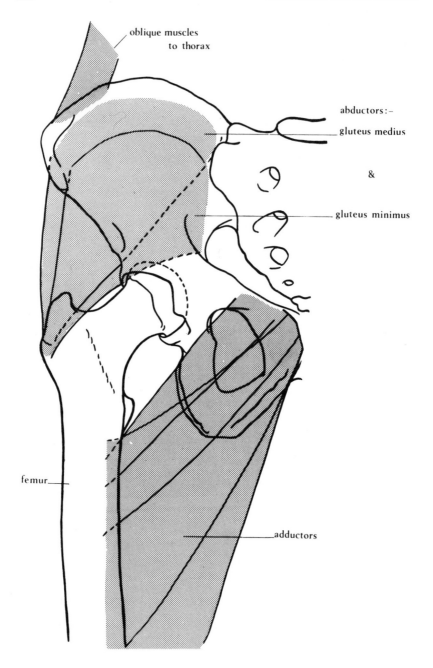

oblique muscles
to thorax

abductors:−

gluteus medius

&

gluteus minimus

femur

adductors

Fig. 5.11. Diagram of abductor and adductor muscles of the thigh in man.

1. The bones are smaller and lighter, being more comparable to those of the Bushman than to the heavier races of modern man. The muscle attachment areas on the blade of the ilium are less marked; the iliac pillar and iliac tubercle are absent. These differences can be seen in Figure 5.12.

2. There is a relatively smaller sacroiliac articulation than in man.

3. The ischial tuberosity is somewhat lower than the acetabulum (when the pelvis is oriented with the body of the ischium in a vertical position) because the body of the ischium is relatively longer than in modern man and is oriented slightly differently in relation to the ilium.

These differences appear to indicate that *Australopithecus* was smaller and lighter than modern man. The slightly longer ischium is, as we have seen, an anthropoid-like character; in an erect form like *Australopithecus* it gives less leverage to the biceps muscle, which flexes the femur, than it could in a more quadrupedal form. In the evolution of man the ischium finally shortened and so increased the power of this lever in an erect animal (Fig. 5.8).

The pelvis of *A. robustus* differs from that of *A. africanus* in its greater overall size, a greater forward projection of the anterior superior iliac spine, a relatively smaller and more lateral-facing acetabulum, and a longer ischium. The forward projection of the spine is clearly an adaptation to erect posture and gives greater leverage to the abdominal muscles: the last two characters are ape-like, and together with the absence of an iliac pillar and tubercle they suggest a much less evolved gait (which Napier has described as waddling) than we find in *A. africanus* (Napier 1964).

No pelvis of *Homo erectus* is known, but a few fragments of early *Homo sapiens* pelves have been collected. The pelves of Mount Carmel (McCown and Keith 1939), Neandertal itself, and La Chapelle are described as indistinguishable from those of modern man and indicate a fully erect posture (Straus and Cave 1957).

5.3 The hindlimb

THE MORPHOLOGY of the limb bones reflects the mode of locomotion of the animal. The relative lengths of the different bones and the extent of movement possible are related to the function of the limb as a whole. The thickness of the bones reflects the size of

FIG. 5.12. The pelvis of a chimpanzee (*A*) compared with that of *Australopithecus africanus* (*B*) and a Bushman (*C*); *on the left,* the left lateral
view, and *on the right,* the entire pelvis from the front. Note the strong
similarity between the human and *Australopithecus* pelves. (Not drawn
to scale.) (Redrawn from Le Gros Clark, 1962, and Dart, 1949.)

the animal and the weight transmitted by each bone; it is to be expected that the bigger animals have longer limbs and heavier bones.

The *femora* or thigh bones of the lower primates and small monkeys are, on the whole, slender and straight, while the *greater* and the *lesser trochanter,* upon which extensor and flexor muscles, respectively, are inserted, are prominent processes. The femora of the larger quadrupedal monkeys and great apes are bowed in the anterior-posterior plane, but those of a semibrachiating form like the langur (*Presbytis*) are not bowed and have a long straight shaft. Remains of fossil femora of *Dryopithecus* and *Proconsul* have been found (Le Gros Clark and Leakey 1951) with a long straight shaft, and they have been compared and found to have much in common with femora of semibrachiators as well as with modern man (Napier 1964) (Fig. 5.13).

The femora of *Australopithecus africanus* are represented only by fragments, though the total length of the Sterkfontein specimen has been estimated to be three hundred and ten mm. (Broom *et al.* 1950), suggesting a stature for the creature of no more than the very smallest Bushmen—between 4 and 5 feet. The head and distal end of this femur are not greatly different in form from those of modern man, though the bone is much lighter than in man, appropriate to the smaller height of the animal, and the muscle attachment areas are less strongly developed. It is also clear that the weight of the animal passed mainly through the outer condyle of the knee as in man but unlike the apes, in which it passes through the inner condyle, with the result that they are bowlegged (Fig. 5.14). Two upper femoral fragments of *Australopithecus robustus* from Swartkrans are much more ape-like; they have a small head (appropriate to the relatively small acetabulum) and a greater trochantur less prominent than in man, and these features suggest a less evolved bipedalism.

Unusually well preserved are fragments of six femora of *Homo erectus* from Java. One was complete and measured 455 mm. giving a supposed stature of 5 ft. 6 in. (168 cm.) (Dubois 1926). Together with a femur of *H. erectus* from Peking (Weidenreich 1938), they appear to be very similar to those of modern man. Femora of Neandertal man are also known and again appear to be little different from those of modern man (Straus and Cave 1957). In all these forms, as in modern man, the increase in weight borne by the leg bones has brought the circumference of the human femur to be second only to that of the very heavy gorilla (Schultz 1953). Human legs are, on the

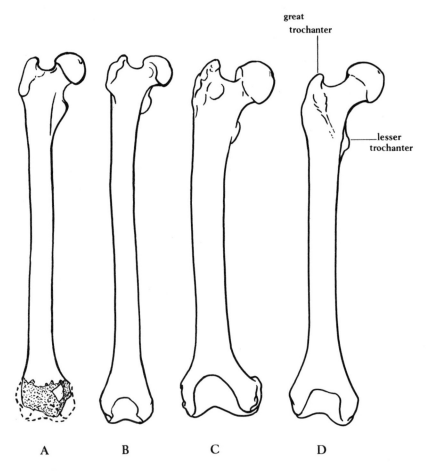

FIG. 5.13. Femora of *Proconsul (A)*, *Dryopithecus (B)*, *Pan (C)*, and modern man *(D)* all drawn the same size. The *Proconsul* femur is a reconstruction from fragments of two different bones.

average, the longest among all the primates, relative to trunk length (Schultz 1950) (see Fig. 5.1). As the weight of the animal increases in evolution so does the weight of the bone, and the bearing surfaces tend to increase in area. Both the articular head of the femur and the acetabulum into which it fits on the pelvis are relatively large in man. However, at the distal end the two condyles (at the knee) form a bearing surface relatively narrower than that found in heavy apes. This results from the improved weight transmission, which is more or less direct down the leg because, as we have seen, it tends to pass through the outer condyle.

The neck of the femur is also longer in the Hominidae than in the monkeys and apes (Fig. 5.13), so the greater trochantur is farther out from the point of pivot (the head of the femur). In this way the abductor muscles gain more leverage in holding the trunk over the leg (see p. 115).

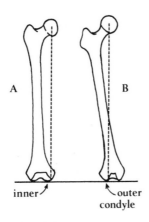

inner   outer
condyle

FIG. 5.14. Femora of gorilla (*A*) and modern man (*B*) drawn the same size to show difference in the line of weight transmission down the leg.

The distal limb bones have also been modified in the course of human evolution. In the primitive mammal, the existence of two distal limb bones rather than one made possible the rotary movement of the hand and foot (*manus* and *pes*). The *tibia* can be considered the fixed bone that transmits the majority of the weight (the *ulna* in the forelimb), while the distal end of the *fibula* (and *radius*) can move in a rotary manner round the base of the tibia, and this movement in turn revolves the pes (or manus) (Fig. 5.6). Such rotation is essential to an arboreal creature for grasping the trunk and branches of trees at all angles. The retention of this generalized feature of primitive limb structure is characteristic of the primates, though modified in *Tarsius* and some lemurs. In the terrestrial forms, the rotation is somewhat limited, and in man the fibula plays no part in this activity.

The size of these bones is again related to the weight transmitted through them, and in the relative circumference of his tibia man leads the primates (Schultz 1953); as a corollary, no weight is transmitted through the fibula, and in man it has become reduced, as is his ability to revolve his foot.

Fossil tibiae and fibulae are rare. The earliest hominoid specimens we have come from Bed I, Olduvai Gorge, and may well belong to *Australopithecus*. Davis (1964) has described the bones and shown them to belong to a creature habitually bipedal, but whose gait may well have differed considerably from that of modern man. The bones are already quite long, and the fibula is reduced and indistinguishable from that of modern man. Fragments of these bones are also known from Neandertal and Rhodesian man; they appear to fall within the range of variation of modern man.

All these changes, which have clearly occurred in human evolution, are directly related to the development of erect posture, to the position of the femur in relation to the pelvis, to its position in relation to the tibia, and to the transmission of weight directly through the bone rather than through a system of stressed and compressed members of muscle and bone. The reduction of the fibula in hominids is related to their reduced power to rotate the foot—an adaptation no longer necessary in an animal that walks and runs on the ground.

5.4 The evolution of the foot

THE HIND FOOT or *pes* has a number of fairly distinct functions in primates, and it is the changing balance between these different functions that characterizes its evolution. The functions may be considered in turn.

1. The foot acts as a lever that adds to the propulsive force of the leg, a function clearly seen in modern man. By contraction of the *gastrocnemius* and *soleus* muscles of the calf of the leg, the body is raised upon the ball of the foot. The point of pivot is the *crural joint* of the *talus* (or *astragalus*). The power arm of the lever is the *calcaneus* (or *os calcis*); the contraction of the gastrocnemius is transmitted through the *Achilles tendon* to the heel. The load arm is the *tarsal* section of the foot anterior to the pivot, together with the *metatarsals* (Fig. 5.15).

The relative lengths of the load arm and power arm have changed in primate evolution according to the mode of locomotion. Extensive movement in the foot lever is characteristic of the leaping prosimians, where power is less essential. The load arm of *Tarsius* is eight times as long as the power arm. In the heavier Hominoidea, power is more important, and, in man, the load arm is less than three times as long as the power arm.

FIG. 5.15. Diagram of the structure and mechanics of the human foot. *C,* cural joint.

Within the load arm itself, the proportions of the tarsal and metatarsal segments have varied, but only in a few prosimians (e.g., *Tarsius*) has the tarsal segment assumed great importance. Among the Anthropoidea, the metatarsals are longer, the tarsal bones remaining short and compressed. Slight lengthening of the tarsal segment is, however, characteristic of human evolution (Fig. 5.16).

When we examine the mechanism for the transmission of weight from above, we see some significant variations in the load line. Among

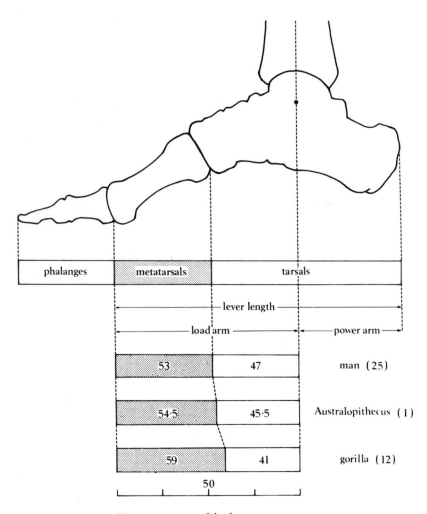

Mean percentage of load arm

FIG. 5.16. Mean proportions of different parts of digit 1 (the hallux) of the feet of three primates suggest that the tarsal section of the load arm has lengthened in human evolution. The number following each name shows the sample size (*n*) used for this calculation. The proportion in modern man is of course variable and overlaps the figures for *Australopithecus*. As always, the significance to be attached to a sample of n = 1 is questionable, but in the absence of further evidence there is no reason to discard these figures as a basis for discussion. (Data from Day and Napier 1964.)

the monkeys that have retained a quadrupedal mode of locomotion, weight is transmitted mainly through the middle digit of the foot, which is the longest. These monkeys retain the primitive phalangeal formula of decreasing length common to quadrupedal mammals, so from the longest to the shortest the order of phalanges is $3 > 4 > 2 > 5 > 1$ (Fig. 5.17). Later in evolution, as body weight increased and the grasping functions of the foot increased to some extent at the expense of the propulsive function, the *hallux* (great toe) became increasingly opposable to the other digits. In the feet of apes, we find the weight is transmitted to the branch not through digit 3 but through the webbing between digits 1 and 2 (Figs. 5.17 and 5.18). This shift in the load line has been extended in the human foot almost to digit 1 (the hallux), and the existence and origin of the shift is of the utmost importance in human evolution. The fact of this shift of load line suggests very strongly that the Hominidae evolved from a primate that had increased somewhat in weight, developed semibrachiation and a partially opposable hallux. In contrast, the baboons have retained the primitive weight line through the third digit, suggesting their origin from quadrupedal monkeys.

The human foot has the formula of phalangeal length $2 > 1 > 3 > 4 > 5$, and Schultz (1950) has shown that this change has been brought about by a reduction of digits 2—5 rather than by an elongation of the hallux. A significant comparison can be made with two subspecies of *Gorilla*. The mountain gorilla (*Gorilla gorilla berengei*) is almost entirely terrestrial, and its foot is much closer to that of man, since the opposability of the hallux is partially lost. It should be compared with the lowland gorilla (*G. gorilla gorilla*), which is still to a considerable extent arboreal (Fig. 5.19). The pattern of robusticity of the metatarsals is also significant in this respect: in the fully terrestrial forms alone, more weight is transmitted through digit 5, which is more robust than digits 2 and 3 (Day and Napier 1964) and which, by making the weight distribution like a tripod, helps lateral balance (Fig. 5.20).

2. The foot may also act as a means of gripping the branches and trunks of trees. This is primarily the property of the phalanges. In an arboreal primate, the phalanges must be of such a length as to enable the animal to grasp the branches among which it moves. As has been mentioned, claws alone are not altogether satisfactory in a fully arboreal animal.

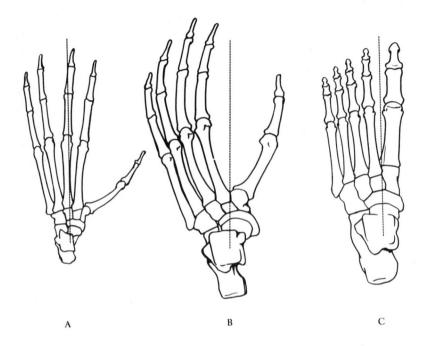

A   B   C

FIG. 5.17. Foot skeleton of *Macaca* (A), *Pan* (B), and man (C), showing the load line in each genus. (After Morton, 1927.)

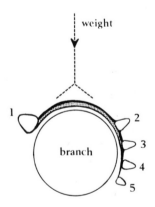

FIG. 5.18. The transmission of weight to the branch in apes is not through a digit but through the musculature between digits 1 and 2. This figure shows a diagrammatic transverse section through foot and branch. (After Morton, 1927.)

The effective size of grasp of the phalanges can be increased by the evolution of an opposable hallux (or *pollex* in the forelimb), a common adaptation among the prosimians, the small size of which poses special problems in gripping the larger branches. Among the relatively large quadrupedal monkeys, opposability of the hallux has not evolved to any great extent; instead, long phalanges are the rule. Only among the slower-moving great apes do we find opposability of the hallux, and, as has been described, this opposability gives rise to a change in the load line, an important feature in human evolution.

A **B** **C** **D**

FIG. 5.19. Feet of *Pan* (*A*), lowland gorilla (*B*), mountain gorilla (*C*), and modern man (*D*). The three centers of weight in the human foot are marked with crosses. (From Morton, 1964.)

A second development of great importance has effected the grasping power of the primate hand and foot (together called the *chiridia*). The function of the hooked claws of the insectivores and lower prosimians has been taken over in the primates not only by the long phalanges but also by the evolution of *volar pads* (friction pads) on the palms, which were enlarged and eventually fused. Volar pads are characterized by a special ridged skin with a microscopic folding of the outer layer. This skin lacks hair but is well supplied with sweat glands. The claws themselves were reduced in evolution and modified to flat plates, the nails, which gave support to the terminal pads (nail pads) that are so important in maintaining a grip on a branch.

3. The foot may also act as a tactile organ, and there was an immense evolutionary proliferation of the tactile receptors in the ridged

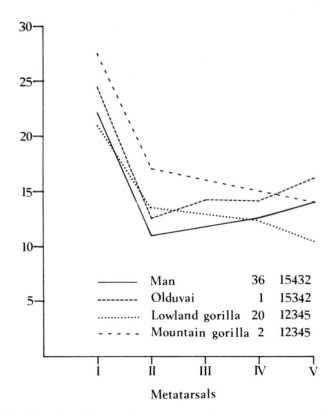

Metatarsals

Fig. 5.20. The robusticity of the metatarsals is an important indicator of weight distribution through the foot. The robusticity index is defined as $\dfrac{\text{mean diameter} \times 100}{\text{mean length}}$ of the different metatarsals. In this diagram, this index is shown for the metatarsals of modern man, the Olduvai foot, and the two gorillas. Both in modern man and in the Olduvai foot, the fifth metatarsal is the second most robust after the first. In the gorillas, it is the least robust, though in the more terrestrial mountain gorilla the index of all metatarsals is greater, especially that of the fifth metatarsal. The five-figure numbers in the key show the order of robusticity (the robusticity formula) of the different samples; the smaller numbers indicate the sample size (n). (After Day and Napier, 1964.)

volar skin. In this way, the chiridia came to replace, as prime organ of touch, the tactile rhinarium and whiskers on the snout that we associate with most other mammals. The importance of this development, particularly as it applies to the hand, is immense in human evolution; it is further discussed in chapters 6 and 7. In the human foot we find an organ perhaps unnecessarily well-endowed with tactile receptors, since its functions have been reduced from three to one, that of locomotion.

Unfortunately, we have little knowledge of early hominid feet. There is a single talus bone from Kromdraai in South Africa, which is said to suggest a form intermediate between ape and man; Napier has described the foot to which it belonged as broad, splayed, and flat, with some divergence of the hallux. If this talus belongs to *Australopithecus robustus,* as seems most probable, we have in this species the most primitive known hominid foot. It is fortunate that the Leakeys have recently excavated a fairly well preserved hominid foot in Bed I at Olduvai, Tanzania. The talus from this Olduvai foot is nearer to that of modern man and suggests a less divergent hallux; the species to which it belonged is uncertain, but it may be ascribed to *A. africanus* or *Homo erectus.* In neither foot is the line of weight transmission through the ankle exactly as it is in modern man. In other respects the Olduvai foot suggests the upright stance and bipedal gait of modern man, to which it lies morphologically close, though it is probably somewhat broader and the relative shortening of the metatarsals has not gone quite so far as in man (see Fig. 5.16) (Day and Napier 1964).

No other fossil foot bones are known of *Homo erectus,* but of Neandertal man we have both bones and a footprint. They indicate a broad, short foot, but they can be matched in modern man, and, although the proportions are unusual, they are not significantly simian, as has been claimed. The best preserved specimens are those of La Ferrassie.

In summary, it is possible to distinguish six different but related trends in the evolution of the human foot:

1. There was probably a reduction of the load arm of the foot lever compared with the power arm in the evolution of the anthropoid foot. This reduction would have occurred as the monkeys became heavier animals. In the Hominoidea, we see a shortening of the phalanges themselves.

2. The volar (friction pad) area of the foot has increased to cover the whole contact surface.

3. With the hairless volar skin, we find sweat glands and a great density of tactile sensory nerve endings; both these features were perhaps a little reduced in the most recent stages of human evolution.

4. There was a change of load line from metatarsal 3 to between metatarsals 1 and 2; this change was a correlate of the hominoid opposable hallux. In human evolution the load line moved on towards the hallux—a significant pointer to human origins.

5. The high proportion of load arm made up by the metatarsals (as compared with tarsals) is somewhat reduced in man by a shortening of metatarsals 2–5.

6. The foot is narrowed, yet at the same time a new secondary load line evolves along phalanx 5, which becomes more robust and thus enables the weight of the bipedal animal to be distributed through three centers in each foot—the heel, the hallux, and the small toe—giving the stable character of a tripod.

These changes, which summarize the evolution of the human foot, involve not so much the evolution of a new function as a reduction in the original primate functions. We see the foot changing from a tactile grasping organ to a locomotor prop. The phalanges are shortened, and the musculature is reduced; although some nonlocomotor function is still possible in the foot (cripples can paint pictures with their feet), we see that it has clearly been evolving from a generalized to a specialized organ.

5.5 Summary

FROM A CONSIDERATION of the lower limbs it is possible to conclude that the evolution of erect posture and bipedalism has involved fundamental changes in the function of two structures, the pelvis and the foot, together with a host of minor changes elsewhere.

The pelvis, structurally very complex already, has changed shape markedly in accordance with the the different characteristic angle of the femur in relation to the spine and the changed function of its associated musculature. In particular, the pelvis, in its role as anchor for the important muscles of forward propulsion and lateral balance, has broadened to give these muscles greater leverage about the hip joint. This broadening has been accompanied by a shortening of the ilium and a closer approximation of the points through which the body weight is transmitted—the sacral articulation and acetabulum. The pelvic basin has undergone re-alignment with the spine and gives essential support to the viscera.

The leg is straight, and in man we see the whole body weight transmitted directly through the knee joint from acetabulum to ankle.

The foot itself has undergone evolution from a generalized to a specialized condition. It has been modified to carry the whole weight of the body in walking, one foot at a time. The points of weight transmission have become precise and threefold rather than general, and the primary line of weight has moved close to the hallux. Digits 2–5 have shortened, and the outer metatarsal has thickened.

The immense power of the human stride comes from three muscles in turn. The biceps brings the body forward over the knee; the gluteus maximus completes extension at the hip; the gastrocnemius gives a final lift by raising the foot lever on the distal end of the metatarsals. The bipedal stride of modern man is unique in the animal world and, as we have seen, was already advanced in *Australopithecus*, although there are still a few minor features in the bones of this genus that have not evolved as far as in modern man. *Australopithecus* was a biped at least two million years ago; by the time of *Homo erectus,* the evolution of bipedalism was evidently complete.

It seems clear that the evolution of bipedalism was one of the early character complexes to appear in human evolution. If it was almost complete two million years ago, it must have begun some millions of years earlier; we shall return to this matter when we come to discuss the origin of the Hominidae in chapter 11.

SUGGESTIONS FOR FURTHER READING

The evolution of the primate and in particular the hominid pelvis has been treated in some detail by W. E. le Gros Clark in two books: *The Antecedents of Man* (Edinburgh: University of Edinburgh Press, 1962) and *The Fossil Evidence for Human Evolution* (2d ed.; Chicago: University of Chicago Press, 1964). The evolution of the human foot has been described by D. J. Morton, in *The Human Foot* (New York: Haffner Publishing Co., 1964).

ᨶ6

Manipulation and the Forelimb

6.1 The mammalian forelimb

ᨶ IN THE LOCOMOTION of the terrestrial quadrupedal mammals, including the quadrupedal primates, the main driving force is derived from the hindlimbs. The body is propelled forward from the rear (not pulled), and mechanical efficiency requires a rigid bone-to-bone connection between the pelvis and the spine. The function of the forelegs, even in a generalized mammal, is different. In such movements as running and jumping, the forelegs usually hit the ground first and take a great deal of shock. This shock would be transmitted throughout the body by a rigid bone-to-bone connection. Such a connection does not exist; the shock is absorbed by the mass of muscle that suspends the spine and thorax from the shoulder girdle (Fig. 6.1).

Although the shoulder or *pectoral* girdle consisted in its primitive condition of three bones, as does the pelvis, it is reduced in mammals to two—the *scapula* and *clavicle*. The scapula is the dorsal bone and is equivalent to the ilium; the clavicle is ventral and equivalent to the pubis. Unlike the pelvis, however, they are not fused but are connected by a movable joint (the *acromioclavicular joint*). The clavicle makes contact with the rest of the skeleton through a second movable joint,

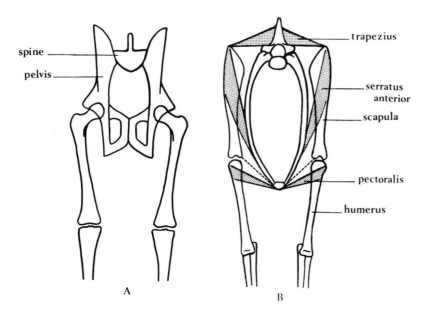

FIG. 6.1. Diagrammatic representation of the limb "suspension" in a typical quadrupedal mammal (such as a horse). The pelvic girdle, supported by the hindlimbs, is fixed to the spine by a rigid bone-to-bone connection (*A*). Upon the pectoral girdle (*B*), the body is suspended mainly by two muscles, the *trapezius* and *serratus anterior,* which transmit the animal's weight from the spine and ribs. The lower end of the scapula is steadied by the *pectoralis,* which holds the head of the humerus near the trunk. The dotted line indicates the position of the clavicle if it is present. It is lost in ungulates, since it serves no function in a strictly quadrupedal animal.

the *sternoclavicular,* where it articulates with the *manubrium* or upper part of the *sternum* (Fig. 6.2). The clavicle maintains the distance of the scapula from the sternum and, acting as a strut, allows movement of the scapula at a constant radius from the manubrium. The weight of the animal is suspended on the *serratus anterior* muscle (or *serratus magnus,* as it is often called). The clavicle merely keeps the *glenoid cavity* (the pectoral equivalent of the acetabulum), into which the *humerus* fits, at a fixed distance from the midline of the body. Figure 6.1 shows, however, that when the body weight alone is transmitted by the pectoral girdle (as among ungulates, which do not leap or climb), the clavicle is not an essential component, because movement occurs only in the anterior-posterior plane, and there is no lateral swing of the forelimbs. The clavicle has been lost in these groups.

The muscle suspension of the forelimbs gives them greater flexibility than the hindlimbs, and this flexibility has been exploited, as we shall see, by the primates.

6.2 The pectoral girdle

UNLIKE MANY quadrupedal mammals, the primates have retained the two-boned pectoral girdle, and both bones are flexibly mounted. They can move some 40 degrees about the sternoclavicular joint in each of two planes. At the same time, the scapula can move freely in relation to the clavicle about the acromioclavicular

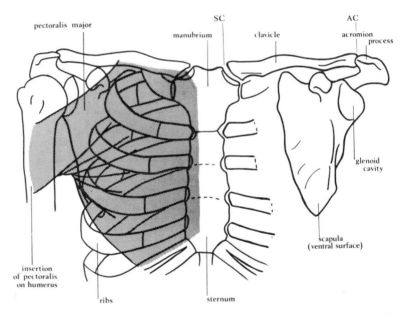

FIG. 6.2. The human thoracic region is here shown cut away on the right so that the clavicle and scapula can be seen from the front. On the left the thorax is intact, and upon it is shown the *pectoralis major* muscle on its ventral side, which in quadrupeds propels the body forward and in brachiating primates lifts the body in brachiation. *SC* = sternoclavicular joint; *AC* = acromioclavicular joint.

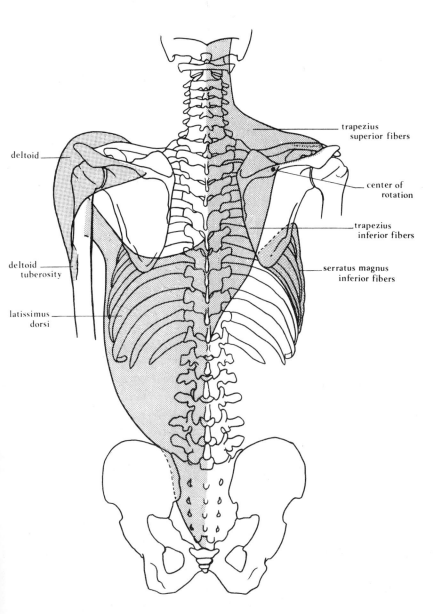

FIG. 6.3. Dorsal view of the human trunk showing (*on the right*) the two muscles that can effect rotation of the scapula about the center of rotation and (*on the left*) muscles that raise and lower the humerus.

joint. These two movable joints allow the scapula to move over the surface of the thorax in both the vertical and the horizontal planes. The acromioclavicular joint allows the scapula to twist in relation to the clavicle and so remain flat on the surface of the thorax, in spite of the fact that the latter is not spherical. The scapula moves forward round the thorax in pushing or thrusting and to the back in pulling the body forward or upward in climbing. In addition, by the action of the *trapezius* and serratus anterior muscles, the scapula can be rotated (Fig. 6.3, right side) so that the glenoid cavity (equivalent to the acetabulum in the pelvis) can face in different directions. This rotation nearly doubles the range of movement of the limb in a vertical plane. It may also be noted that the glenoid cavity is more open than the acetabulum and therefore allows a greater arc of movement in the forelimb than in the hindlimb. Here, stability has been sacrificed to mobility.

From this short account of the pectoral girdle, it can be seen that, in accordance with its different function, its structure is different from that of the pelvis. In fact, the strucure is more generalized—that is, capable of more kinds of movement—and we might accordingly predict a greater variety of adaptations in the course of primate evolution. Such is indeed the case. While differences in the clavicles are slight, a glance at Figure 6.4 will show the differences between the scapula of the tree shrew, gibbon, gorilla, and man. Figure 4.10 (page 96) shows rather more striking differences in the position of the shoulder girdle upon the thorax, differences related to the change of function of the forelimbs in the evolution of the primates.

We can trace three distinct functions of the forelimbs and follow the changing proportion of each. These functions are as follows:

1. To support the weight of the body in quadrupedal locomotion
2. To suspend the weight of the body in brachiation
3. To manipulate objects

The change from quadrupedalism to brachiation is reflected in the form of the scapula and its musculature. As mentioned above, the shoulder girdle can be rotated to allow the arm to rise vertically, a movement that is clearly important in brachiation (Fig. 6.3). Oxnard (1963) has shown how the importance of the two rotatory muscles, the serratus anterior and the trapezius, varies among the main locomotor

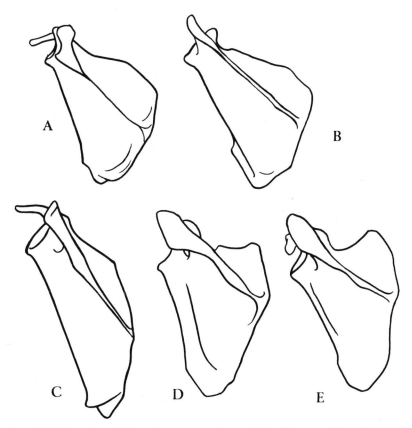

FIG. 6.4. Scapulae of *Tupaia,* a tree shrew (*A*), *Macaca* (*B*), *Hylobates* (*C*), modern man (*D*), and gorilla (*E*), all drawn the same size.

groups of primates (Fig. 6.5). The data show that, as might be expected, the muscles are better developed in brachiators than in quadrupeds and that in this character man is close to the brachiators. At the same time, there is a relative increase in length in the bony lever to which these muscles are attached (as we saw in our consideration of leverage about the hip joint). That is to say, the insertion area of the muscles on the scapula tends to move away from the central point around which the scapula rotates. Therefore in brachiating forms we find that the scapula is lengthened; it is longer in the monkeys, especially the semibrachiators, and longest in the Hominoidea, in which the *acromion process* (which, with the spine of the scapula, carries the trapezius and *deltoid* muscles) is also well developed, for the same reason (Figs. 6.3, 6.4).

The actual plane of the glenoid cavity has similarly changed in relation to the rest of the scapula, reflecting the "characteristic" position of the arms in relation to the body, and the greater mobility of the brachiators' shoulder joint. Quadrupeds therefore tend to have the glenoid cavity pointing more or less horizontally; brachiators have the cavity pointing upward. The way the angle is measured and the figures for it are shown in Figure 6.6.

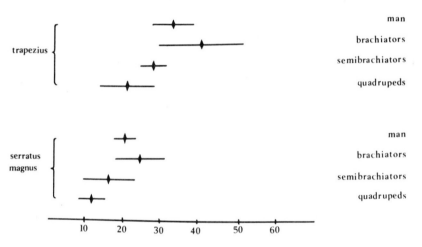

FIG. 6.5. Diagram illustrating the relative mass of the trapezius and serratus anterior (or magnus) muscles in the three main locomotor groups of higher primates and in man. Note that in these two features man lies near the brachiators and semibrachiators. The numbers are units of relative mass. (Data from Oxnard, 1963.)

We see that in this angle man is aligned with the quadrupeds, since the plane of man's glenoid cavity is more nearly parallel to the lateral margin of the scapula than it is in brachiators. The reason is that man does not brachiate but, on the contrary, carries his arms hanging downward from the shoulder. His bipedal stance has clearly changed the shape of the scapula in this respect; we need not necessarily conclude that the larger angle indicates a history of quadrupedal locomotion.

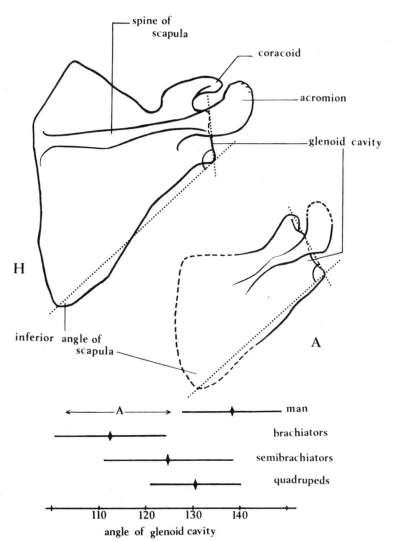

spine of
scapula

coracoid

acromion

glenoid cavity

H

glenoid cavity

inferior angle of
scapula

A

←——A——→   man

brachiators

semibrachiators

quadrupeds

110   120   130   140

angle of glenoid cavity

FIG. 6.6. The angle of the plane of the glenoid cavity can be measured in relation to the lateral margin of the scapula, as shown in the human scapula (*H*). This angle has been measured by Oxnard in many different primates, and his results are recorded in diagrammatic form below the drawings. The smaller, incomplete scapula on the right (*A*) belongs to *Australopithecus*. Although observation of the specimen (which is still in its rocky matrix) suggests the angle of the glenoid cavity to be greater than that indicated by Broom (103°), even the highest estimate places it among the semibrachiators (about 126°), and it may have been much less. It is shown on the chart as *A*. (After Broom *et al.*, 1950.)

On the other hand, when we turn to fossil hominid clavicles and scapulae we find a different situation. Up to the present, fossil remains of pectoral girdles are rare. The lightness of the scapula and its position within the surrounding musculature probably render it liable to destruction by predators and scavengers. Clavicles are rather more common. There are two fragments belonging to the Miocene *Proconsul,* but, apart from their obviously hominoid character, they are too incomplete for further diagnosis (Le Gros Clark and Leakey 1951). Of *Australopithecus* we have fragments of three clavicles, one from Makapansgat, which is very fragmentary, and two from Olduvai. Of the latter, which are quite well preserved, one is described as only slightly different from that of modern man (Napier, in Tobias *et al.* 1965). One clavicle is known of Peking man from Choukoutien (*Homo erectus*), and it appears to be quite similar to the clavicle of modern man (Weidenreich 1938).

There is one fragmentary scapula from Sterkfontein, described by Broom *et al.* (1950), attributed to *Australopithecus africanus.* Fortunately, it consists of the anterior part, including the glenoid cavity, the *coracoid process,* and part of the spine (Fig. 6.6, *A*). The coracoid is curved strongly and carries a large attachment area for the biceps muscle—a brachiating character. The acromion process projects well out over the glenoid cavity, as it does in other Hominoidea. The angle between the spine and the lateral margin of the bone (the *axilospinal angle*) is such that they are nearly parallel. Oxnard (1963) has shown that these two characters are associated with brachiation, and Figures 6.4 and 6.6, *A* suggest this association. Also, the considerable angle that the plane of the glenoid cavity makes with the lateral margin of the scapula again puts the bone into the semibrachiating class (chart in Fig. 6.6). Broom summarizes his description by stating that the bone falls between that of the orang and modern man in its overall form; or, to put it another way, it has a more brachiating form than has the scapula of modern man.

Although it is only a small fragment, this scapula may provide an important clue to the locomotor history of *Australopithecus africanus* from Sterkfontein. A single bone is a small sample, but it does suggest either that *Australopithecus* used his arms to brachiate, at least to some extent, or that his ancestors did so. Which of these hypotheses is correct will perhaps be clarified by the evidence of the skull and our discussion of the ecology of the group (chapter 7).

We can distinguish, therefore, three types of scapula, associated with three locomotor patterns: the quadrupedal scapula, shorter and squarer in proportion, with a downward-pointing glenoid cavity; the brachiating scapula, elongated, with an upward-pointing glenoid cavity; and the human scapula, still elongated, but with a downward-pointing glenoid cavity. The anatomy of the australopithecine scapula suggests some degree of brachiation in the ancestry of hominids, and in the final evolution of man we see a change in the angle of the glenoid cavity, associated with bipedalism.

6.3 The evolution of the upper arm

THE MOST striking differences among the primate humeri are in length and thickness, the functional significance of which has already been broadly discussed. As might be expected, the brachiators have longer humeri than the quadrupeds, while the heavier primates have thicker bones. Figure 5.1 (p. 110) shows the intermembral index, and Table 6.1 shows arm length in relation to trunk length.

TABLE 6.1 MEAN ARM LENGTH (HUMERUS AND RADIUS) AS A PERCENTAGE OF TRUNK LENGTH (DATA FROM SCHULTZ 1953, P. 287)

Primate	Index
Macaca	83
Hylobates	184
Pongo	148
Gorilla	121
Pan	113
Homo	113

The humerus is a powerful bone, which carries a considerable proportion of the body weight in quadrupedal mammals; the forward muscles of propulsion, the *pectorales,* are attached to it (Fig. 6.2, *left*). Among brachiators, these muscles are used to lift and support the body, and the *latissimus dorsi* muscles, which are dorsal to the thorax, also help to lift the body in climbing (Fig. 6.3, *left*). Oxnard (1963) has shown that they are relatively larger in brachiators than in quadrupeds, for only in the former do they lift the total body weight. (Fig. 6.7). The arm itself, on the other hand, is lifted by the deltoid muscle (Fig. 6.3), which again is larger in brachiators (Fig. 6.7). At the same time, the point of insertion of the muscle on the humerus moves down the bone to give greater leverage (Fig. 6.8 and Table 6.2).

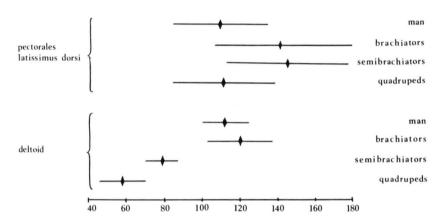

FIG. 6.7. Relative mass of the propulsive muscles, the pectorales and latissimus dorsi and the arm-raising deltoid muscle, in the three main locomotor groups of higher primates and in man. With respect to the first group of muscles, man lies near the quadrupeds; to the second, with the brachiators. The numbers are units of relative mass. (Data from Oxnard, 1963.)

TABLE 6.2 CORRELATES OF BRACHIATION IN THE FORELIMB OF HIGHER PRIMATES

Primate	DELTOID INDEX: Per Cent Distance along Humerus of Lower Limit of Deltoid Insertion	BRACHIAL INDEX $\dfrac{Length\ of\ Radius \times 100}{Length\ of\ Humerus}$
Cercopithecus	44	100
Presbytis	48	101
Proconsul	—	Approx. 86
Hylobates	—	113
Pongo	—	101
Pan	56	93
Gorilla (lowland)	—	80
Homo	53	65–85

Less striking differences include the plane of the articular head of the humerus in relation to the elbow joint. This relationship has changed in evolution according to the position of the scapula on the thorax (Fig. 4.10, p. 96). Thus in quadrupedal forms, the center line of the ball joint of the humerus, which fits into the glenoid cavity, is just about at right angles to the elbow (Fig. 6.9, *C*) facing directly backward, while in a brachiating form such as the chimpanzee or *Presbytis,* the humerus has twisted so that the angle between elbow and head is near 30 degrees, and the head points inward (Fig. 6.9, *A* and *D*). Modern man shares this character with the brachiating groups: in both semibrachiators and bipeds the arm is able to move laterally as well as backward and forward.

Finally, it is characteristic of brachiators—and, to a lesser extent, of semi-brachiators, as well as of man—that the hinge joint at the

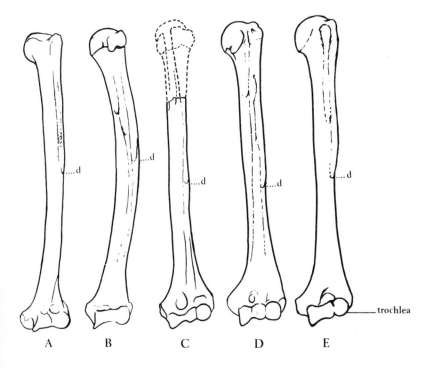

A   B   C   D   E

FIG. 6.8. Humeri of *Presbytis* (*A*), *Cercopithecus* (*B*), *Proconsul* (*C*), *Pan* (*D*), and modern man (*E*), all drawn the same size; *d* marks the lowest extent of the insertion of the deltoid muscle.

elbow, the *trochlea,* allows full extension of the forearm and is relatively broad, giving much greater lateral stability at that point (Fig. 6.8).

In the upper arm, therefore, we find that man shares four characters with the brachiators.

1. A relatively long and stout humerus
2. Relatively large arm-raising muscles and a low point of insertion of the deltoid
3. The head of the humerus pointing inward rather than straight backward
4. A fairly broad trochlea at the elbow

In one character, however, man's upright stance has led to a reduction in musculature, compared with all other primates and especially the brachiators—that is, in the propulsive muscles, the pectorales and latissimus dorsi.

Let us now turn to the fossil evidence for the evolution of the hominoid forelimb. We have fragments of two humeri of *Proconsul,*

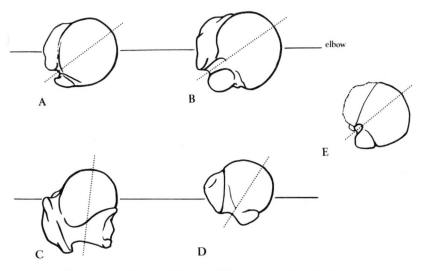

Fig. 6.9. View from above of heads of humeri of *Pan* (*A*), modern man (*B*), *Macaca* (*C*), and *Presbytis* (*D*). They are aligned according to the plane of the elbow joint. *E* is the humerus head of *Australopithecus;* it is not correctly aligned since the elbow joint is missing. It is, however, added for comparison of the form of the head and groove.

four of *Australopithecus,* and one of *Homo erectus.* One *Proconsul* humerus is associated with a radius and ulna, and these important fossil bones, which belong to the small species *Proconsul africanus,* have been described by Napier and Davis (1959). The humerus has been well reconstructed and in form and dimensions appears most similar to that of the semibrachiating monkey *Presbytis.* The point of insertion of the deltoid muscle is well down in the brachiator position, and the trochlea closely approaches the condition seen in *Pan,* allowing great extension at the elbow joint and (by its broadness) great stability (Fig. 6.8).

Small portions of a femur and humeral shaft have also been reported from the *Pan*-sized *Proconsul nyanzae* (Le Gros Clark and Leakey 1951). These fragments do not bear any characters of brachiators, but this may be accounted for by the fact that larger forms of living primates (apart from *Pongo*) do not show such extreme specialization in this respect as do the smaller forms (such as the gibbon).

It is not possible to draw more than very limited conclusions from these few fragments of *Proconsul,* but it is fair to admit evidence of a semi-brachiating primate in the Miocene—*Proconsul africanus.* It is of great interest that the dentition of this genus shows affinities to the great apes (see 7.7). While we can never know for sure what place this Miocene species had in the evolution of the Hominoidea, at least the limbs do not preclude its close association with a hypothetical Miocene pongid stock, as well as a hominid stock.

Humeri of *Australopithecus* were found at the following sites:

A. africanus	Sterkfontein	Almost complete bone (Broom *et al.* 1950)
	Makapansgat	Small piece of shaft
A. robustus	Kromdraai	Distal shaft and trochlea with ulna fragment (Broom and Schepers 1946)
Australopithecus Species uncertain	Olduvai	Distal shaft and trochlea

The Makapansgat fragment is too small to be of great interest, and the Olduvai fragments have not yet been described. The Sterkfontein humerus consists of the head and greater part of the shaft and has been described by Broom (Broom *et al.* 1950). In general, he finds the head of the humerus almost typically human, but the lesser tuberosity is very well developed and suggests a powerful *subscapularis*

muscle—the muscle that draws the humerus forward and downward—
an important muscle to a brachiator. In other characters, the bone appears almost human, but, according to Broom, it has characters that
recall those of the brachiating orang.

The Kromdraai bone includes the trochlea and was associated with
the proximal end of the ulna. It has been assigned to *Australopithecus
robustus* and is clearly hominoid in form, with a rather broad elbow
joint (Broom and Schepers 1946).

A humerus shaft has been described from Choukoutien, associated
with the fossils of Peking man. Though unusually slender and thick-
walled, this bone appears to fall within the range of that of modern
man. The specimens of femora and humeri are few, yet it seems clear
that *Homo erectus* had limbs not dissimilar to our own. If it were
not for the evidence of the skull, we would certainly assess these limb
bones as belonging to *Homo sapiens*.

From the data presented here, it seems clear not only that the upper
arm of modern man carries characters associated with the brachiating
primates but that his fossil relatives, in particular *Australopithecus*,
show quite strongly the characteristics of brachiation. Broom's comment on both the scapula and the humerus of *Australopithecus* was
that in his opinion these bones were intermediate between the bones of
modern man and the orang, the most advanced of the great apes in
the direction of full brachiation. The evidence for brachiation in man's
ancestry accumulates.

6.4 The forearm

THE BRACHIAL INDEX has been devised as an indicator of the
relative lengths of the humerus and radius. Table 6.2 gives
some figures for this index and shows that an elongation of the forearm relative to the upper arm is a correlate of brachiation. The spider
monkey (*Ateles*) is an extreme case in the New World, and the gibbon
(*Hylobates*) is extreme in this respect in the Old World. Some secondary shortening may have occurred in the gorilla; if so, it is possibly
associated with that heavy animal's more quadrupedal mode of locomotion. The brachial index of man varies a great deal but is always
well under 100, which places him with the quadrupedal primates. The

same general proportions of length and thickness are shown in the radius and ulna as in the humerus.

These bones of the forearm, the radius and ulna, are flexed and extended about the hinge-like elbow joint by muscles that originate on the humerus and lie along it. The *triceps* is the extensor of the forearm; the *biceps* is the flexor (Fig. 6.10). As might be expected, the extensor is the important muscle in a quadrupedal mammal because it supports the weight of the animal at the elbow, and the flexor is

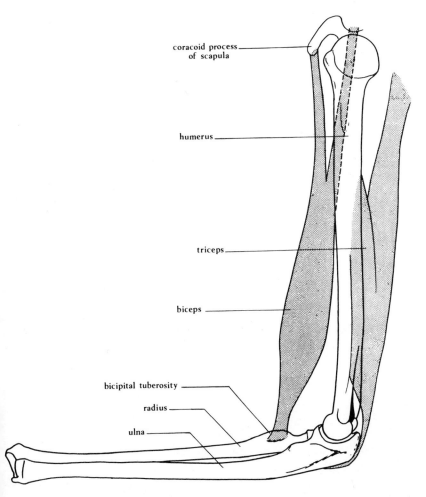

Fig. 6.10. Diagram showing the flexor and extensor muscles of the human forearm.

important in a brachiating form because it flexes the arm and lifts
the animal. Oxnard (1963) has again shown that the relative mass
of the triceps is, as we might expect, diminished in brachiators (Fig.
6.11). The length of the power arm of the forearm lever (that is, the
distance of the *bicipital tuberosity* from the elbow joint) also varies
with locomotor function (see Fig. 6.10). In this character, modern
man shows a shift from the quadrupedal condition toward the brachiating condition.

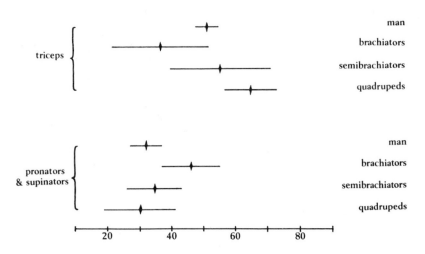

FIG. 6.11. Above, the relative mass of the triceps muscles, and below, the
relative mass of the pronators and supinators, in four locomotor groups.
The numbers refer to units of relative mass. (From Oxnard, 1963.)

The retention of the two bones in the forelimb is of course due to
the need for effective rotation of the hand—*pronation* and *supination*
(in pronation the thumb lies nearer the body—in supination digit 5
does so; Fig. 6.12). The articulation at the elbow joint is primarily
between humerus and ulna, and at the wrist between radius and the
carpal bones (Fig. 6.13). Forces of compression and tension are transmitted between the two forearm bones by the *interosseous membrane*.
The extent of rotation is limited by the extent to which the radius and
ulna are bowed. While the supination of quadrupedal monkeys is about
90 degrees, that of apes and man is nearer 180 degrees. The power of
rotation is dependent on the mass of the rotator muscles, and this

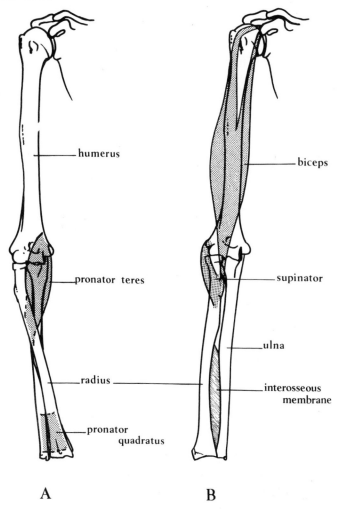

A   B

FIG. 6.12. Pronation (*A*) and supination (*B*) in man, shown from the front. The muscles used are shown in each drawing.

factor is recorded statistically in Figure 6.11. There is, again, a correlation between extensive rotation of the forearm and brachiation, as might be expected. In this character man lies with the semibrachiators and brachiators; the great power of rotation of the arm is clearly of great value in manipulation as well as in brachiation.

Fossil bones of the forearm are extremely rare, and worthwhile fragments have been found to date only from *Homo* and *Proconsul africanus*. Bones from the latter suggest a relatively short forearm and give a low brachial index (Table 6.2; Fig. 6.13). If, as we believe, *Proconsul* is ancestral to the apes, this evidence suggests that the elongation of the forearm typical of the living apes had not yet begun

FIG. 6.13. Forelimb skeleton of chimpanzee (*A*), *Proconsul* (*B*), and modern man (*C*) (reduced to the same total length). (After Le Gros Clark, 1962.)

in the Miocene (Napier and Davis 1959). Man shares this low brachial index with *Proconsul,* and, if the hominid line split away from the pongid line before the elongation of the forearm occurred, then the brachial index may have remained more or less constant in human evolution.

In other characters, the *Proconsul* fragments show an intermediate condition between quadruped and brachiator, as we might expect. Fragments of the forearm bones belonging to Neandertal man are as usual within the variation of form found among living *Homo sapiens.*

6.5 *The hands of primates*

THE MANUS of the tree shrew (Fig. 6.14, *A*) is a simple, five-fingered (*pentadactyl*) organ, the rather short phalanges making it appear little more than a paw. Each *phalanx* carries a claw, and there are six volar pads of friction skin on the palm and one terminal pad on each phalanx. Just above the wrist lies a small skin projection (*papilla*) from which grow long hairs, the *carpal vibrissae.* This papilla is a tactile sense organ common to most mammals, similar to those that bear whiskers on the face in dogs and cats. The vibrissae are implanted in richly innervated skin and form an extremely sensitive but quite undiscriminating tactile sense organ.

Studies of comparative anatomy make it clear that, as the volar pads increase in area and sensitivity in primate evolution, the importance of the carpal vibrissae decreases. They are poorly developed in the New World and absent in the Old World Anthropoidea. In the human fetus, a small transient cutaneous papilla can sometimes be seen in the carpal region (Schultz 1924). During evolution, the innervation of the volar pads, and particularly in the terminal digital pads, increases in density so that they become tactile sense organs of great importance (see sec. 6.6 and Fig. 6.14).

While it happens that in man the tactile function of the hand completely replaces the locomotor function, the manus remains an important locomotor organ in all other primates. In the Old World monkeys the forelimb may not be as important as the hindlimb in the propulsion of the quadrupedal groups, yet as a grasping organ it is very important. This grasping function is enhanced among the brachiators. There are two means of achieving a hold on a branch with the manus. The first, which is typical of the prosimians, involves a *pollex* (thumb), which diverges from the phalanges and can be opposed to

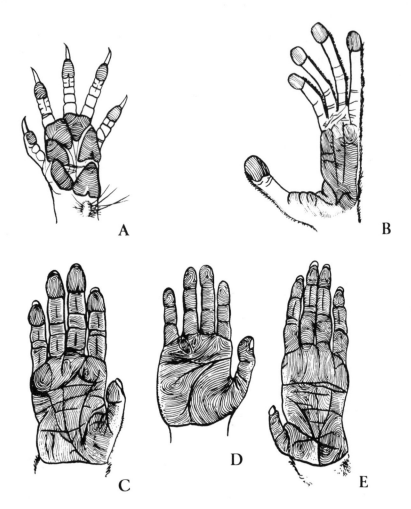

FIG. 6.14. The hands of primates: *Tupaia* (*A*), *Indri* (*B*), *Pan* (*C*), *Homo* (*D*), and *Pongo* (*E*). Note the carpal papilla on the wrist of *Tupaia*, the tree shrew, and the increase in the area of the volar skin in the higher primates. Note also the elongated pollex of *Indri* and the short pollex of *Pongo*. (After Biegert, 1963.)

them round the branch (Fig. 6.14, *B*). The second, typical of brachiators, involves the lengthening of the phalanges and, in many cases, a reduction of the pollex (see Fig. 6.14, *E* and Table 6.3). In the Old World monkeys, however, the opposable thumb of the prosimians is not lost, but, rather than for locomotion, it is retained as a result of the evolutionary development of the hand for use in other functions, such as the procurement of food, hygiene, defense, care of offspring, improved three-dimensional tactile sense and so forth (Biegert 1963). In fact, the Old World monkeys use their hands not only in locomotion but in a wide variety of basic functions, including grooming, carrying offspring and other objects, and throwing sticks and stones. A baboon has a precision grip between thumb and fingers sufficiently well evolved to extract the sting from a scorpion (Schultz 1961).

TABLE 6.3 MEAN PROPORTIONS OF THE HAND AND THUMB IN PRIMATES (DATA FROM SCHULTZ 1956)

Primate	$\dfrac{Hand\ Breadth \times 100}{Hand\ Length}$	$\dfrac{Pollex \times 100}{Hand\ Length}$
Presbytis	29	40
Macaca	35	56
Pan	34	47
Pongo	34	43
Gorilla	51	54
Hylobates	20	52
Homo	43	67

In the brachiating Hominoidea, however, we find the pollex much reduced, since the more the manus is involved in locomotion as a brachiating organ, the less it is available as a hand. The manus becomes a hook, and the phalanges lengthen further (Table 6.3) This is a specialization and reaches the condition in which the hand can no longer be used flat (*pronograde*) as a means of support because the ligaments permanently retain a curved, hook-like shape. When the African apes walk quadrupedally, therefore, their weight is borne on the phalangeal knuckles of their fingers, which cannot be flattened. A more extreme instance is found in the gibbons, which walk quadrupedally upon their metatarsal knuckles—a striking contrast with the condition found in the human infant and the baboon (Fig. 3.5, p. 67). The proportions of the hands of apes have been investigated by Schultz

(1956), and some figures are reproduced in Table 6.3. When hand length was compared to body trunk length, it was found that while in monkeys hand length is usually less than one-third of trunk length, it rises to an average of 47 per cent in semibrachiating New World monkeys and as much as 59 per cent in the gibbon.

We see, therefore, that except in certain prosimians, such as *Indri* (Fig. 6.14, *B*), the thumb has not developed as an opposable digit to increase the effective grasp of branches. On the contrary, among the brachiators the thumb is relatively reduced from a longer primitive condition. Napier (1960) has shown that the great apes *Pan* and *Pongo* have such short thumbs that they cannot achieve the powerful "pulp-to-pulp" contact of thumb and digits (Fig. 6.15) that forms the anatomical basis of man's precision grip. While the gorilla thumb is somewhat longer, it is still short of the human condition (see Fig. 6.17). Apart from the prosimians, therefore, a fairly long thumb can be found only among the quadrupedal Old World monkeys and man, and, as we have seen, it is used in these groups for the manipulation of objects.

FIG. 6.15. Man's precision grip, because of the full opposition of thumb and finger, is precise and delicate, yet strong.

A fairly complete hand has been described belonging to the Miocene *Proconsul africanus* (Napier and Davis 1959). It appears to be basically the hand of a quadrupedal Old World monkey with certain signs of brachiating adaptations. The hand is unfortunately not complete, and in particular it is not known how long the thumb was; nevertheless, its assessment as showing similarity to a semibrachiating species seems justified. This conclusion accords with that drawn on the basis of the forelimb bones. It seems clear that in *P. africanus* we have an incipient brachiator with much in common with our modern semibrachiators, and one that, on the basis of the limb bones, could conceivably be ancestral to both the living Pongidae and the living Hominidae. But this conclusion must be subject to the examination of the features of the skulls of all these forms.

6.6 *The evolution of the human hand*

WE HAVE SEEN that monkeys use their hands for a wide variety of purposes, and one of the most important, which we must now consider, is their contribution to the satisfaction of effectance motivation (see 2.6) : the hands make possible a detailed examination of parts of the environment that can be manipulated. Monkeys, apes, and man are almost the only animals that fiddle about with things, that turn them over and examine their form and texture. This manipulation of objects is not necessarily directly related to the procurement of food but is simply a process of investigation, equivalent to the olfactory investigation of the environment so characteristic of a dog. But in manipulation a monkey is investigating not the whole environment but only one particular part of it—and frequently a part that can be separated physically from the rest. This ability of higher primates to extract an object from its setting and examine it visually and three-dimensionally from all sides is a development of the utmost importance in human evolution. A carnivore will examine the olfactory nature of objects but cannot at the same time see them as part of the visual pattern of the environment because during examination by the nose the objects are more or less out of sight. Admittedly, a ball or bone can be manipulated with the paws and tossed with the mouth, but the range of objects examined is limited, and, compared with the primate hand, the paws and mouth give only a rough indication of shape and texture.

As will become apparent in chapter 10, the detachment of objects from the environment appears to be a most important prerequisite for the evolution of primate perception. This examination of things as objects we owe to the evolution of the primate hand and the opposable thumb. The recognition of different kinds of objects we owe to primate visual and tactile examination. Only a primate can, as it were, extract an object from the environment, examine it by smell, touch, and sight, and then return it to its place in its surroundings. In this way the higher primates have come to see the environment not as a continuum of events in a world of pattern but as an encounter with objects that proved to make up these events and this pattern. We shall return to this development in considering perception and conceptual thought (10.2).

This all-important development may have come quite early in primate evolution, with the appearance of the opposable thumb. In man, a further advance in opposability has perfected this remarkable organ of manipulation. Napier (1961) has examined the thumb of the

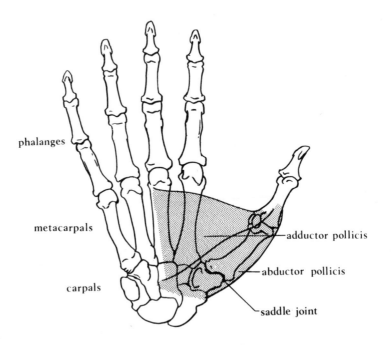

Fɪɢ. 6.16. The musculature of the thumb is well developed on the palm of the human hand. The two powerful muscles shown move the thumb toward and away from the palm. (After Napier, 1962.)

primate in order to analyze the development of opposability in hominid evolution. It reaches its most evolved condition in modern man and involves "a compound movement of abduction, flexion and medial rotation at the carpal-metacarpal articulation of the pollex." That is to say, a saddle joint evolves at the base of the thumb that allows a 45-degree rotation as well as movement in two planes (Fig. 6.16).

Though monkeys have an opposable thumb, it is only in man that the thumb is long enough and divergent enough to carry a heavy musculature (Fig. 6.16). This length and strength make possible a precision grip, strong yet delicate (Fig. 6.15). At the same time, with

A   B   C

FIG. 6.17. Hand bones of *Gorilla* (*A*), *Australopithecus* (*B*), and modern ern man (*C*). Note the straightening of the fingers in this series, the broadening and lengthening of the last phalanx of the thumb, and the lengthening of the thumb as a whole. Some of the *Australopithecus* thumb bones are reconstructions on the basis of other evidence. (Redrawn from Napier, 1962.)

the hand no longer functioning to grasp branches, the *metacarpals* and phalanges straighten out in the course of human evolution, and the terminal segments broaden (Fig. 6.17).

When apes and monkeys carry objects about, which they often do, their locomotor efficiency is impaired. Tool-carrying, food-carrying, and food-sharing (which is possible only if the food is first carried) all have been reported to a limited extent among chimpanzees (Goodall 1965), but they cannot move fast with a handful of objects and do so only for very limited distances. In early man the survival value of being able to carry objects without any disadvantageous effect on locomotion is of the greatest importance. Not only is it most advantageous to be able to carry food when surprised by a predator, but it can lead eventually to food sharing, and in particular to hunting. A weapon at the ready is also of great survival value. The survival value of carrying also serves in turn to promote a physical structure adapted to bipedal locomotion.

Tool-using is not so rare as might be supposed in the animal kingdom. The use of sticks and rocks in agonistic display by chimpanzees and baboons is familiar (Hall 1963a). Tool modification—the next stage in the evolution of material culture—has been reported among chimpanzees, which prepare and collect sticks of a certain length for extracting termites from their nests. At Olduvai, stone tools have been found at an early level dated nearly 1.8 million years B.P. (Before Present) in direct association with one or more species of *Australopithecus* (J. D. Clark 1963, and Evernden and Curtis 1965) (Fig. 6.18).

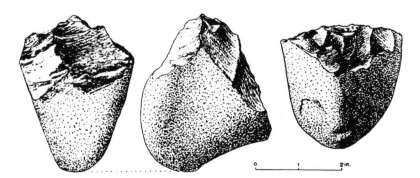

FIG. 6.18. Primitive pebble tools of the kind associated with *Australopithecus* at Olduvai, Tanzania. (By permission of the trustees of the British Museum [Natural History].)

Here we see pebbles obviously used for pounding roots and other vegetable matter, preserved, after flaking, as cutting tools for the preparation of meat. From South Africa we have evidence of bones modified as tools from a site and stratum inhabited by *Australopithecus africanus* (Dart 1957). The transition from tool-modifying to tool-making is slow and continuous, but there is no doubt that a cutting tool was a great asset and is particularly necessary in the evolution of a carnivorous diet (see 7.2, 7.10).

But the tools we have found associated with the man-ape *Australopithecus* are relatively simple, and it is relevant that this creature had a brain not really much bigger in absolute size than that of a gorilla (see Table 8.2). Fragments of a hand are known, and they are reported to be somewhat less than fully human (Napier 1962) (Fig. 6.17). Finely flaked stone tools are found—to date—only in association with the bones of hominids that had larger brains. Fine Acheulian hand-axes are known from Ternifine as well as Olduvai, where they are associated with remains of *Homo erectus;* in this hominid the brain may well have amounted to nearly 1,000 cc. Clearly, the final perfection of the hand was a perfection not only in anatomy but in sensory perception and motor control, with a highly developed brain. The most clear-cut neural correlate of the evolution of the human hand is the increase in representation that this organ carries on the motor and somatic sensory cortexes of the brain (see Fig. 8.10, p. 226). We have also noted significant improvement in the direct nervous pathways to the hand of the ascending and descending fibers (see 3.6).

We can summarize the evolution of the human hand by marking two stages in its development. First, the primate terrestrial environment selects the opposable thumb, for grasping branches, and this thumb appears among the prosimians and in turn makes possible manipulation among Old World monkeys. Second, the ecological move to the open plains correlated with bipedalism frees the hand from all locomotor function and allows the perfection of the precision grip by some minor modifications of the thumb. The hand has contributed as much as the eye to the making of man; together they gave him a new perception of his environment and, with his material culture, a new control of it.

6.7 Man's ancestors as semibrachiators

FROM THE EVIDENCE presented in this chapter, it seems in-
controvertible that modern man's ancestors were either semibrachiating monkeys or apes. Not only does living *Homo sapiens* share
many characters with living semibrachiators but so does the genus
Australopithecus. In this connection we must recall the much earlier
form *Proconsul,* which also carries a variety of semibrachiating characters.

Modern man does, of course, bear certain characters in the forelimbs that are adaptations to erect posture, and in particular these
characters result from the downward-hanging characteristic position
of the arms. This result is to be expected, and, although some of the
characters have something in common with quadrupedal monkeys, they
need not lead us to suppose that man's ancestors were quadrupedal
monkeys. The character of the *Australopithecus* scapula and humerus
is important evidence in this hypothesis.

Finally, we need not be surprised to find that the muscles that carry
the weight of the body in brachiators are, with their areas of attachment, reduced in man (Ziegler 1964). Although man uses the same
muscles in carrying as do the brachiators, these muscles do very much
less work.

Man is, of course, a much more recent arrival on the earth than the
kangaroo or the dinosaur, so it is not surprising that his forearms show
in comparison little or no sign of reduction (see Fig. 4.5, p. 91). It
is not impossible that the arms have been slightly reduced, though
as yet we have no evidence on this matter from such an intermediate
form as *Australopithecus,* since the long bones known at present are
fragmentary. On the whole, though, it seems likely that the value of
man's arms is such as not to result in the selection of reduced length.
For throwing stones and spears, a long arm is invaluable; for writing,
it is perhaps less necessary.

SUGGESTIONS FOR FURTHER READING

Few authors have given much attention to the evolution of the forelimb. As a general introduction that runs parallel to this discussion see

the appropriate chapter in W. E. le Gros Clark, *The Antecedents of Man* (Edinburgh: University of Edinburgh Press, 1963). An important study of the forearm is to be found in J. R. Napier and P. R. Davis, *The Forelimb Skeleton and Associated Remains of* Proconsul africanus (London: British Museum [Nat. Hist.], 1959). For reference to the primate hand see J. Biegert, "Volarhaut der Hände und Füsse," *Handbuch der Primatenkunde,* II/1 Lieferung 3, pp. 1-326 (Basel and New York: S. Karger, 1961).

7

Feeding, Ecology, and Behavior

7.1 Functions of the head

IN APPROACHING the subject of this chapter we cannot avoid consideration of the head as a whole, as an organ that has come to assume an increasing number of functions in animal evolution. To understand the evolution of the human head, we must examine these different functions carefully. In order to reveal their phylogenetic origin, let us turn for a moment to consider the structure of a primitive living creature, the lancelet (*Amphioxus*), which is believed to be very similar to the ancestor of all vertebrates. This small marine animal looks like a minute fish, about an inch long (Fig. 7.1).

In this creature (as well as in more primitive invertebrate forms) the head can be recognized by three characteristics. First, it may be defined as the part of the body of the animal that precedes the rest in locomotion; second, it is near to, or incorporates, the mouth; and, third, it contains at least one sense organ. In preceding the body, the head is able to investigate the environment that the organism is approaching, to direct the organism toward food (in many instances by moving toward light or up a "desirable" chemical gradient), and to receive food by the mouth. Since movement toward food is a simple kind of behavior, we find the nervous system developing between the head receptors and the effectors (the swimming muscles), which lie behind it along the animal's body. In the course of the evolution of both invertebrate and vertebrate animals, a small knot or *ganglion* of nerves appears near the receptors and the mouth. Within this small ganglion of nervous tissue, the primitive brain, information about the environment (or about the food) is analyzed and an appropriate pattern of behavior is effected. In the evolution of vertebrates, the extent of sensory investigation of the environment has vastly increased, for increased sensory input relating to environmental conditions has characterized the appearance of more complex individuals. The evolution of multiple sense organs has been accompanied by the evolution of a relatively massive central nervous system, which analyzes the vast input from the receptors and mediates a wide range of behavioral activity.

FIG. 7.1. The lancelet, a primitive animal still found in shallow sea water, believed to be very like the ancestor of vertebrates; *m* = mouth, *in* = intestine, *a* = anus, *g* = gills, *no* = notocord (the primitive spine), *nc* = nerve cord, *my* = myotomes (the lateral swimming muscles) and *f* = fin. (From Colbert, 1955.)

In vertebrates, therefore, with the brain evolving near the sense receptors in the head, we find that the head serves the animal in two quite separate ways, first as a complex organ of interaction with the environment and second as a protective box for the brain. The functions of the head may be summarized as follows:

I. Relations with environment
   A. Metabolic
      1. Food intake through mouth and masticatory apparatus
      2. Inspiration and expiration of air through the mouth, with which the gills or lungs are connected (for they arose as outgrowths from the alimentary canal)

B. Sensory and motor
  1. Deployment of sense receptors concerned with input from environment, both distant and contact (especially food recognition, mate recognition, and enemy recognition)
  2. Communication (a secondary function of metabolic structures): movement of facial muscles, and sound production through trachea and mouth
  3. Defense and offense: a secondary function of teeth of masticatory apparatus, and evolution of horns on the skull in some groups
II. Protective case for the brain

The evolution of these functions of the head will be considered in the following chapters. Here, we are concerned with the part played by the head in feeding and digestion, including the sensory receptors concerned with food-finding and -testing (I, A, 1 above, together with B, 1). Other functions of the masticatory apparatus will also be considered (B, 3). Chapter 8 refers to further aspects of the evolution of the head (I, B, 1 and II), and chapter 10 refers to the evolution of communication (I, B, 2).

Before investigating the evolution of feeding in primates, it is convenient to classify the sense organs functionally into two kinds: the *contact receptors,* which supply data about the immediate environment (taste and touch), and the *distance receptors,* which measure intensity and direction (or extent of change) of external conditions. We recognize three kinds of distance receptor: the *chemo-receptors* measure the density of certain vaporized substances in the air (smell), the *photo-receptors* measure the intensity and wavelength of certain electro-magnetic waves (vision), and the *mechanoreceptors* measure vibration, sound waves, and gravity (hearing and balance). The evolution of these senses will be discussed in this and the following chapters.

7.2 Food-finding and diet

TOGETHER WITH mating behavior, food-finding is a basic activity of all animals. An animal may spend most of its waking lifetime searching for food, and only an increase in food availability will allow for the development of other behavior patterns less immediately essential. It is an important fact of primate biology that in their adaptation to an arboreal environment primates were able to exploit a rich source of food, which had not been tapped before to any great extent. An enormous proportion of the energy received from the sun is converted into trees, as distinct from herbs, and the primates were able to consume not only the foliage but also the fruit and seeds of the forest. Fruit and seeds have high food value, and arboreal animals obtained access to food resources of quite a different order of richness from those available to the grazing mammals of the plains. Plants have evolved a highly concentrated food store in seeds to nourish the developing seedling, and a very attractive food source in fruit. Edible fruits have evolved specifically for the consumption of animals, which in turn serve the plant by distributing the seeds in their feces. Thus, though the primates are broadly herbivorous, it is clear that the type of food they live on is different in texture and quality from that available to the plains mammals.

Primates identify their food by sight, smell, touch, and finally taste. The pre-eminent importance of primate vision has already been mentioned, and it is certain that such an acute sense is of value in recognizing fruits and seeds, especially the former, which are often brightly colored. Birds and primates are the two groups of vertebrates known to have a well-developed color sense, and the colored fruits of the forest have evolved, no doubt, in conjunction with their developed color sense. The development of the visual receptors and visual cortex has been of very great survival value to primates, in this as well as in other ways.

Although the visual sense is highly evolved in the carnivores and some ungulates, the sense of smell is by far the most important distance receptor in most mammals other than primates, and even in primates its importance should not be underestimated. The early mammals (which were probably nocturnal) and most recent mammals depend almost entirely on distance chemo-reception in food-finding and mate-finding. For that reason, the olfactory sense is an essential determinant of behavior. While sexual behavior is probably predominately innate (see chapter 9), a great deal of food-finding behavior is known to be learned, and the olfactory lobes are closely connected with the cerebral cortex (see 8.6). It is significant that the cortex itself, with its vast memory store, evolved from the part of the brain originally concerned with smell (the *rhinencephalon*). It is not surprising, therefore, that, although in the evolution of the primates the visual sense overtakes the olfactory sense in overall importance, the latter plays some part in the deeply rooted behavior patterns of feeding and mating, and this importance is not altogether lost in modern man.

When food has been located and approached, the evolving primate hand plays an important part. The evolution of an organ of manipulation has not greatly affected the diet, but it has enabled the animal to carry food to the mouth, rather than having to pluck food with the mouth alone. Therefore the neck of primates has never lengthened as an adaptation to food-gathering; the prehensile and sensory hand has evolved instead.

When food has been identified by the eyes and tactile senses of the hand it is passed to the lips, where again we find a tactile sense organ of great importance. The sensory and motor areas of the cerebral cortex that relate to the lips (see Fig. 8.10, p. 226) are very large; the primate lips are a highly innervated organ of investigation, and this character is not lost in human evolution. As the food is brought to the mouth, it is held close to the nostrils, which can thus obtain reliable olfactory information about it. Innate physiological responses follow olfactory stimulation, such as the secretion of saliva and other digestive substances. Any food that has passed the lips and been subjected to so much investigation is unlikely to be falsely identified.

Though it is probable that all primates were originally insectivorous, today different primates have different feeding habits and diets according to the nature of their various environments. Flora varies with climate, altitude, and continent, and diet varies accordingly. The diet of species that remain almost permanently in the highest tree-tops will be confined mainly to vegetable matter, leaves, fruit, young shoots, and new bark. Primates that visit the ground from time to time will eat roots and even some meat, besides termites, ants, and tree frogs. The mountain gorilla, though predominantly ground-living, is, however, fully vegetarian (Schaller 1963). The chimpanzee, on the other hand, is not averse to eating termites and even small mammals (Goodall 1965). The fully terrestrial baboons also eat meat when they can catch a young animal, but all are predominantly herbivorous (DeVore and Washburn 1963). The baboon lives mainly on grass, shoots, and other succulent vegetation.

Schultz (1961) claims that some animal food is consumed by all primates and that some New World monkeys and most prosimians eat more worms, insects, frogs, lizards, and bird eggs than plant food. The important conclusion for our studies is that primates have at all times been able to consume and digest animal food—indeed, they appear to enjoy it. The limiting factor in the evolution of a more carnivorous diet among higher primates was, first, probably a lack of any selection pressure to do so, since the forest contained a nearly unlimited supply of plant food of good quality, and, second, the fact that primates are not in any way preadapted to catch animals larger than frogs, lizards, and so forth.

Modern man is an omnivore, and his diet varies a great deal; it is probably more variable than that of any other animal species. Meat represents a large portion of the diet only in north-temperate peoples who live in an environment short of vegetables during the winter. For that reason, Eskimos are almost completely carnivorous. Tropical man eats meat, and some will go to much trouble to obtain it by hunting, but most tribes, even the pastoralists, have a primarily vegetarian diet. (Exceptions include the Masai tribe of eastern Africa, which subsists on blood and milk obtained from their cattle, and the Bushmen of southern Africa, who are hunters. Both tribes live in arid regions, where the supply of vegetable matter is limited.)

It therefore appears that there was no really fundamental change of diet between the primate ancestors of man and *Homo sapiens*. An analysis of animal bones on the early Pleistocene living floors at Olduvai in Tanzania shows that at that stage the meat diet of *Australopithecus* was still confined mainly to small animals, such as birds, lizards, and rodents (Leakey 1959). The change that occurred, therefore, in the diet of evolving man, was to the consumption of larger animals—the plains mammals—which could be caught only with the technology and social organization associated with hunting.

The evolution of the social hunt brought varying proportions of mammal meat into man's diet. Clearly, this new and virtually unlimited food source was of immense survival value to groups of primitive men living on the open plains, where good vegetables were neither common nor succulent, especially during the dry seasons. But man remained to some extent dependent on insects, reptiles, and birds, as he does to this day.

It is an important fact that every new evolutionary radiation has involved the exploitation of a new major source of food. Of course, the herbivorous mammals of the wide grass plains had already been exploited by the carnivores, such as the lion and leopard, but the natural balance between those two groups appears to be about one carnivore to every hundred herbivores. The effectiveness of social hunting among humans enabled them to tap this huge reserve more effectively; there was enough food for both men and lions.

It seems possible that the availability of an immense supply of mammal meat made the synthesis of certain proteins a much simpler matter for *Homo*; they were already synthesized by the herbivorous mammals and, though broken down in the process of human digestion to their component amino acids, were available in the right proportions for re-synthesis. The availability of mammal meat may have been very important in the final evolution of *Homo*. It is of interest that the baboon, another plains-living primate, has also shown carnivorous tendencies, and Dart (1963) claims that it needs a regular supply of animal protein.

Meat is a concentrated form of food, comparable to seeds, which have been exploited by the rodents and are no doubt a contributory factor to their great success. Meat contains a high percentage of protein and, when digested, will release the whole range of amino acids necessary for the synthesis of body tissues. It also contains vitamins (in particular in the liver), which are not readily available in a vegetable diet. There is little doubt that the final stage in human evolution (since the Middle Pleistocene) was correlated with the exploitation by man of the plains mammals. Man's immensely successful evolutionary radiation must be associated, then, not with a fundamental change in diet, but with an important change in emphasis from a diet that was mainly vegetarian to one that was increasingly omniverous, if not distinctly carnivorous. The change was not so much one of internal evolution of the alimentary canal and masticatory apparatus as a change in ecology, in man's whole environment. In leaving the forest for the plains, man's ancestors changed not only their diet but their whole way of life. The change in diet was a reflection of the new environment, not the reason for it.

7.3 Taste and the tongue

THE TESTING and identification of food does not end when it is placed in the mouth. The inside of the mouth is rich in tactile sensory nerve endings, as is the tongue. In addition, the tongue carries numerous *papillae,* containing nerve endings sensitive to taste (the taste buds), which in man (and presumably other primates) can distinguish the flavors sweet, bitter, acid, and salt. Such particular characteristics of food are not readily detectable by the nose (one cannot smell the sweetness or saltiness of a dish), for the relevant molecules are not easily vaporized. But the identification of these flavors is important: sugar is a valuable source of food, and salt is an essential mineral. Our marine origin has left us with saline body fluids, the salinity of which must be exactly maintained. Primates have been observed licking rocks containing salt and obtaining it from the salty sweat deposits in each other's fur. Bitterness and acidity are the characteristics of some natural poisons.

The human sense of "taste" is of course for the most part due to the activity of the olfactory organ, the nose. The smell of food in the mouth enters the nose by the *pharynx,* the internal passage from the mouth to the nose. There is no doubt that, although the sense of smell is now less important to man than it was to some of his ancestors, he still has the power of great chemical discrimination (in a "trained palate"); while the total volume of the brain involved with this sense may be relatively reduced, it is probably not absolutely reduced and is still of considerable magnitude. In man, the importance of smell has been more strikingly reduced as a determinant of sexual behavior than in feeding behavior.

Since the tongue lies between the teeth, it is able to sample food during mastication. Stimuli interpreted as undesirable can still result in rejection of the food. It is interesting that the nerve fibers from the taste buds lead to the brainstem and are strongly tied to innate reflexes, such as salivation or rejection. The significance of taste is primarily innate, that of smell is to a great extent learned.

The tongue has other functions besides bearing the taste buds. In prosimians as well as in many other animals it has a roughened horny surface and aids in grasping the food in the mouth. The tongue initiates the process of swallowing and is important as a means of removing food particles from the teeth and in keeping them clean. In the Hominoidea this function is still important, ranking after tasting, swallowing, and speech, though the rough surface has been sacrificed to increased sensory discrimination.

The musculature of the tongue is an important consideration in a study of human evolution because the tongue makes possible the act of speech. This musculature is well developed in most mammals for the various functions described above, and little anatomical change was needed to turn it into an organ of speech. The tongue is anchored to the skeleton at two points, one the inner surface of the *mandible* or jawbone at the *genial tubercle* (Fig. 7.9, p. 186) and the second the *hyoid* bone (Fig. 10.2, p. 309). The tongue also carries its own internal muscle, which makes possible its complex changes of shape. However, the important changes that occurred in the evolution of speech were not so much in the tongue's anatomy as in the motor control of the tongue by the brain (see 10.6).

7.4 The masticatory apparatus

MASTICATION is an essential process in the realization of the total value of foods. The enzymes and other substances that effect digestion cannot operate on large masses of food except very slowly. It is remarkable that some reptiles (such as snakes) are able to digest entire animals without any form of mastication, but the resulting rate of output of digested food substances is low and the animals undergo a period of postprandial sluggishness, or even coma. The warm-blooded mammal and the bird require a constant and high rate of digestion, and each has developed its own masticatory apparatus; among mammals, it evolved from the jaws, and, among birds, the gizzard evolved from the alimentary canal. Besides breaking down large pieces of food, mastication also destroys plant cellular structure and frees the proteins, fats, and sugars from the insoluble cellulose cell walls that enclose the living cell contents, thus releasing an immense quantity of food for immediate digestion—a development clearly essential to the mammal way of life.

The evolution of primate dentition is indeed of great interest, not least insofar as the structure of the teeth reflects different diets. But there is another reason for its interest to us: of all parts of the body, the teeth have been most successfully preserved as fossils, and these fossil teeth have enabled us to understand something of the evolution of the living primates. Jawbones, too, are very strong structures and for that reason have also been preserved in considerable numbers. The evolution of the human masticatory apparatus is probably more completely documented than that of any other part of the body, and it deserves a detailed description.

In accord with changes in tooth function, the mammal jaw itself has evolved. As we have seen, the reptile jaw was primarily a food trap, so it needed to be large, quick-operating, and escape-proof. It was not necessary for the jaws to develop large compressive forces between the teeth. In the python, for example, all the bones of the forepart of the skull and mandible are loosely connected, to allow the swallowing of large food animals without mastication (Fig. 2.3, p. 40). The most primitive primate jaw is to be found among the tree shrews, where little more than grasping action is required. As grinding action evolved, more power was required, and the jaw changed shape. Before consideration of these important shape changes, however, it is necessary to review briefly the musculature of the primate jaw.

The jaw is operated by paired muscles that move the mandible about its pivots, the *mandibular condyles*. The maxillary bones (or *maxillae*) that carry the upper teeth are firmly fixed to the skull, and the compressive force used in crushing and grinding is achieved by raising the mandible against the maxilla. The muscles that raise the mandible and close the jaw are the *temporalis* muscles, assisted by the *masseter* and *medial pterygoids* (also called *internal pterygoids*). The mandible is moved forward and sideways by the *lateral* (or *external*) *pterygoids*. Figures 7.2, 7.3, and 7.4 show the arrangement

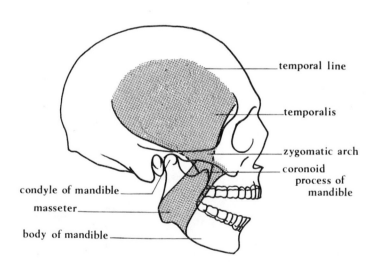

temporal line

temporalis

zygomatic arch

coronoid
process of
mandible

condyle of mandible

masseter

body of mandible

FIG. 7.2. The human skull, showing the masseter and temporalis muscles, which raise the mandible to bite. The medial pterygoids (which also raise the mandible) are not shown, since they lie within the skull.

of these muscles. The architecture of the skull is such as to form a framework around the nasal passages and orbits to transmit these forces of mastication (imposed upon the maxillary bone) to the top and sides of the skull. The heavy browridges—the *supraorbital torus*— have evolved partly in order to spread this force and may be considered as part of the masticatory apparatus. Their form and function is discussed in greater detail in chapter 8.

In the evolution of chewing among primates, two features of the jaw itself have changed:

1. The *occlusal plane* is the line on which the teeth meet when the jaw is closed. In primitive primates, the point of pivot—the mandibular condyle—lies more or less on this plane; in higher primates, it has moved up well above this plane (Fig. 7.5). The result is that, while

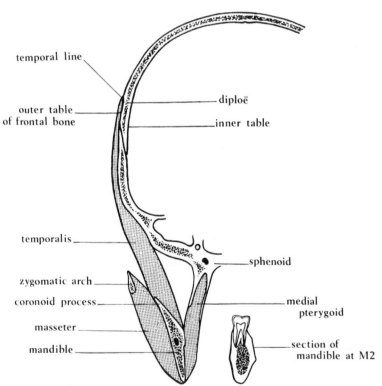

temporal line

outer table
of frontal bone

diploë

inner table

temporalis

zygomatic arch

coronoid process

masseter

mandible

sphenoid

medial
pterygoid

section of
mandible at M2

Fig. 7.3. A section through the right side of the skull and mandible at the coronoid process showing the arrangement of the three biting muscles. *Bottom right,* a section of the mandible at the second molar showing the bone structure into which the tooth is embedded.

in the lower primates the molar teeth meet first and the incisors later (like a pair of scissors), in the higher forms the whole dentition occludes simultaneously, which means that all the molars are equally effective as crushers and grinders. At the same time, the increased distance between pivot and teeth allows the lateral movement necessary for grinding. The overall form and musculature of the jaw is modified accordingly. Thus the jaw becomes an angled bone instead of a more or less straight one, the *ramal* portion (the part bearing no teeth) being ascending rather than horizontal (Fig. 7.5). The displacement has been achieved in the skull itself by lowering the floor of the nasal chamber and the dental arcade in relation to the braincase and orbits, and in

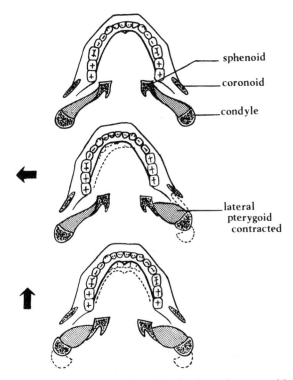

FIG. 7.4. Diagram showing the action of the lateral pterygoid muscles, which are attached medially to the sphenoid bone of the skull and latererally to the mandibular condyle on the inner surface. In the middle drawing the mandible is pulled to the left by the action of one muscle only—the right lateral pterygoid. In the lower drawing the mandible is pulled forward by the contraction of both lateral pterygoid muscles. (Redrawn from Testut, 1928.)

some species the palate is vaulted. The changes in the general form of the skull resulting from this modification are discussed in chapter 8.

2. The second primate development relates to the power developed between the molar teeth. This power is proportional to the relationship between the length of the power arm and the load arm of the mandible lever, for a given volume of muscle. The shorter the load arm (that is, the distance between the teeth and pivot point projected onto the occlusal plane), the greater the power of compression developed between

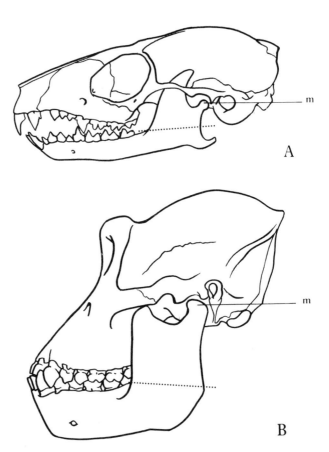

A

m

m

B

Fɪɢ. 7.5. Skulls of the tree shrew (*Ptilocerus*) (*A*) and a female gorilla (*B*). Note the relative sizes of the jaw and neurocranium and their relative positions. In particular, note the height of the mandibular condyle (*m*) above the occlusal plane of the teeth (*dotted line*). (From drawings in Le Gros Clark, 1962.)

the molars for grinding food (Fig. 7.6). In the evolution of the primates the relative shortening of the load arm has been achieved to a
great extent by bringing the dental arcades backward and under the
braincase, which has had the added advantage that the maxillary bone
can transmit the forces of compression more directly to the skull vault
from which arise the temporal muscles. Development of a short and
powerful jaw was made possible when the need for snapping action
by the mouth became of secondary importance in the evolution of a
herbivorous diet.

These two trends have operated simultaneously in the evolution of
the human dentition. Only in the last stages of the process was jaw size
reduced relative to body size, and this reduction now deserves consideration.

7.5 *The human jaw*

THE CONCEPT OF BIOLOGICAL efficiency suggests that if an
organ is larger than necessary it will be reduced by genetic
adjustment in the course of evolution. But in human evolution there
was another distinct advantage in having a smaller jaw, for a reduc-

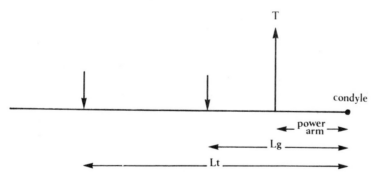

FIG. 7.6. Diagram showing the length of the load arm of the mandible
lever in relation to the power arm in the tree shrew and gorilla. The
horizontal line represents the occlusal plane, and upon it are projected
the condyle or pivot of the mandible, and the position of the force developed by the temporalis muscle and transmitted through the coronoid
process (*T*). The relative length of the load arm is calculated on the
basis of a constant power-arm length and is defined as the distance of
the first molar tooth from the condyles. This length is indicated by *Lt*
for the tree shrew and by *Lg* for the gorilla.

tion in the size of the masticatory apparatus in an erect animal will help toward achieving a true balance of the head upon the spine. Such a balance has been almost achieved in modern man, and the reduction in the size of the masticatory apparatus (a reduction of subnasal prognathism) is a factor of prime importance in this evolutionary development (4.4). We see this development as early as the Pliocene in the mandible of *Ramapithecus,* which in Figure 7.7 is shown alongside that of a typical fossil pongid (of the subfamily Dryopithecinae) of the same antiquity. The reduction of the teeth has allowed the mandible to curve inward at the level of the first molar in *Ramapithacus*; in the dryopithecine animal it curves much farther out, level with the premolar teeth (see also Figure 7.14).

Experiments on animals have demonstrated conclusively that in ontogeny the final size of the mandible and masticatory muscles depends on the amount of use the masticatory apparatus is put to during growth —an example of developmental homeostasis. On the other hand, the size of the teeth is not affected in this way by environmental influence but is under more or less direct genetic control. The crowns of the teeth are of course subject to wear, but the length and breadth of the crown is not modified unless the tooth is damaged.

There is always a delay between a change in selection pressure and the appropriate genetic (evolutionary) modification, a delay beautifully demonstrated in the fossilized dentition of *Australopithecus robustus,* in which marked tooth-crowding is quite characteristic (Oppenheimer 1964) (Fig. 7.8). This phenomenon indicates that the jaw did not grow to the size for which the teeth had evolved. The need for a heavy jaw was lost, but the teeth had not yet been reduced; the phenotype had made some adjustment to altered environmental conditions, but the genotype as yet had not. Tooth-crowding is seen in modern man for similar reasons.

What were the altered environmental conditions? *Australopithecus* was eating less tough food, which may have been the direct result of the development of tools to cut up meat and break up roots and grain. It is possible that here we have evidence of the development of tools for cutting and as weapons, initiating the reduction of the jaws in the evolution of man.

Two other more detailed features must concern us in a study of the later stages of human evolution: the form of the *mandibular body* and the evolution of the chin.

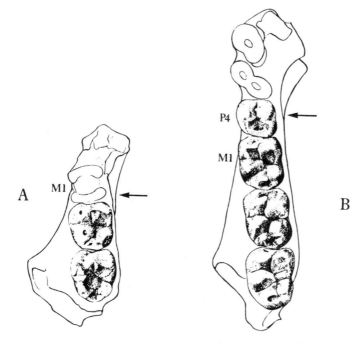

FIG. 7.7. Comparison of Mio-Pliocene hominid mandible fragment of *Ramapithecus* (*A*), with contemporary ape *Dryopithecus* (*B*). In the hominid, the mandible begins to turn inward toward the midline at the level of the first molar (*M1*), while in *Dryopithecus* the curve does not begin until the second premolar (*P4*). This feature shows that the reduction typical of the hominid jaw and dentition was already apparent at this early date. (From Simons, 1964.)

The mandibular body or *corpus* is the part of the mandible that carries the teeth. Its function, besides carrying teeth, is to transmit to the teeth themselves the forces put upon the ramal part of the mandible by the contraction of the masticatory muscles. Large teeth like canines have large roots as anchors, and of course it follows that a deep mandibular body is necessary to carry large teeth. In man, with much-reduced teeth, especially canines, the body may be quite shallow, but the bone structure has to transmit various forces and so must be of a certain cross-section beyond that necessary to house the roots of the teeth. The depth of the mandible allows it to transmit the vertical forces involved in closing the jaw when the temporalis, masseter, and medial pterygoid muscles contract; the body of the mandible can be considered

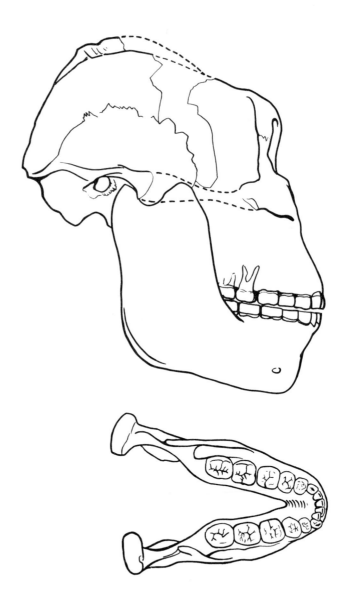

FIG. 7.8. The heavily built *Australopithecus robustus* skull and mandible. Note the level tooth rows without projecting canines and the crowding among the lower incisors. A small sagittal crest is clearly present. (Drawn from a photograph of the Olduvai specimen; the mandible is from Swartkrans.)

as a girder, and its depth is directly related to the bending stress developed at each point along its length. The teeth make it, in effect, a U-girder with internal webbing (see Fig. 7.3).

Forces in the vertical plane are not, however, the only forces acting on the body of the mandible. The lateral grinding movement of the mandible is an important masticatory movement and is brought about by the lateral pterygoid muscles (the action of these muscles is shown in Figure 7.4). Lateral movement is caused by the action of each muscle alternately: the right lateral pterygoid pulls the mandible to the left; the left lateral pterygoid pulls it to the right. The power for lateral grinding action therefore comes from one side only and is transmitted through the body of the mandible to the molar teeth on the other side. The bending stress on the mandible in the horizontal plane can therefore be very great, especially when the jaw muscles are strongly contracted and the friction between the molars is at its maximum.

In species that have evolved a powerful lateral grinding action of the molar teeth, therefore, we find a thickening of the body of the mandible in the horizontal plane. Thickening is most apparent at the point at which the mandible is most curved, at the *symphyseal region* (the midline between the first incisor teeth). In the mandibles of higher primates, this point is strengthened by the development of internal buttressing, which may occur either at the lower margin, when it is called a *simian shelf,* or halfway up the body of the mandible, when it is called a *mandibular torus.* In some forms both kinds of buttressing occur together (Fig. 7.9).

In the evolution of man both kinds of buttressing have been lost, although their traces can be identified in some mandibles. The internal buttress has been replaced by a weakly developed external buttress, the chin. Clearly the stresses set up in the mandible of modern man are not great, but, as can be seen in the wear of human teeth, grinding action has by no means been entirely lost and some strengthening is still necessary. The reason for this change of structure in the buttressing of the mandible of *Homo* has been revealed by a functional analysis by DuBrul and Sicher (1954).

Both the recession of the dental arcade and the movement of the head backward on top of the spine (with the forward movement of the occipital condyles) to achieve a better balance have brought the mandible into very close proximity to the neck. If the form of the lower margin of the mandible had not changed, it would certainly have con-

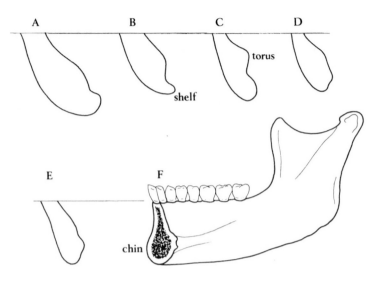

FIG. 7.9. Section of the symphyseal region of different jaws: gorilla (*A*), chimpanzee (*B*), *Australopithecus africanus* (*C*), *Homo erectus* (Heidelberg) (*D*), *Homo sapiens* (early form from Krapina) (*E*), and modern man (*F*). Note the different means of horizontal stiffening: the simian shelf, mandibular torus, and chin. On the inner symphyseal surface of (*F*) are to be seen two small protuberances, the genial tubercles, to which are attached the muscles supporting the tongue.

stricted the windpipe, larynx, and soft viscera of the neck, including the vital veins and arteries to the brain, which lie just behind the angle of the mandible. DuBrul and Sicher have shown how the lower margin of the mandible has been everted to avoid this state of affairs (Fig. 7.10). The chin is the result of the eversion of the lightly buttressed *symphysis*; it is a necessary result of the reduced masticatory apparatus of modern man.

It is of interest to study the skull topography of the orang in this context. Biegert (1963) has pointed out that in order to accommodate the laryngeal sacs, in the laryngeal space under the jaws, the occipital condyles have moved back under the skull; the jaws have come forward and a more "primitive" alignment of the skull has resulted. This development appears to be an alternative means of protecting the neck viscera.

The changes in the primate jaw that led to that of modern man can therefore be summarized as follows:

1. Evolution of the ascending ramus, at right angles to the corpus
2. Retraction of the dental arcade under the skull
3. Reduction of the jaws and dentition
4. Eversion of the lower border of the mandible

7.6 Dentition: the incisors

BEFORE WE CONSIDER the different kinds of teeth, it is necessary to review their arrangement in the jawbones (maxilla and mandible). This arrangement is termed the *dental arcade,* since in man it is seen to take the form of an arc. In other primates, however, the teeth lie either in two converging rows or as three sides of a rectangle (Fig. 7.11). Fossil evidence suggests that human evolution involved a change in the dental arcade from one with straight rows to a continuous curved row of teeth, as we shall see (7.7). At the same time, the jaws shortened and became smaller in relation to the rest of the head. This

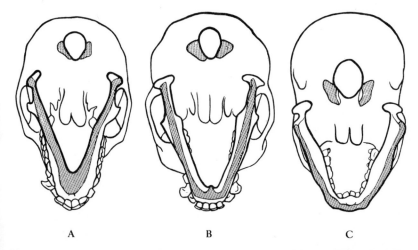

A   B   C

FIG. 7.10. Basal views of the skulls of a monkey (*Cercopithecus*) (*A*), the gibbon (*Hylobates*) (*B*), and modern man (*C*) drawn the same size. Note that the lower margin of the mandible (*shaded*) remains a more or less constant distance from the occipital condyles (*also shaded*), which support the head upon the neck. The buttressing of the jaw in man takes the form of a chin in place of a "simian shelf," visible in the monkey. (After DuBrul 1958.)

reduction in the size of the masticatory apparatus has already been discussed (7.5).

Since the different kinds of heterodont mammalian teeth have evolved from the similar teeth of a homodont reptile, there are no very fundamental historical differences among them, and they are in some species indistinguishable in form or function. In most primates, however, the four kinds of teeth remain distinct, though they are often reduced in number. They are the incisors (abbreviated as I) the ca-

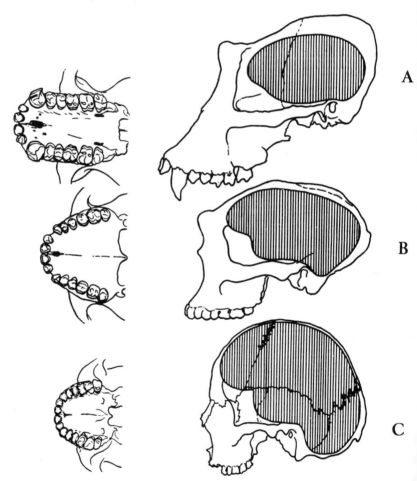

FIG. 7.11. Upper dentition (*left*) and complete skulls (*right*) of *Gorilla* (*A*), *Homo erectus* (*B*), and modern man (*C*). Note size and form of dental arcade and compare the size of the jaws and that of the cranial cavities (*shaded*). (From Weidenreich, 1941.)

nines (C), premolars (P), and molars (M). The teeth are conventionally numbered from the front backward, so the primitive hypothetical mammal shown in Figure 7.12 had four rows of teeth as follows: I1, I2, I3, C, P1, P2, P3, P4, M1, M2, M3, making a total of twenty-two in each jaw.

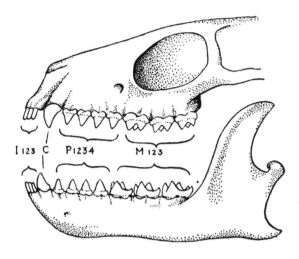

FIG. 7.12. Diagram of the dentition of a hypothetical early placental mammal showing the arrangement and grouping of teeth from which we presume the various primate dentitions evolved. (From Le Gros Clark, 1962).

The incisors, the most anterior of the whole dentition, are generally cutting teeth, as their name implies (though they grow into the tusks of elephants and walruses). Exceptions do occur among the primates, and in the lemurs we find a total change in function: the incisors of the upper jaw are very small, and those of the mandible are modified into pointed pegs to form a comb for cleaning the fur. They no longer serve any function related to feeding. In the higher primates, however, the incisors are spatulate (chisel-shaped), and serve to cut food. They are used for biting into fruit, nuts, and shoots, for chopping leaves and stripping bark. They have enabled mammals to utilize food that is too big to swallow whole and thus have made available a vastly increased food supply.

Among higher primates there are only four incisors in each jaw, two on each side (I1, I2). In most primates they tend to lie in a nearly straight line (Fig. 7.11*A*) and together form an efficient cutting edge. The incisors of the Pongidae are the largest and broadest and tend to make the dental arcade rectangular, though the lateral upper incisors do not share this enlargement.

In the evolution of man no great changes have occurred in the function of the incisor teeth, so their form has remained more or less unchanged. Their size has decreased in accordance with the reduction in size of the whole masticatory apparatus. They lie in a curve instead of in a straight line (Fig. 7.11,*C*).

We have incisors of *Australopithecus* showing no very significant differences from human incisors apart from size. (Fig. 7.14) The incisors themselves tell us less about hominid evolution than do the other teeth, which we shall now consider.

7.7 Dentition: the canines

THE CANINE is a more interesting tooth than the incisor for the study of human evolution. Throughout mammalian evolution as a whole, the canine has tended to retain the pointed and rounded form of reptile teeth. Its function has been primarily that of grasping food, and its importance in this respect has been greatest among carnivores. It receives its name from its well-known developed form as seen in the dog (*Canis*). Among herbivores it has often assumed a different function: that of a weapon. The tusks of wild pigs are obvious examples, and this adaptation is not absent among the primates. The upper canines of lemurs and the canines of both jaws of the larger monkeys and the Pongidae are a case of this special adaptation. In the absence of claws, the importance of these large canines is probably enhanced. Since the animals are primarily herbivorous, the function of the canines in feeding is clearly not responsible for this unusual enlargement.

In the Pongidae, and especially in the gorilla, the canines are larger in the male animal than in the female, as is the supporting bone structure and skull. This is an instance of *sexual dimorphism,*—of the form of a character varying between the sexes. The enlargement of the teeth is due to some behavior unique to the male animal—fighting for defense of the social group and sexual competition by threat or display.

The development of sexual dimorphism is a character of social significance, since it affects the status of different individuals within the social group; it will be discussed in chapter 9.

Animals with large canines necessarily have a *diastema,* a gap in the opposing tooth row into which the canine fits so that the jaws may be closed. The lower canines always fall into a diastema in front of the upper canines, and the upper canines fall behind the lower (Fig. 7.13). Le Gros Clark (1962) points out that the diastema is absent until the canines have fully erupted. It appears that the diastema is merely the result of active tooth occlusion (the way the teeth of the two jaws in fact interlock) rather than a genetically predetermined character.

The *hypertrophy* (enlargement) of the canines has evolved as a striking feature of the living Pongidae, and if *Proconsul* is a pongid ancestor (which is probable), the condition of modern pongids appears to be an instance of steady evolution from an ancestor whose canines resembled those of modern monkeys (Fig. 7.14).

In the evolution of man, the opposite trend has occurred. The exact form of the canine varies among individuals (as the reader may easily verify) from a spatulate tooth, indistinguishable from an incisor, to a rather pointed tooth. It is significant that the root of the modern canine is longer than that of the neighboring teeth, suggesting

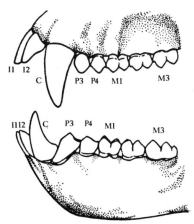

FIG. 7.13. Dentition of the catarrhine monkey *Macaca.* Note the canine teeth (*C*), diastemata, sectorial lower premolar (*P3*) (see 7.7) and bilophodont molars (*M1—3*) (see sec. 7.9). (From Le Gros Clark, 1962.)

that it may have been reduced from a larger tooth in the course of human evolution. Indeed, the fossil evidence supports such a conclusion. From Figure 3.14 (p. 83) we can see that, as early as the late Miocene, *Ramapithecus* was equipped with a canine of reduced length as compared with *Proconsul,* suggesting that evolution of the typical *Australopithecus*-like dentition was already begun. The Pliocene monkey (*Mesopithecus*) and living monkeys and apes (Fig. 7.15) all have relatively larger canines than *Proconsul.* The available evidence suggests, therefore, the following:

1. The canine of modern man has been reduced in evolution.
2. It is unlikely at any time to have been of the size found in the Pongidae.
3. We can see from *Australopithecus robustus* (Fig. 7.8), in which the canine is like an incisor, that the canine could have been reduced still more completely at an earlier stage in evolution.

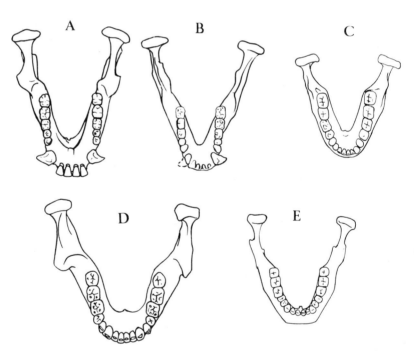

FIG. 7.14. Lower dentition of various primates: *Pan* (*A*), *Proconsul nyanzae* (*B*), *Australopithecus robustus* (*C*), *Homo erectus* (*D*), modern man (*E*). Note the different forms of the dental arcade and canine teeth. (Not drawn to scale.)

The fact that it was not so reduced suggests that it retained some important function. *Australopithecus robustus* is a species closely related to *A. africanus* and approximately contemporary with it. It is remarkable in having a canine tooth that does not project at all beyond the level of the incisors and premolars. For that reason (among others) we can conclude that it was ancestral to neither *A. africanus* nor *Homo erectus*, both of which have larger canines. It seems probable that *robustus* maintained a wholly herbivorous diet and had lost the need

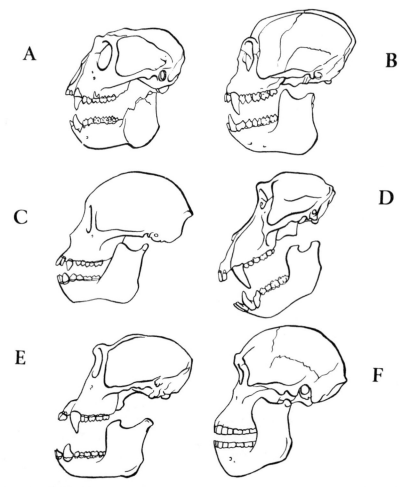

A

B

C

D

E

F

FIG. 7.15. Skulls of *Mesopithecus* (*A*), *Presbytis* (*B*), *Proconsul* (*C*), *Papio* (*D*), *Pan* (*E*), and *Australopithecus* (*F*). (Redrawn from Le Gros Clark, 1962.) (Not drawn to scale.)

for a grasping tooth. It had apparently also lost the need for such a tooth in fighting or display, which suggests that *A. robustus* had perfected the use of weapons (such as stones and bones) for defense and offense and did not use dental display for threat as do many other higher primates.

In the human lineage, we can assume that there was at least an equal skill in weaponry, suggesting that the retention of a somewhat larger canine tooth was associated with its functions of grasping and tearing. This in turn suggests a diet that came to consist more of meat than did that of *A. robustus*. But the human canine is nevertheless relatively small, and the overall reduction in this tooth which we associate with the Hominidae seems to be the main reason for the change in the dental arcade from a rectangular to a curved form.

7.8 Dentition: the premolars

THE PREMOLAR TEETH have served a variety of functions in mammalian evolution. In general, they have slowly evolved from their peg-like original condition as grasping teeth to flatter teeth for crushing and even for grinding; that is, they have tended to become increasingly molar-like in function, for the molars have evolved mainly as crushing and grinding teeth. In the primates, however, the premolars have retained their peg-like form to some extent, especially in the prosimians (Fig. 7.16). Their evolution toward the molar condition has been termed "molarization," but the teeth become fully "molarized" only in the lemurs. In most species of higher primates the premolars and molars are still clearly distinct.

From an original four premolars in early mammals (Fig. 7.12), we find only two surviving in catarrhine monkeys and hominoids (the third and fourth of the primitive series, known appropriately as P3 and P4) (Fig. 7.13). In Old World monkeys, the molars are typically *biscuspid* (with two *cusps* or points), which makes possible crushing as well as grasping, for the cusps interlock when the jaw is closed. One premolar has a special function, however, in this group. The anterior lower premolar is somewhat enlarged, and it shears against the upper canine when the jaw is closed so as to make an effective cutting organ. That is why this modified premolar (lower P3) is termed *sectorial*

(Fig. 7.13). The same character is also typical of the Pongidae; the lower P3 is functionally correlated with the large upper canine.

This sectorial lower premolar is not characteristic of the Hominidae, which lack a large upper canine. Hominid premolars are all bicuspid, with the cusps more or less equal in size. In modern man the *lingual* (inner) cusp is slightly reduced. The shape of the premolar crown has been considered an important character in the classification of early Hominidae (Leakey *et al.* 1964). However, in both the known species of *Australopithecus* and in modern man the shape is quite variable, and, as Robinson (1965) has shown, the shape in these different species overlaps. The canine and molar teeth are of more interest in this connection.

The pleistocene hominid *Australopithecus robustus* has taken molarization of the premolars to its most advanced condition in the

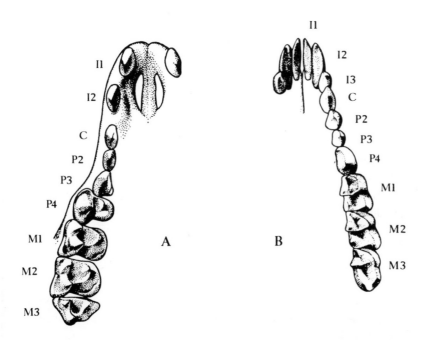

Fig. 7.16. Upper (*A*) and lower dentition (*B*) of the tree shrew *Ptilocerus*. Note the primitive arrangement of three incisors in the lower dentition and their strange shape, due to their use as a comb rather than for cutting food. The three premolars are still rather like canines in form, with the exception of the upper *P4*. (From Le Gros Clark, 1962.)

higher primates.* As a result of the grinding action of the jaw, the premolars are large and flattened like the molars. The absence of protruding canines makes possible a rotary movement, which is most effective for the mastication of tough plant material (Fig. 7.8).

7.9 Dentition: the molars

THE EVOLUTION of the mammalian molar tooth has been subject to a great deal of study and has been recently summarized elsewhere (Le Gros Clark 1962). For our purposes, we need only accept that a more or less quadrilateral four-cusped tooth is found in both jaws of all higher primates, though a fifth cusp is present in the lower molars of the Pongidae. Apart from the exceptional New World marmosets, there are always three molars in each jaw, and their general form is surprisingly constant.

In the Old World monkeys, each of the molar teeth is divided by a "valley" or constriction between the anterior and posterior pairs of cusps (Fig. 7.13 shows this feature). This type of molar shows what is called the *bilophodont* condition, and it produces a deeply interlocking type of occlusion. While the teeth are perhaps most effective in crushing vegetation, the jaws do allow a lateral grinding motion and the teeth move from side to side in relation to each other (Fig. 7.17). Full rotary grinding is inhibited by the canines, which allow some lateral movement but no movement in the backward and forward plane. It is surely significant that in this feature the herbivorous primates differ from the herbivorous ungulates and rodents; in the latter, rotary grinding is the function of the molar teeth. The plants of the open plains are much tougher than the tender fruit and shoots of the tropical forest; crushing and lateral grinding alone will serve to release the nutriment only from the succulent forest foods.

In the Pongidae, the bilophodont condition is not found. Instead, the cusp pattern is more complex and a fifth cusp has been retained in the lower molars. The pongid molars are perhaps slightly more effective grinders, for in occlusion the teeth do not interlock so deeply, though rotary movement of the jaw is still restricted by the huge interlocking canines.

* A possible exception is the fossil ape *Gigantopithecus*.

Among the Hominidae, there are two functional trends in the evolution of the molar teeth:

1. The evolution in *Australopithecus robustus* of relatively flat and large grinding molars and premolars, accompanied by rotary action of the jaw, was, as already stated, made possible by a reduction of the canines and was accompanied by molarization of the premolars. This trend appears to be an adaptation to a coarse vegetable diet, such as would be available to a plains-living animal that had not widely exploited animal food (Fig. 7.8).

FIG. 7.17. Occlusion in an Old World monkey, *Macaca*. The first two maxillary molars are drawn with a heavy line, the mandibular molars with a thin line. The first molar is shown on the left. The central drawing shows the resting position; in the other two drawings the mandible is moved from side to side. The cusps are paired and alternate and side-to-side movement alone is possible. (From Mills, 1963.)

2. The reduction of the molar series as a whole and, in particular, reduction of the third molar (the wisdom tooth, M3) in both jaws is a trend seen in the latter stages of human evolution and probably associated with the preparation of food by cooking, when the need for effective mastication is reduced. In modern man, the third molar is always considerably smaller than the other two and is sometimes missing altogether (Figs. 7.11 and 7.14).

A character of some interest in studies of human evolution is the order of tooth eruption. Schultz (1935) has shown that the order in the permanent dentition of the Pongidae and *Homo* is as shown in the accompanying chart.

	Order of Eruption							
	1	2	3	4	5	6	7	8
Pongids	M1	I1	I2	M2	P	P	C	M3
Homo (and rarely among pongids)	M1	I1	I2	P	C	P	M2	M3

The absolute and relative ages of eruption are shown in Figure 7.18. These data together demonstrate the much slower development of the human dentition as a whole (which is correlated with the slower growth rate of the whole body) and the slower development of the molars in particular (which is related to the reduction in importance of the molar series in modern man). Further such data are presented by Garn and Lewis (1963). Unfortunately, information about the tooth eruption sequence of *Australopithecus* is not considered by those authors to be reliable.

7.10 Digestion

AFTER MASTICATION, the breakdown of foodstuffs by digestion and their assimilation into the body does not vary greatly among mammals. Studies in comparative anatomy (Straus 1936) suggest that no remarkable changes have occurred in the evolution of the human alimentary canal, but there is of course no fossil record of these soft parts, and such a statement cannot be verified by direct evidence.

There is, however, one variable in mammalian digestion that is of overriding importance: the extent to which specializations have evolved to make possible the digestion of cellulose. (Cellulose is a polysaccharide—though a multiple of a sugar molecule it is normally indigestible because it is insoluble.) Such a specialization as that for cellulose digestion is typical of fully adapted herbivores. It takes the form of an increase in the total volume of the alimentary canal to allow the development of a large population of microorganisms that are able to break down cellulose to synthesize protein and produce sugars. The microorganisms and sugars are in turn digested by the mammal. This development is typical of ruminants (such as cattle and sheep), which have multiple stomachs, and the herbivorous lagomorphs (such as the rabbit), which have a large *cecum,* a special, blindly ending branch of the alimentary canal.

It might be expected that some extension of the alimentary canal would be apparent among the herbivorous primates. This, however, is not very general, though some instances can be found. There is, for example, one unusual specialization in the mouth of certain primates

FIG. 7.18. On the left, the absolute ages and, on the right, the relative ages of eruption of the teeth of *Macaca, Pan,* and modern man. (From Schultz, 1935.)

in the evolution of cheek pouches. This character, confined to the Old World monkeys, allows food to be retained in the mouth for some time before swallowing, but while it presumably aids the digestion of starch by the salivary enzyme ptyalin, there is no reason to suppose that it is an adaptation for cellulose digestion. It is, however, an adaptive character, in view of the high starch content of the diet of these arboreal forms.

The primate stomach is not greatly different from the human stomach, and only in one subfamily of the Old World monkeys is the area of lining of the stomach increased by subdivision into different compartments. This subfamily is the Old World Colobinae, whose diet is confined almost entirely to leaves and shoots with high cellulose content. Schultz (1961) believes them to be the only true vegetarians among primates. This feature appears to be an instance of parallel evolution with the ruminants, and it is perhaps surprising that it is not more widespread in the order.

An alternative adaptation is, however, found in the lower primates, where the cecum is often elongated and dilated—perhaps another case of parallel evolution, this time with the lagomorphs. In the Anthropoidea, however, the cecum is as small as in man and appears to have no digestive function. There is one character that separates the Hominoidea from the monkeys: the former have a vermiform appendix attached to the cecum. This tubular extension from the cecum contains in the Pongidae some lymphoid tissue, and in man somewhat more (Straus 1936). While its function is not yet understood, it does not appear to be vestigial, as has often been claimed, but rather is a hominoid specialization that has reached its greatest elaboration in man. We can, however, have no certain knowledge of its evolutionary history.

Sidney Smith said that the secret of life lay in good digestion. While this vital process is under the automatic control of the lower centers of the brain, it also affects and is affected by the cerebral cortex. Bad digestion can poison our waking and sleeping hours, while our daily problems can equally upset our digestive processes. A digestion that can easily handle a wide range of foodstuffs has been of immense benefit to the species; it makes possible man's wide geographical distribution and great population growth. The variety of succulent food we can enjoy appears to be a direct consequence of our ancestry, yet it may carry with it some dangers, for there is no doubt that the arboreal primates also had to learn what fruit and leaves could and could not be eaten. Fruits poisonous to primates, evolved for the delectation of birds, can be a disaster for any primate with too much initiative or too little ability to learn.

7.11 Ecology, diet, and behavior

THE OMNIVOROUS NATURE of primates, and of their dentition and digestive processes in particular, made it possible for man's ancestors to evolve from forest-living to plains-living creatures. The flexibility in diet and behavior so typical of primates allowed an adaptation in food-finding behavior and food choice that made it possible for the early hominids to undergo a fundamental change in their environment.

On the basis of present conditions in east and south Africa, we can attempt retrospectively to predict the conditions in the early Pleistocene. During the Pliocene and Miocene, however, the climate is less certainly known. All we can say with some certainty is that in the early Pleistocene at Olduvai, climatic conditions were somewhat similar to those at present (Hay, *in* Evernden and Curtis 1965, p. 383) and *Australopithecus* was living on small reptiles, birds, and small mammals (such as rodents), as well as presumably on roots and fruits (though no evidence of vegetable diet remains). This sort

FIG. 7.19. Reconstruction of autralopithecines living in the grasslands of the Transvaal in Lower Pleistocene times, obtaining meat by scavenging and perhaps by hunting small or young animals. (By permission of the trustees of the British Museum [Natural History].)

of mixed diet is nourishing, yet hard to get. Like modern baboons, *Australopithecus* must have spent a large part of each day gathering food and scavenging, perhaps with the help of simple tools (Fig. 7.19). Although the use of stone tools is established by the Pleistocene, it would not be unreasonable to suppose that bones in particular would have already been used as weapons for killing small animals in the Pliocene (see Dart 1957).

Only in the Middle Pleistocene do we find evidence of a major change in early man's adaptation to plains living, and this change involved *cooperative hunting*—a change in food-getting behavior of central importance to the story of human evolution. It seems clear that man survived the climatic changes of the Middle Pleistocene by a new behavioral adaptation that affected fundamentally and irrevocably his psychosocial character; it was this change in food-finding behavior that finally made man and that, as I shall show (chapter 11), can justify our recognition of the change from *Australopithecus* the man-ape to *Homo* the man.

For mammals, food-finding and feeding is normally not a social occupation, except among a few carnivores (such as dogs and killer whales). Most primates live in social groups, but such groups are not primarily based on the need for social hunting and feeding. Social hunting is typical only of rather small carnivorous mammals that feed on species larger than themselves. Wolves and jackals hunt in packs, particularly in winter, when small animals are scarce and they have to attack larger species.

It was in this way that early man must have evolved cooperative hunting behavior. It seems clear that the prizes available as food make the evolution of cooperative hunting highly adaptive. If a group of males could cooperate to corner and kill an antelope, they would have enough meat for more than one individual and for more than one day. Of course newborn animals would have been the first victims, and only later would adults have been killed, but in time the necessary techniques were developed, and they changed the whole way of life of early man. Not only was cooperation essential, but food-sharing followed. The sharing of a small kill serves little purpose; the sharing of a large kill is necessary and highly adaptive. It is clear that cooperative hunting and food-sharing changed the social and physical attributes of early man in a number of very important ways.

1. Success in hunting required cooperation among males.

2. Nursing and pregnant mothers would not have the endurance to carry their young long distances, so the females would have been left together, possibly guarded by a few males, thus involving the establishment of a home base.

3. Traveling long distances and carrying heavy burdens put strong selective pressure on the evolution of really efficient bipedalism.

4. The exertions of the chase may, it has been suggested (Hockett and Ascher 1964), have been responsible for the diminution of subcutaneous fat deposits, loss of body hair, and the considerable development of sweat glands (which are not found in large numbers of forest animals), all of which aid the rapid diffusion of metabolic heat.

5. Catching and killing large animals required ingenuity and technological skill. The earliest implements were probably stones and clubs (sometimes used by living pongids). In the Middle Pleistocene, round stones are found that may have been used for throwing, possibly as a *bolas,* an ingenious and deadly device consisting of three stones strung together with long leather thongs. On impact the thongs will wrap round the animal and probably bring it to the ground.

6. The need to cut up large mammals must have stimulated the development of better chopping and cutting tools; hominid teeth were clearly unsuitable for this function.

7. The meat would be in sufficient quantity to be shared by all males and carried back to females. Bipedalism makes hand carrying possible and frees the mouth for speech. In the absence of a suitable alternative diet, bringing meat to the females would be strongly selected as a behavior pattern, and indeed there is evidence for it from the Middle Pleistocene, especially at Choukoutien.

8. Food-sharing within a social group would certainly bring the group together in a very intimate way, a situation that probably encouraged speech, especially for planning the hunt and in accounts of what happened during the hunt. As Roe (1963) has said, speech was perhaps born of the need of intercourse as a result of the division of labor. For the first time, primates had something essential to communicate (see 10.5).

9. Geographical knowledge obviously became of prime importance; the locality of waterholes and herds of game must have become a vital subject for communication. Clearly, improved powers of perception, memory, and prediction were of immense value and probably evolved conjointly with speech.

10. The absence of males from the home base on hunting expeditions must in turn have increased the overall division of labor between the sexes. The females would have taken over all other group activities. Sexual dimorphism might have changed its character in this new way of life (see 9.6).

11. Longer periods of sexual receptivity in the females might have been selected in evolution if the males were away hunting for a considerable portion of the time (see 9.3).

It would be possible to list many other important changes that might have followed the evolution of social hunting, but even from those listed it seems clear that the exploitation of the larger herbivorous mammals as a source of meat required cooperation, endurance, intelligence, foresight, and a precise means of communication. At the same time, it initiated the selection of an evolutionary trend toward further socialization with the development of speech and technology, all of central importance in our survey of human evolution.

We shall return to these socializing factors again in more detail in the following chapters. Here it is necessary only to emphasize, first, that primate feeding habits preadapted bipedal hominids to a terrestrial existence (as they preadapted baboons); second, that the exploitation of plains mammals was made possible by, and also immensely stimulated, the evolution of human society. Thus the final determinant of the direction of human evolution was necessarily environmental and ecological, not obscure, but striking and fundamental. Like all great evolutionary radiations of animals, man's appearance on the earth involved the exploitation of a new food source, and a very rich one.

7.12 Food and fire

FIRE HAS A NUMBER of functions in human culture, and cooking is by no means the most important. However, the use of fire has affected the digestion of food, and therefore this chapter may be taken as the place to discuss the history and functions of fire in human evolution.

The history of man's use of fire is being pieced together by archeologists and has recently been reviewed by Oakley (1961). The first traces of man-made hearths come not from Africa but from

Europe and Asia. At a site in Hungary called Vértesszöllös (Oakley 1966) we have traces of hearths together with hominid remains dating from the Mindel glaciation of Europe, that is, the very beginning of the Middle Pleistocene (Fig. 7.20). Hearths of about the same date have also been found at Choukoutien in China, the site and level of which has also revealed the fossils of Peking man, *Homo erectus pekinensis* (Black *et al.* 1933).

At a much later date, fire is recorded in Africa at the famous Cave of Hearths (Lowe 1954), but the oldest trace there is probably a natural combustion of bat guano. However, above the thick, ashy layer formed by the burning bat guano, there is a succession of man-made hearths dating from the final Acheulian period. Although of relatively recent date (perhaps little more than 50,000 years B.P.), it does show us how fire might first have been used by man. Without an appropriate technology, man must have relied at first on capturing fire from natural conflagrations caused by lightning, or possibly by seepages of mineral oil or gas, or even by deposits of coal revealed by landslide; all these have been known to show spontaneous combustion. The myth of Prometheus describes how man stole fire from the gods; by means of myth, this achievement is recorded in our racial memory and celebrated in some tribes (among Bushmen, for example). It was an achievement of vital importance to mankind.

Only after man had learned to handle fire could he have learned to make it, possibly as a result of striking stones in the manufacture of tools. However it came about, man learned to make, conserve, feed, and handle fire, and it became a precious tool in the advance of his culture. By the time of *Homo erectus,* fire began to assume many important functions, for it was able to provide protection against predators, a center point at the home base, warmth, light, a means of cooking, and an aid to tool-making.

It is interesting that according to the present evidence the use of fire arose first in Europe and Asia at about the time of the Mindel ice age. No traces of fire have been found on the open living floors of East Africa or in the only known rock-shelter used by *Australopithecus,* at Sterkfontein in South Africa (Robinson and Mason 1957). It appears first in the north-temperate cave-dwellings. It seems highly probable that fire made cave-dwelling practicable because it gave man warmth and protection at night from wild animals (such as the cave bear), which in cooler climates were dangerous as predators and at

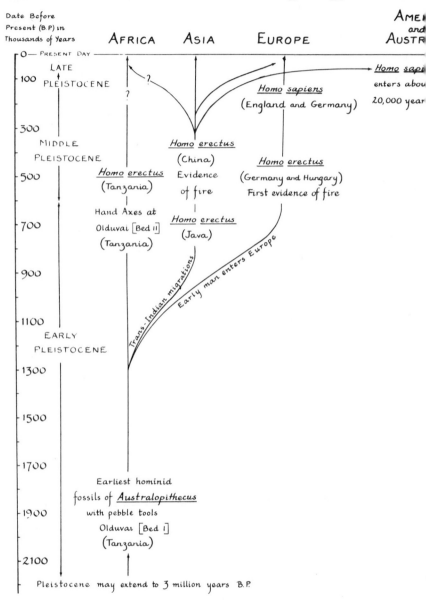

FIG. 7.20. This chart indicates approximately some of the dated archeological discoveries from the Pleistocene and their possible relationships
in terms of the migrations of human ancestral groups. From at least
one million years ago migrations between Africa, Europe, and Asia
were probably continuous, and no attempt has been made to show the
complexity of these movements.

the same time competitors for shelter. Fire is still used in parts of Canada for driving bears out of caves.

The achievement of handling and making fire would have resulted in a less nomadic existence, and the cave would have become not merely a temporary base but a home. The fire might have been maintained day and night by the women, and it would have supplied vital warmth and light against the long winter evenings and the cool, wet climate of the glacial period. The effective day would have been lengthened, and work—toolmaking and the preparation of skins and other animal products—could have been continued by firelight in the evening.

The established fire must have led to cooking, perhaps inadvertently at first. Heat will break down the tough structural components of vegetables and meat and release the nourishing juices. Complex organic compounds are in some cases broken down into simpler forms by heat, so that the process of digestion is already begun, as is the process of mastication. Roasting must have been the usual way of cooking for a long time; boiling is a much more recent development, since it involves a water-tight, fireproof container. It is perhaps not surprising, then, that the overall recession and reduction of the human masticatory apparatus, which is still continuing today, began with the appearance of hearths in cave shelters. A powerful jaw is no longer necessary for the mastication of cooked food. In the process of evolution it has been modified accordingly.

Finally, fire was used in tool-making. Large stones can be split by heating followed by sudden cooling, wood can be hardened in fire to form effective arrow-heads. Only a few millennia ago, fire was first used to smelt ores, and the use of metal has resulted in the rise of modern civilization.

7.13 Summary

IN THIS CHAPTER on food and feeding we have touched on matters that are important in two ways. First, teeth and jaws form the most abundant evidence for human evolution, and, second, the environment determines the direction and rate of evolution directly and obviously by the way the animal interacts with it in the act of feeding.

We have examined the structure and function of the primate jaw and dentition and have noted the lack of full herbivore specializations except in a few groups. The omnivorous diet of primates has made them adaptable to a greater range of environments than most other groups of mammals; it allowed adaptation to a terrestrial life. We have seen that such adaptation among hominids has taken two courses, both involving reduction in the canine tooth: in *Australopithecus robustus* a trend toward molarization for maximum grinding efficiency and in the *A. africanus–Homo* line a trend toward an omnivorous dentition, with reduction in the molar series and finally in the whole masticatory apparatus.

Such a hominizing trend is accelerated by the evolution of social hunting, by the making of tools for cutting and chopping meat and bones, and by the mastery of fire. The social correlates of cooperative hunting have also been briefly considered, and it seems clear that this cultural development was the most important single step in the final evolution of man. Human beings and their society are no exception to the general observation that animal groups evolve as homeostatic adjustments to changing environmental conditions, relating primarily to the interaction of organism and environment that is involved in getting food.

SUGGESTIONS FOR FURTHER READING

The best general account of the evolution of the primate dentition is again W. E. le Gros Clark, *The Antecedents of Man* (Edinburgh: University of Edinburgh Press, 1962).

A good account of the ecological adaptations of the Australopithecines is to be found in J. T. Robinson, "Adaptive Radiation in the Australopithecines and the Origin of Man," in F. Clark Howell and F. Bourlière (eds.), *African Ecology and Human Evolution,* pp. 385-416 (*Viking Fund Publs. Anthrop,* No. 36 [Chicago: Aldine Publishing Co., 1963]). Beyond this, the most interesting paper on these aspects of human evolution is C. F. Hockett and R. Ascher, "The Human Revolution," *Curr. Anthrop.* 5 (1964): 135–68. An important account of some adaptations of modern man are to be found in G. A. Harrison, J. S. Weiner, J. M. Tanner and N. A. Barnicot, *Human Biology* (Oxford: Oxford University Press, 1964).

⮑ 8

The Evolution
of the Head

8.1 Factors determining head form

IN STUDYING the evolution of the human head, we must examine not only the masticatory apparatus but also the evolution of the senses and the correlated changes that took place in the brain, all of which have contributed to the present form of the human skull.

In many marine and fresh-water animals the head is streamlined for swimming, and its shape is therefore dictated primarily by hydrodynamic factors. In terrestrial vertebrates the overall shape of the head depends on two factors: first, the form of the masticatory apparatus, sense organs, and brain; second, its position in relation to the body and in relation to gravitation. The shape reflects the function and size of the different parts and by examining the evolution of those parts we can understand the evolution of the skull.

The sense organs situated in the head are listed in Table 8.1. Not all of them affect skull form. The ones that do, together with the other factors mentioned above, add up to the following major determinants of head form.

1. The masticatory apparatus
2. The eyes

TABLE 8.1 THE SENSORY RECEPTORS OF MAMMALS

Organ	Sense	Stimulus	See Section
Eyes	Vision (optic)	Radiant energy: light	8.3
Nose	Smell (olfactory)	Certain volatile chemicals	8.4
Ears, cochlea	Hearing (aural)	Vibrations in air (or water)	8.5
Ears, semi-circular canals, etc.	Balance and movement	Direction of gravity and rate of change of direction of movement, i.e., acceleration	8.5
Taste buds	Taste	Certain nonvolatile chemicals	7.3
Skin, lips, and tongue	Touch, temperature, and pain	Local pressure change on skin, temperature change, damage to body tissues	8.9

3. The nose and nasal chamber, which make up the muzzle
4. The brain
5. The position of the skull on the spine

The evolution of the masticatory apparatus has already been discussed (see 7.4, 7.5). It remains only to consider the influence of this apparatus on the form of the head as a whole.

8.2 *The masticatory apparatus and the head*

THE SIZE AND POWER of the masticatory apparatus obviously affects head form. A large mandible needs a large maxilla to carry the upper dentition, and together they will make an animal appear *prognathous* (with its muzzle protruding) if the other parts of the skull are not expanded equally. Not only will the bony parts of the apparatus affect head form, but so will the related muscles and the extent of their attachment areas.

All the muscles of mastication have their origin on the skull, and the extent of their attachment areas has changed in evolution according to the degree of their development, a fact that is particularly relevant to skull architecture when we study the origin of the *temporal muscle* on the skull. Its origin is on the brain case (*neurocranium*) in the area of the *temporal* and *parietal* bones (Figs. 8.1, 8.2; see also Figs. 7.2, 7.3, pp. 177–178).

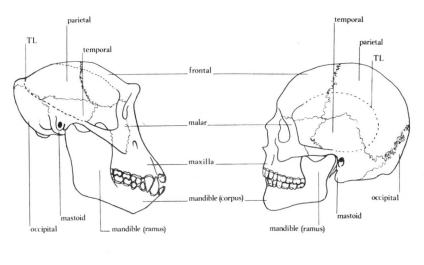

FIG. 8.1. Skulls of a chimpanzee (A) and a man (B) showing the different bones mentioned in this chapter. TL = temporal line.

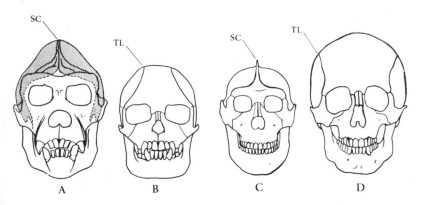

FIG. 8.2. Facial views of Gorilla (A), Proconsul (B), Australopithecus robustus (C), and modern man (D); skulls drawn approximately the same size. Note the different development of the sagittal crest in each genus. Upon the gorilla skull have been superimposed the temporal muscles that originate on the sagittal crest and surface of the neurocranium and are inserted upon the mandibular condyles. TL = temporal line; SC = sagittal crest.

The extent of this area of attachment varies in accordance with the power developed in the masticatory apparatus. In the large-jawed primates, such as the gorilla, the area of attachment is so large that the areas on each side meet on top of the cranium, and the bone grows to form a ridge at this meeting point to increase the anchorage still further (Fig. 8.2, *A*). The height of the ridge varies according to the development of the jaws, so in the lighter-jawed female gorilla it is smaller than in the male or absent altogether. This ridge is the *sagittal crest,* and it is peculiar to primates whose jaws are proportionally larger than their neurocrania—those in which the temporal muscles cover the neurocranium and actually meet in the sagittal plane along the top of the skull. A second crest, the *nuchal crest,* develops in heavy-jawed primates where the extended temporal attachment area meets the proportionally large attachment area of the neck muscles (see 4.4 and Fig. 4.14, p. 101). We have seen how the size of the masticatory apparatus is not only genetically controlled but also depends on the use it receives (see 7.5), and it therefore follows that these two factors similarly affect the size of the attachment areas of the temporal muscles and, ultimately, the size of the sagittal and nuchal crests.

Many of the fossil skulls of *Australopithecus* carry a marked sagittal crest (Fig. 8.2), but the attachment areas were reduced in evolution along with the masticatory apparatus, so that in *Homo erectus* the areas have retreated down the sides of the skull. The areas of attachment are bordered by the *temporal line,* which shows distinctly on the surface of the skull bones, and in the evolution of man this line moves down the side of the skull as the relative size of the jaws is reduced and the size of the neurocranium increases (Figs. 4.14, p. 101, and 8.2).

Since the activity of all the powerful masticatory muscles occurs within the perimeter of the head, the stresses developed by their action must be entirely absorbed by the skull architecture. When the muscles contract and the jaw is closed the force exerted for chewing pulls the mandible and neurocranium together. The force is very considerable and the bony structure between the roof of the neurocranium and the maxillary teeth—that is, the face and brows (all of which receive the force from the lower dentition)—must be very strong. Thus the thickness and form of the facial bones is related to the power developed by the masticatory apparatus.

Nearly all this force is transmitted by the molar and premolar teeth and passed up the side of the face to the cranial vault. Owing to the position of the nasal cavity and orbits, the force must be carried round these openings by the maxilla and *malar* bones. Like the mandibular torus and chin, the supraorbital torus (which is the anterior edge of the *frontal bone* of the skull) acts as an essential cross-member at the top of the face to transmit the masticatory forces across the whole vault of the neurocranium rather than at each side only. Thus the size and form of the facial bones and supraorbital torus is related to the size of the masticatory apparatus (Fig. 8.3).

Finally, it should be mentioned that the cheekbones—each the *zygomatic arch* of the temporal bone—carry the origin of the masseter muscle, which is an important masticatory muscle. These bones, which form a bridge across the temporal muscle, also vary in form according to the development of the jaws (see Fig. 7.2, p. 177).

The masticatory apparatus and brain are certainly the two most striking determinants of head form (Fig. 8.4). Before we consider the brain, we must, however, consider the part played by the different senses in determining the form of the head both directly and indirectly, through their influence on the evolution of the brain.

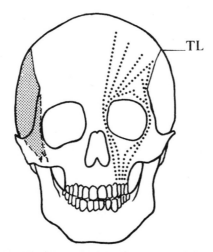

FIR. 8.3. Diagram showing how the forces developed by the masticatory muscles, in particular the *temporalis* (shown on left passing behind the zygomatic arch), are transmitted from the lower jaw to the vault of the skull in man. The lines of compression that pass through the facial bones are shown as dots on the right side of the skull. *TL* = temporal line.

8.3 The eyes

THE IMPORTANCE of eyes in the evolution of the primates has already been mentioned; we have described how vision evolved in response to the demands of the forest environment, where a sense of smell was of less value. Receptive to radiant energy of a certain range of wavelengths (380–760 mμ), the eyes came to provide information at a distance about size, color, texture, movement, pattern, spatial relationships, and distance—information not accurately obtainable by other means. Here we must discuss three aspects of the evolution of vision: (1) the retina, (2) the neural correlates of vision, and (3) the orbital region of the skull.

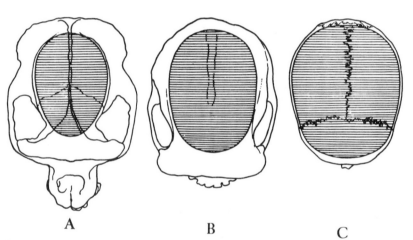

A   B   C

FIG. 8.4. Skulls of *Gorilla* (*A*), *Homo erectus* (*B*), and modern man (*C*) from above showing the relative sizes of the cranial cavity (*shaded*) and masticatory apparatus protruding below the neurocranium. (From Weidenreich, 1941.)

1. Cats have relatively large eyes, but, apart from a few such carnivores, the eyes of primates are outstandingly large. The amount of light that will enter the eye depends upon the aperture of the lens, and discrimination and sensitivity depend upon the concentration and kinds of photoreceptors on the surface of the retina. A large eye will allow the entry of more light, and thus permit greater sensitivity. The

first stimulus to increased eye size may have been the nocturnal habits which may have been characteristic of some early primates, and today many prosimian eyes are specially adapted for nocturnal vision, with a high density of photoreceptors in the retina of the very sensitive "rod" type. The amount of information received by the brain from the eyes is probably approximately related to the size of the optic nerves. The dog and cat have about 150,000 fibers in each nerve; man has 1,200,000 (von Bonin 1963).

The eyes of the higher primates, however, are adapted for daylight vision, and their structure is fairly consistent (Woollard 1927): the differences between the eye of man and that of monkey are slight. Both have a high proportion of the so-called "cone" type of photoreceptor, which is specialized for discrimination rather than sensitivity. Fine visual discrimination seems to have assumed great importance in the forest, for in the primate we find the evolution of the *fovea centralis* ("yellow spot"), which is a small area of the retina where the usual layer of nerves and blood vessels does not lie over the actual photoreceptor cells, which here form a dense layer of cones. At this point the surface is pitted so that light will fall directly on the receptors. In man, the *fovea* makes possible the kind of discrimination required in reading and other fine work. But the fovea had already evolved in the forest and in fact is more marked in the monkey *Cercocebus* than in modern man (Woollard 1927). It is clear that the remarkable quality of vision that we enjoy arose as an adaptation to forest life. There is no doubt, however, that changes were also necessary in the brain as a correlate of the greatly increased quantity of visual information that became available, and it is these changes which above all have carried human perception beyond that which may be attributed to monkeys.

2. We have already mentioned the evolution of stereoscopic vision among the primates (see 3.4 and 3.7). This important development has involved changes in the position of the eyes, in the structure of the optic nerve paths and brain, and finally in perception.

The evolution of the primate visual sense has involved a large expansion of the part of the brain concerned with vision, the visual cortex of the cerebral hemispheres. In Figure 8.5 the brains of three primates are drawn the same size. The visual cortex is already well developed in the tree shrew, and this development is especially striking when the brain of an insectivore with a minute visual cortex is compared with it. However, in the tree shrew the visual sense has not yet replaced the

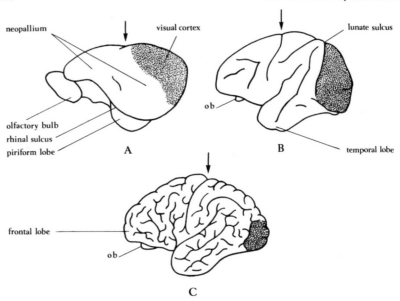

C

FIG. 8.5. Cerebral hemispheres of the tree shrew *Tupaia* (*A*), *Macaca* (*B*), and man (*C*), drawn the same size. Note the variation in extent of folding of the cortex and the relative size of the olfactory bulbs (*ob*) and visual cortex (*shaded*). The temporal and frontal lobes of the neopallium hide the Piriform lobe of the archipallium in the higher primates, which is visible here only in the brain of *Tupaia*. The arrow points in each drawing to the central sulcus, which separates the frontal and parietal lobes. The rhinal sulcus separates the archipallium and neopallium, and the lunate or "simian" sulcus demarcates the visual cortex. (For a diagram showing the different lobes of the brain, see Fig. 8.8.)

olfactory sense, as can be seen from the relatively large size of the olfactory bulbs. In the higher primates, such replacement has occurred, and, although the visual cortex gets smaller relative to the rest of the brain, it is still absolutely expanding. This expansion is even more true of the visual association area, the part of the cortex nearest to the visual cortex, which, as we have seen (Fig. 3.10, p. 78), carries the connections between the visual cortex and other parts of the brain. In primates the expansion of the brain begins with the expansion of the visual cortex, and throughout primate evolution the visual system is increasingly integrated with total brain function. The fact that the *occipital lobe* (that part of the brain which includes the visual areas of the cortex at the back of the head) of the hemispheres expands does not, however, mean a localized expansion of the neurocranium: it means merely an increase in the total cranial capacity, reflected in the size of the neurocranium as a whole.

3. The eye has played an important part in molding the skull, in addition to its psychological and neurological importance in the evolution of man. We have seen that primate eyes have increased in size and have come to face forward (Fig. 3.4, p. 61). The eye sockets— the *orbits*—have appropriately enlarged and moved into a more central position in the face. The eyeball is a delicate structure, and its form is of necessity optically precise, so it must at no time be subjected to stress or pressure. It must also be at the surface of the body and under precise motor control. As a result, the eye is rather like the ball of a universal joint in a well-lubricated and well-padded bony socket, which gives it support and protection. The eye muscles move it within this socket, and facial muscles can be contracted across the socket to protect it from direct blows. Hairs protect it from sweat, rain, and dust.

As the eye sockets enlarged in evolution, the loss of the muzzle made room for them in the face and allowed them a more central position. With the muzzle, they also moved back into the head, and in man they lie closer under the anterior part of the brain than in other primates (Fig. 8.6). The bony rim of the orbit serves to protect the

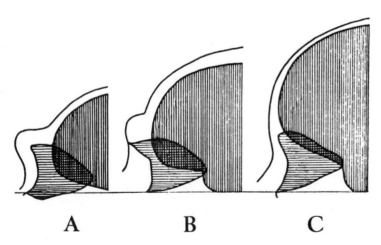

A   B   C

FIG. 8.6. The relation between the orbit and the frontal part of the cranial cavity in *Pan* (*A*), *Homo erectus* (*B*), and modern man (*C*). (From Weidenreich, 1941.)

eye as well as to transmit the forces developed by the masticatory apparatus. The upper part of this rim assumes the greatest size (and gets the name of supraorbital torus) in big jawed forms, in which the eyes have not fully retreated under the forepart of the brain. Such is the case in the gorilla and chimpanzee, while in man, the orang, and the gibbon, the torus is less well-developed, since the jaw is smaller and the eye is better protected by the forepart of the neurocranium (Biegert 1963). It is of interest that the torus is quite heavily built in all the Hominidae except modern man, for it was only in the last stages of human evolution that the jaws finally retreated and the anterior part of the neurocranium finally expanded over the top of the eyes. This expansion of the brain has resulted in the flat vertical forehead of man and his more or less vertical face, which carries the deep eye sockets.

8.4 *The nose*

THE RHINARIUM, the sensitive skin around the nostrils, was an important sense organ in the lower primates, and its wet surface no doubt enhanced its sensitivity to air currents, which would be interpreted directionally. In the open plains, the direction of the wind, coupled with the scent it carries, is a datum of first importance. In the forest, the sense of smell will be of significance only in relation to an object seen or touched, because the nose is unable to receive directional information. It is no longer a distance receptor, so, with the ascendance of the visual sense, the olfactory sense has come to be relatively less important in primates. In the arboreal environment it supplies information limited to the quality and intensity of odor, with no direct spatial implications.

The air required for respiration is drawn into the nostrils and over the olfactory *mucoperiosteum* (the "skin" bearing olfactory receptors) within the nasal cavity on its way to the lungs. By means of a complex maze of fine bones, the *turbinal bones,* the actual area of mucoperiosteum may be very considerable, and in the rabbit (for example) it has been estimated to carry 100 million chemoreceptor cells. In the higher primates both the size of the nasal cavity and the complexity of the turbinal bones has been much reduced, together with the total area of mucoperiosteum. That both the muzzle and the jaws are reduced in modern man is coincidental. In some animals they have receded independently: in the gorilla, the muzzle is slight, the jaws large; in the little elephant shrew (*Elephantulus*), the muzzle is far more developed than the small jaws.

It is the reduction of both the muzzle and the jaws in man that has resulted in his flat face. This change has altered the center of gravity of the head and contributed to the balance of the skull upon the spine. The reduction of the muzzle came early in the evolution of the primates; the reduction of the jaws came late in the evolution of man (see Fig. 4.12, p. 98).

A visit to the zoo will, however, reveal the human nose to be rather more prominent than that of most monkeys and apes—perhaps partly due to the recession of the jaws and the expansion of the brain, which left only a small space for the nasal cavity. However, the mucoperiosteum covers in fact only a small part (2.5 sq. cm.) of the lining of this cavity, so it is not unreasonable to suppose that some other function is performed by the human nose besides smelling. The fleshy surroundings of the nostrils contain fatty tissue, and, within, they are lined with a thick, moist mucous membrane with many blood vessels, suggesting that the function of the nose is to warm and moisten the air on inspiration. The fatty tissue insulates the nasal cavity, and the blood maintains the temperature within. The mucous membrane itself acts like flypaper to catch dust and small insects, and to that end there is a clump of hair near the opening of each nostril. Clearly, the warming of air could be important to the north-temperate peoples not only to protect the delicate membranes lining their lungs but perhaps also to increase the effectiveness of their olfactory organ.

The moist mucous membrane also acts to humidify the inspired air. It has been shown that it secretes up to one liter of water per day and maintains the relative humidity of the inspired air at 95 per cent (at body temperature). Its function is clearly to protect from desiccation the delicate inner surfaces of the nasal and oral passages and the lungs. The nasal index of modern man (which indicates the shape of the nasal openings) is highly correlated with the absolute humidity of the air of the region he inhabits (Weiner 1954). Thus many of the tropical races of man have flatter, more open noses than have those occupying dry areas, such as Mongolia. The prominent human nose is an organ for filtering, warming, and moistening the air and has perhaps evolved in size for that purpose since the movement of man into the dry plains and later into the temperate zones at the beginning of the Middle Pleistocene.

The sense of smell is much reduced in the higher primates, but it retains some value in modern man (though less than in the apes and monkeys). It has already been pointed out that its functions are closely related to the basic drives of feeding and sex. In modern man, smell is an important stimulant to feeding, but individuals in which this sense has been destroyed can survive with little difficulty if dependent upon the civilized preparation of foods. In its second function, sex, smell has again been replaced mainly by sight, but scent is still used by modern man as a sexual stimulant.

The relative size of the olfactory "bulbs" of the brain, to which the olfactory nerves run, can be seen in Figure 8.5. Analysis of the olfactory impulses begins in the olfactory bulbs, and from them, fibers pass to the lower lateral parts of the cerebral hemisphere (the *piriform lobe*), where further analysis presumably occurs. In mammals, electrical stimulation at this point results in such reflexes as licking, salivation, chewing, etc. From the piriform lobe, connections run to the areas of the cerebral cortex, where patterns are memorized and recognized. Though olfactory bulbs have been reduced in primate evolution, in man the olfactory sense is still capable of considerable discrimination and the nose is capable of remarkable sensitivity in spite of the fact that the importance in behavior of the olfactory stimulus is much reduced. This final loss of importance has almost certainly been a recent event.

8.5 The ears

STUDY OF THE EVOLUTION of the head must include consideration of the ear and the other soft parts of the face. The ear and the organs associated with it in the head form a complex mechanoreceptor that is sensitive to sound waves in air, to gravity, and to movement. Like light but unlike scent, sound waves travel in straight lines and therefore can be used in direction-finding. For that reason, the ears are separated (as are the eyes, but not the olfactory organ) and can function as a stereophonic organ. They can supply data about the direction, frequency, and amplitude of sound waves.

The different parts of the ear serve the following functions among primates.

1. The *outer ear* is primarily a directional receiver of sound waves. As in many mammals, the primate external ear can be moved by both its own and associated muscles to receive the maximum amplitude of sound waves and to aid discrimination among different sources of sound. The outer ear also plays some part in thermoregulation, as it does in mammals generally. There are a large number of blood vessels in the outer ear, and like the rest of the skin they are subject to dilation and contraction to regulate heat loss. This is important to animals with heavy fur (like lemurs) but almost naked ears. At the same time, ears held close to or away from the body can adjust the effective surface area for heat loss. The different sizes of the ears in different primates may be due as much to their function as thermoregulators as to their function as organs of hearing.

2. *The middle ear* receives the sound waves at a diaphragm (the ear drum) and transmits them mechanically (with a reduction of amplitude) to the *cochlea* through a second diaphragm (the *fenestra ovalis*).

3. Sound waves of reduced amplitude are transmitted to the liquid-filled cochlea in the *inner ear,* where the vibrations in this liquid are detected by the mechanically stimulated cells of the *organ of Corti.* The small hair-like processes attached to these cells respond selectively to movements in the surrounding liquid and send nerve impulses to the brain by the auditory nerve.

4. In connection with the cochlea are other liquid-filled vessels; the *utricle* and *sacculus,* organs that are lined with similar mechanoreceptors and transmit information to the brain about the posture of the head in relation to gravity.

5. Associated with this system of mechanoreceptors are the *semicircular canals,* which lie in the three planes of space. Sensory cells here detect the direction and acceleration of movement of the head (Fig. 8.7).

It is certain that a fast-moving arboreal animal like a primate needs a very efficient sense of movement and posture, but in fact the organs described are really not very different from those found in fishes, reptiles, and birds. Such organs are necessary to any mobile vertebrate. In its function as an organ of hearing, the ear has also changed very little in the evolution of the primates.

In the evolution of man the functions of the ear have not changed greatly. The ear still occasionally functions as an organ of thermoregulation when, as a result of the dilation of blood vessels, the ear turns bright pink (sometimes caused by blushing). The musculature of the ear has been greatly reduced, however, and few people can move their ears more than a small amount. This reduction of motility begins among the higher primates, and the reason for it can only be guessed, though it may be associated with increased motility of the head. Presumably, an acute sense of hearing is of less vital importance to noisy diurnal animals with few predators than to silent creatures that hunt by night or walk in fear of death. The tendency in primate evolution has been to lose acuity of hearing but to gain discrimination in detecting sound frequency patterns. This change is probably correlated with the development of communication within the group, using sounds

FIG. 8.7. The mechanoreceptors of the inner ear are a system of interconnected liquid-filled tubes. They are shown here with their nerve supply. *Lat.*, the horizontal semicircular canal; *Post* and *Sup.*, the two vertical canals at right angles. The utricle (*Utr.*), sacculus, and cochlea are labeled. (After Hardy, 1934.)

of widely different kinds. It is certain that, in spite of the great auditory discrimination of man (and in particular of musical man), he may not be able to detect noise as well as his dog, who guards him by listening for unusual sounds.

The high degree of auditory discrimination that man possesses enables him to understand the complex sounds of language and music. This discrimination is probably due to some improvement in the cochlea itself, where it concerns frequency, but is certainly and more emphatically due to the evolution of the auditory cortex, where the incoming signals are analyzed. The auditory cortex lies in the temporal lobe (Fig. 8.8), and it may be no coincidence that memory, which also appears to be to some extent localized in this area, is closely concerned with language as well as with visual images and that words and music may be memorized in an almost infinite variety of patterns.

In summary, it may be said that the ear has become concerned with investigation not so much of the general environment as of the part of the environment that consists of other members of the species, that it is concerned with the kind of auditory discrimination required in human communication. Appreciation of music is perhaps a by-product of the ablty to analyze speech sounds.

8.6 *Changes in brain structure and function*

BY MICROSCOPIC EXAMINATION and electrical stimulation and recording within the living brain it has proved possible to identify to some extent the functions of its different parts. Figure 8.5 shows some of the main functional areas of the tree shrew, macaque, and human cerebral cortex. The evolution of these different areas in the primates may be related to the evolution of the sense organs we have discussed, and may be summarized as follows.

1. The *olfactory bulbs* and *piriform lobes* are concerned, as we have seen, with the analysis of the olfactory stimuli from the nose. The piriform lobes form part of the *archipallium*, which is the most archaic part of the cerebral cortex. The archipallium is separated from the *neopallium* (which lies above it) by the *rhinal sulcus*. The neopallium effects, among other things, analysis of the sensory input other than that from the olfactory organ. In the evolution of the primates, the

value of the sense of smell diminishes and with it the relative size of the archipallium. With the increasing importance of the other senses, the neopallium expands, the rhinal sulcus moves down the side of the brain, and the archipallium, including the piriform lobe, comes to lie underneath the brain rather than to one side. These changes are indicated in Figure 8.5.

2. The *occipital* (posterior) *lobe* of the brain has been shown to be associated with the analysis of visual images, and the cortical layers here are, as we have seen, known as the *visual cortex*. As might be expected from what has been said of the importance of sight in primate evolution, the visual cortex has greatly expanded, even in the lower primates. This area of the cortex is clearly defined by a curved *sulcus* (fissure), the *lunate sulcus,* or, as it is often (appropriately) called, the *simian sulcus*. The development of the visual cortex is one of the most striking features of the primate brain.

3. The *temporal lobe* has also expanded at an early stage in primate evolution. A small area on its surface constitutes the *auditory cortex* (Fig. 8.8), but the rest appears to be concerned with the elaboration of visual analysis and with visual and auditory memory. These functions are clearly important in a group of animals that has increasingly come to rely on the visual memory more than on other imprinted sensory patterns.

Clearly, the temporal lobes also play an important part in the human brain. Not only is memory to a major extent visual, but so is the stream of consciousness. Evidence suggests (Penfield and Roberts 1959) that in man the temporal cortex is involved with the whole record of experience and with the reactivation of that experience.

4. The *frontal* and *parietal lobes* have also expanded in primate evolution, an expansion that has exceeded that of the other parts of the cortex in the latter stages of the evolution of man. It is indeed the enlarged frontal lobes that are always considered characteristic of man, that have given him in the last stages of his evolution a neurocranium that has expanded over his eye sockets, protects them, and forms his vertical forehead. The parietal lobes, which lie behind the frontal lobes, have also expanded possibly more than the frontal lobes (von Bonin and Bailey 1961); the total effect is very striking compared with other primates (see Fig. 8.5). As has been stated, the actual area of the cortex has increased far more than might appear, since its folding is much more complex than in other animals (Fig. 8.9). In man, 64

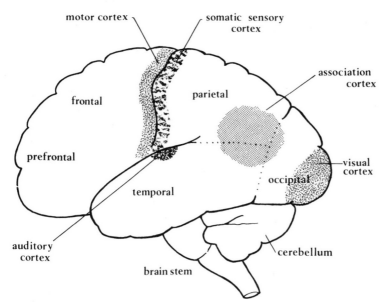

FIG. 8.8. View of the left side of the human brain, showing the main sub-divisions of the cerebral cortex, together with the somatic sensory and motor cortexes. The dotted area in the inferior posterior parietal region shows very approximately the "association cortex of association cortexes" discussed in the text. (Compare Fig. 10.4).

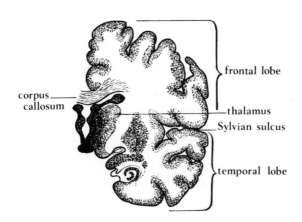

FIG. 8.9. Section through one cerebral hemisphere of man showing the extent of folding of the cerebral cortex.

per cent of the surface of the cortex is hidden in the sulci (or fissures); in primitive monkeys, only 7 per cent.

The function of the frontal and parietal lobes is partly known, partly obscure. Parts of the cortex lying between them are clearly identified as *motor cortex* and *somatic sensory cortex* (see Fig. 8.8). In these areas are located the transmitting and receiving neurons for the motor and *somesthetic* organs (skin sensory receptors) of the body. The "mapping" of these areas has been carried out by electrical stimulation and recording in conscious human beings and other animals (Fig. 8.10).

To the front of the motor cortex lie the frontal lobes, also termed the *prefrontal area*. Since no clear reaction can be obtained from this area by electrical stimulation, it has been termed "silent," and the only evidence of function comes from the striking but complex changes

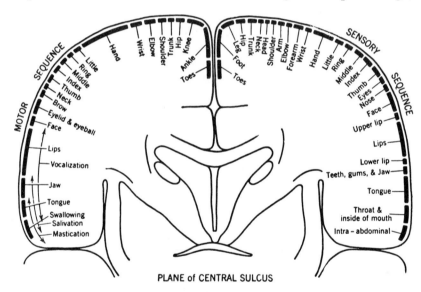

PLANE of CENTRAL SULCUS

FIG. 8.10. Schematic diagram combining a cross-section of the motor cortex (*left*) and the somatic sensory cortex (*right*) of man, in the plane of the central sulcus. The diagram shows the motor and sensory sequence of representation determined by electrical stimulation of conscious patients. With stronger stimulation, wider zones for a given part might be found, and there is considerable variation from individual to individual. Note that the sensory area devoted to the fingers and hand is greater than that devoted to the much larger skin area lying between forearm and shoulder. (From Rasmussen and Penfield, 1947.)

in personality that result from its removal in human subjects. Evidence of this kind suggests that these areas are concerned with the maintenance of drive and with its inhibition and restraint. The prefrontal areas appear to make possible both initiative and sustained attention in human behavior.

Man's ability to sustain his attention and concentrate on a particular goal may be an important development in his evolution. Kortlandt (1965) states that as a rule nonhuman primates cannot concentrate on one issue for longer than a quarter of an hour, or, at the most, half an hour. He contrasts this short attention span with carnivores like wolves, which may continue to lie in ambush, follow the same prey, or dig a den for many hours or even several days at a stretch. Clearly, a herbivore that persistently searched for one kind of food not readily available would be likely to die of starvation, whereas a carnivore diverted from its chosen prey would never succeed in running that prey to exhaustion. The evidence seems to suggest that insofar as man was a hunter he necessarily evolved the ability to work persistently toward a remote goal, and sustained attention was clearly a most important feature of early man's evolving nervous mechanism. We can see here, and we shall see again, how a change in man's ecology and in his way of life required the evolution of new kinds of mental processes, which proved an essential basis for his culture.

We know a little more about the function of the parietal lobes, and it appears that their expansion was of the greatest importance to evolving man. In charts of brain function the parietal areas of the cortex are usually labeled the *association cortex,* a descriptive term arising from the fact that the area receives intracortical connections from the three sensory receiving areas: the auditory (in the temporal lobe), the somatic sensory, and the visual (in the occipital lobe), concerned with hearing, touch, and sight, respectively. In monkeys and apes these areas connect directly with the surrounding cortex, so the nearby areas are labeled "auditory association," "somatic sensory association" and "visual association." But in man we find an expansion of the parietal lobe between these three areas to form what has been described as "the association cortex of association cortexes" (Geschwind 1964). This secondary association area is very small in apes but immense in man. All its connections are with the neighboring cortex rather than with the lower centers of the brain.

The association cortex of association cortexes is the inferior posterior parietal region approximately delineated in Figure 8.8, and it is of the greatest interest that part of it, at least, seems to coincide with the major speech area (see Fig. 10.4, p. 312). In this area of the cortex, so particularly human, as von Bonin and Bailey (1961) point out, it seems possible that we may identify at least one place in which integration of the signals from the different sense organs takes place. There is not only some evidence of integration here, but, as in the speech area, there is also evidence of abstraction. As we shall see (10.6), the so-called "speech area" is to be found only on one side of the brain; on the other side there is evidence of neural activity associated with the elaboration of notions of space and body movement. Such elaboration can again result only from integration of sensory input.

The striking result of this expansion of the frontal and parietal lobes in the last stages of human evolution is that they have covered not only the archipallium but even the large and quite newly evolved visual cortex. The simian sulcus, which demarcates the visual cortex in monkeys and apes, is almost obliterated in man, and the visual cortex comes to lie for the most part underneath the brain, rather than on top, and is hardly visible from above. The primary motor, somatic sensory, visual, and auditory areas, which bulk so large on the surface of the cerebral hemispheres of a monkey, are in man crowded down into the sulci.

While the primates have developed advanced sense reception and motor control, it looks as though the specifically human achievement lies in the special and evolved integrative functions of the brain. These functions appear to have developed with the anatomical correlates of cortical expansion in the secondary and association areas and extensive intracortical connections (see Fig. 3.10, p. 78). These increased intracortical connections are particularly apparent in the greatly increased area of cross-section of the *corpus callosum,* the body of fibers connecting the two hemispheres of the *cerebrum* (Figs. 8.9 and 8.11). It would be wrong, however, to suppose that it is in the cortex alone that we must look for the neurological correlates of humanity, for the other parts of the brain, the so-called "lower centers," have evolved and expanded in conjunction with the cortex, with which they function in close reciprocal collaboration.

The *thalamus,* which lies beneath the cortex and part of which relays signals to and from the cortex, has expanded in the posterior region to form a rounded projection called the *pulvinar,* which is characteristic of higher primates. The thalamus is to some extent the "telephone exchange" of the cortex, and corticothalamic connections exist alongside the corticocortical conections within the cortex.

Another important structure is the *cerebellum,* which, like the cerebral cortex, has become deeply fissured in evolution (Fig. 8.11). Also like the cortex, it can be separated anatomically into a central *medulla* and a cortex (mantle), and its function is the regulation of the action of all skeletal muscles (Herrick 1961, p. 369). The pattern of muscular activity is determined elsewhere; the cerebellum, like a servomechanism,

CS

T

OB

cerebellum

ON

P

H

FIG. 8.11. Median sagittal section of the human brain showing (*upper part*) the internal (medial) surfaces of the left cerebral hemisphere, below which lie the transverse fibers of the corpus callosum that connect the two hemispheres (*shaded*). The central sulcus (*CS*) separates the somatic sensory and motor cortexes (*shaded,* as in Fig. 8.8), which continue on the median side of the hemisphere. The left olfactory bulb (*OB*) and optic nerve (*ON*) are shown at the base of the brain, together with the thalamus (*T*), hypothalamus (*H*), and pituitary (*P*). Like the cerebellum and brainstem, these organs lie medially and are cut in this view.

controls the strength and timing of contraction of the separate muscles involved in any movement. Its activity is involuntary but of immense importance in any vertebrate with rapid movements requiring accurate control. Clearly, primates, of all mammals, depend on the cerebellum to integrate and control their rapid muscular activity. Man has inherited a highly evolved cerebellum from his primate ancestry, which no doubt plays an important part not only in his locomotion but in the delicate motor control required in toolmaking and in the more sophisticated activities of modern man, such as piano-playing.

From this brief summary we can see that different parts of the brain have expanded at different stages of primate and human evolution. Each expansion has presumably been related to a new functional need of the primate order, and each has played a part in the creation of *Homo sapiens*. But it appears that the expansion of the temporal, frontal, and parietal lobes, which came last, has contributed to make man the creature he is. The temporal and parietal lobes appear to have given man new possibilities of integrating his experience, the frontal lobes have given him new control over his behavior. It is important to stress, however, that in no sense did the brain *cause* the evolution of human behavior. The human brain and human behavior evolved together in response to environmental change as necessary correlates.

8.7 The brain as a determinant of skull form

THE IMPORTANCE of the brain in the maintenance of life at all homeostatic levels necessitates its protection in a bony case, the neurocranium. In order to give maximum strength for a given amount of material and weight, the neurocranium has tended in evolution to be spherical in form, which is mechanically the most efficient use of protective material. The brain itself is soft and does not appear to dictate greatly the form of the neurocranium, only its volume. But the neurocranium is in fact normally far from spherical, since the actual form is dictated by the development of the various bony appendages to it that we have discussed—in particular, the orbits, muzzle, and jaws, which make up the face. The relative size of the neurocranium and these components, together with the neck musculature, establishes the form of the head; the brain itself establishes only the volume of the cranial cavity.

The neurocranium itself, with which we are here concerned, consists of two layers of bone, the so-called *inner* and *outer tables*. The inner table surrounds the brain itself; the outer table follows the structural demands of the other components of head form (Moss and Young 1960). Between them is a light-weight, webbed bony structure, the *diploë,* and, where the inner and outer tables do not very closely coincide, air spaces are formed called *sinuses.* Any section through the neurocranium shows the diploë, which can be seen in Figure 7.3 (p. 178). According to mechanical principles, the strength of such a girder can be increased, without increasing the weight of the structure significantly, by moving the two outer components apart, and that is what has happened in the evolution of the neurocranium; skulls with a thick diploë weigh little more, yet give more protection to the brain than do thin ones.

The size and shape of the brain is well known in the living primates, and in the fossil forms it can be estimated by making a cast (an *endocast*) of the inside of a complete fossilized skull (Fig. 8.12). It should not be supposed, however, that the cranial capacity is equivalent to the volume of the brain: owing to the presence of associated structures, such as membranes and blood vessels, the human brain occupies only two-thirds of the total cranial volume, and in other primates the proportion of the brain itself may be even less (Mettler 1956). The size of the brain varies a great deal in modern man and may have varied in more primitive forms as well, so the figures we have, which are based on a few fossils, may be misleading but are unlikely to be very far from correct (Table 8.2).

TABLE 8.2 CRANIAL CAPACITIES OF SOME PRIMATES, INCLUDING FOSSIL HOMINIDS (FROM TOBIAS 1963)

Primate	Range (cc.)	Mean (cc.)
Macaca	—	100
Papio	—	200
Hylobates	87–130	89
Pan	320–480	394
Gorilla	340–752	498
Pongo	295–475	411
Australopithecus	435–600	508
Homo erectus	775–1225	978
Homo sapiens	1000–2000	1300

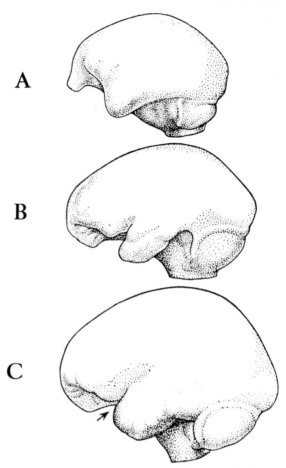

Fig. 8.12. Lateral view of the endocranial casts of *Gorilla* (*A*), *Homo erectus* (*B*), and modern man (*C*). The arrow points to the notch that indicates the position of the sylvian sulcus between the temporal and frontal lobes. (From Le Gros Clark, 1962.)

Among mammals generally, the larger animals have, of course, the larger brains, and a large brain as such is not necessarily an evolutionary novelty, nor does it necessarily indicate special mental power (the brains of elephants and whales may reach 4000 and 6700 cc., respectively). In order to discover whether a brain is unusually large in an animal, it is necessary to relate its size to that of the animal's body. Study of evolutionary lineages in different orders of mammals has shown that the brain increases not in simple proportion to the increase in body size but by the power of approximately 0.66 of that increase.

Thus, if the body size doubles, the brain size will increase to $2^{0.66} = 1.6$ times its original size. It is interesting that this relationship is about the same as that relating the increase of body surface area to body size, so there seems to be a fairly constant relationship between brain size and surface area (Rensch 1959).

The body size and brain size of the primates have been investigated most recently by Jerison (1955). Much data have been collected showing that in some lineages and groups of animals the brain is proportionately larger than in others, and this relationship has been termed the *index of cephalization*. Figures gathered by Jerison for this index are shown in Table 8.3. The relative position of the great apes and

TABLE 8.3 INDEX OF CEPHALIZATION: $K = \dfrac{\text{Brain weight}}{\text{Body weight}^{0.66}}$

Faunal Group	Index of Cephalization
Mammals (excluding primates) ($n = 108$)	0.06
Three great apes ($n = 35$)	0.29
Monkeys* ($n = 50$)	0.41
Modern man ($n = 50$)	0.92

n = sample size.
Data from Jerison (1955).

* Including *Ateles, Cynopithecus, Macaca, Papio, Presbytis.*

monkeys in this table may at first sight be surprising; it is due to the relatively large bodies of the great apes, and it is highly suggestive: monkeys are nearest to man in their relative development of the brain. We do not know the body weight of fossils and therefore do not know their index of cephalization, but it seems probable that *Australopithecus* was already beginning to show this *Homo*-like increase in brain size, which is not associated with an appropriate increase in body size (such as is found among the great apes). The relationship between brain growth and body growth was no longer the same, for the index of cephalization itself has increased in hominid evolution.

From our knowledge of the dating of fossil remains (see Appendix) and their cranial capacity (Table 8.2), it is clear that the great spurt in brain size occurred between the Lower and the Middle Pleistocene. We have, however, noted that there may have been at the same time a slight increase in stature, from perhaps 5 feet to 5 feet 6 inches, though the sample size is extremely small. However, this increase, if it occurred, is not enough to lower very greatly the ratio of brain size to body weight, so the increase in the index of cephalization appears to be very close to the absolute increase in brain size. It is significant that the increase in brain size coincided approximately with the beginning of cooperative hunting by hominids (see 7.11).

The great increase in man's brain size, which was occurring during the Middle Pleistocene, has involved increase in all its parts but perhaps most obviously in the cerebral cortex, as we have seen. The surface layers of the cerebral hemispheres are in man deeply folded (Fig. 8.9), so the total surface area of the cortex is far greater than that of the inside of the neurocranium; the surface area of the human brain is four times as great as that of the gorilla s, although the volume has increased by a factor of only 2.5. The expansion in endocranial volume has meant that in man the neurocranium has enlarged at the same time that the facial bones and jaws have been reduced. The effect of the jawbones on the form of the head is therefore less than that of the brain, which as a result in man comes quite near to its "ideal" spherical form. Man is an "egghead" because his brain is the prime determinant of skull form: the face and jaws are a relatively minor appendage. At the same time, the reduced nuchal and masticatory muscles leave their areas of anchorage rather small, smooth, and no longer bordered by crests. With this change in emphasis of head function and structure, we see the rounded skull vault rising above the orbits in human evolution, and this development has been quantified by Le Gros Clark (1962) (Table 8.4 and Fig. 8.13).

TABLE 8.4 SUPRAORBITAL HEIGHT INDICES (FOR MEANING SEE FIG. 8.13)

Primate	Mean Supraorbital Height Index and Source	
Gorilla	48	
Pan	47	Le Gros Clark (1950)
Pongo	49	
Proconsul africanus	56	Davis and Napier (1963)
Australopithecus robustus	50	Robinson (1963)
A. africanus	61	
Homo erectus	63–67	Ashton and Zuckerman (1951)
Modern man	64–77	

When, therefore, we visualize the overall form of the neurocranium in the final stages of human evolution, we see that its shape becomes increasingly spherical: in the horizontal plane the cranium becomes less dolichocephalic (elongated) and more brachycephalic (round-headed). This brachycephalization has been demonstrated in the most recent stages of human evolution as well as in earlier times, and it seems to reflect the continuing trend toward reduction of the jaws and face and improvement in cranial balance. As can be seen from Fig. 8.13, the supra-orbital height index (FB/AB) measures the height of the skull vault above the level of the top of the orbit, and so indicates the height of the neurocranium and cranial cavity relative to the orbital region of the face. From these figures, it is clear that in this character *Australopithecus robustus* forms a group with the great apes (index 47–50) and *A. africanus* forms a group with *Homo* (index 61–77). There is a considerable gap between these two groups which reflects the fundamental difference between the two species of *Australopithecus*. The gap is occupied by the Miocene fossil ape *Proconsul*.

8.8 The face

THE CHARACTERISTIC features of the human face we owe both to its underlying bone structure and to the form of the soft parts, which now require consideration.

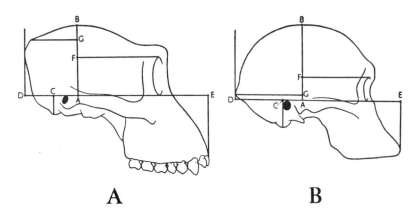

A   **B**

FIG. 8.13. Outlines of skulls of female *Gorilla* (*A*) and *Australopithecus* (*B*), with construction lines to calculate the skull indices introduced by Le Gros Clark: *supraorbital height index FB/AB, condylar position index CD/CE.* (From Le Gros Clark, 1962.)

The eyes have been discussed; their sensitive and delicate movements give the face a liveliness that no other feature can impart. The surrounding muscles serve to protect the eye and at the same time add to muscular activity in this region—particularly that associated with frowning and smiling. The nose is a most prominent feature of the face; its form and function have already been described. The muscles that move the nostrils are rather less developed in man than in other primates, as are those of the ears.

The lips serve both a sensory and a motor function. As a tactile sense organ, not only do they carry a high density of sensory nerve endings, but the surrounding skin also carries hairs, around the follicles of which are wrapped further sensory nerve endings—a condition reminiscent of the facial vibrissae of mammals. This great sensitivity relates to their function in food investigation and is reflected in the area of cortex devoted to them (see Fig. 8.10).

The first motor function of the lips was in eating and swallowing, but even in the lower mammals they play a part in communication, as one of the most mobile parts of the face. In man, the lips have come to have immense importance in speech as well as in facial expression. The area of motor cortex associated with the lips is therefore also very large, as can be seen from Figure 8.10.

The facial musculature as a whole is not only concerned with the masticatory apparatus and the protection of the eyes but also plays a most important part in communication through facial expression. The differentiation of the facial musculature is peculiar to mammals and strikingly advanced in primate evolution. In many mammals, facial muscles are involved in behavior patterns not directly concerned with feeding. Teeth are often displayed to frighten away intruders, as well as in response to pleasure. The faces of the baboon and mandrill carry features that are not merely mechanical but *sematic* (that is, concerned with signaling, with communication within the group); they clearly contribute effects that may be imposing and even terrifying in appearance. There is no doubt that natural selection controls not only the mechanical function of the head but also its appearance, through its shape, color, and distribution of hair (8.9), which is important in a social context.

In the higher primates, facial expressions usually take the form of signals between members of the same species. Most animals perform a courtship ceremony, which is a signaling device to bring the sexes together with proper timing and stimulation; it is hard to say exactly how large a part facial expression plays in these rituals, but in man it seems certain that it is important. Although dance is often a preliminary to sexual communication, speech and facial expression are paramount.

Studies of primates have revealed that in the monkeys and apes facial expressions are varied and important. Examples are manifold

FIG. 8.14. Facial expressions of a young chimpanzee in various moods. Some of the creases are marked with numbers to emphasize that each is by no means confined to one expression. (From Kohts, 1935.)

when photographs are examined (DeVore 1965), and part of the range of expression visible in the face of the chimpanzee is reproduced in Figure 8.14. The origins of facial expression in man are discussed by Andrew (1965): they are an important means of communication in all social primates.

It seems clear then that, in assessing the determinants of head form, we must not omit the soft parts that effect facial appearance and expression. Natural selection operates on the form of the head to evolve a structure with varied functions. The function of the head as an organ of communication in a social primate is not by any means less important than the functions that determine the form of its bones.

8.9 Hair and skin

MAN'S NAKEDNESS is one of his most striking features. The loss of body hair that has occurred in his evolution powerfully suggests his origin as tropical. But his nakedness cannot be the result of his origin alone, since the other tropical primates have retained their hair. The minority of tropical mammals that have lost their body hair, including the elephant, rhinoceros, and hippopotamus, are large animals with thick, heavy skin and subcutaneous fat. The majority of mammals are protected by their hair or fur from the sun's heat as well as from cold in temperate regions. The advantage of nakedness must lie elsewhere; it has been postulated as the need to lose very rapidly the metabolic heat developed in daylight hunting activities, for most carnivores hunt by night or during dawn and dusk. There is no better explanation, and it gains strength from the evidence of the sweat glands given below. It is relevant that we have no evidence of man in north-temperate regions before the early Middle Pleistocene, when it is most probable that he had learned to utilize skins as well as fire for protection against cold. The evolution of nakedness has not involved any major evolutionary novelty. Man has about the same number of hair follicles as have the great apes; the difference is that the majority of man's hairs grow very little (Montagna 1965).

The fact that man retains certain areas of hair is perhaps more surprising than his loss of it. The hair on the head gives protection to the brain in tropical climates. Metabolic heat is not generated in the brain and scalp, and there is no advantage in nakedness here; indeed, it is surely a disadvantage. It is possibly relevant that in north-temperate peoples baldness is stated to be on the increase (Montagna 1965), which may be because hair serves a less vital protective function in cool climates. Yet it will serve to keep the head warm, and thermoregulation in the brain is very important. There seem to be other factors at work here, especially when we remember that among women baldness is rare, yet they have to survive the same climatic conditions as men. Man, incidentally, is not unique in his baldness; one species of macaque and the orang both go bald in middle age, while the uakari monkey has a completely bald head when adult.

In fact, it is certain that the presence and absence of hair on the head, as well as elsewhere, is controlled by other than purely mechanical factors. Hair has been retained around the eyes (brows and lashes), the ears and nose, where its function is primarily protective, but elsewhere it appears to be mainly sematic in function, acting as a signal to other members of the species (Goodhart 1960). A glance at Figure 8.15 suggests that this is indeed the case, for many species of monkeys have striking patches of hair that correspond to our own. In monkeys it is *epigamic* in function—that is, it is used in signaling in relation to sexual dominance. The guenon illustrated here has not only a very smart hairstyle but also a white beard and mustache. The beard is quite common among species of *Cercopithecus,* and a flowing mustache is found in the South American emperor tamarin. Such hair patches, which develop at puberty and are found in males only, are likely to have some sexual function and, in that case, are related to intermale rivalry; it is not that the female selects the most impressive male but that the most impressive-looking male frightens away his rivals. This hierarchy of dominance in sexual prestige is based on appearance rather than physical force, hence the evolution of epigamic hair. There is considerable variation among different races of modern man in the development of facial and head hair, and it is not purely a matter of cultural convention (Fig. 8.16).

Pubic hair and *axillary* (armpit) hair must have a different function, however, since they are found in both sexes and axillary hair is hardly visible unless the arms are raised. These two hair patches coincide with areas of skin containing scent glands (see below), and it seems probable that the hair has some function relating to scent. Goodhart (1960) points out that the scented apocrine secretion (to be

The Evolution of the Head

FIG. 8.15. This *Cercopithecus* monkey (the guenon) has striking patches of distinctive hair, corresponding to man's head hair, mustache, and beard. These patches are important as signals in sexual competition, just as they are in man (see Fig. 8.16). (Courtesy Belle Vue Zoological Gardens.)

described below) is at first odorless and develops a scent only on exposure to air. He suggests that the pubic and axillary hair serves to provide a surface for oxidative reactions and to facilitate the dispersion of scent in the air. However, there is reason to believe that pubic hair also has an epigamic function in men, especially when it grows right up the belly, and it may have been selected as an attractive adornment in women too. There is a useful confirmation of the theory of epigamic hair patches to be derived from warrior dress. The British guardsman's bearskin, the field marshall's plumed hat, and indeed the Highlander's sporran—the ornament of animal fur worn over the pubic region—all serve to accentuate our natural epigamic hair distribution. The most recent to evolve perhaps was the pubic hair, which tends to be sparse in primates and which also would be visible to other individuals only in a bipedal primate.

The glands of the skin have evolved with man's loss of hair. The *sebaceous* (fat-producing) glands are more numerous and active in man than in most other mammals, but their function is still obscure. While they may protect the hair and skin from drying out in the tropical heat, their remarkable distribution on the human body (such as inside the cheeks and on the inner edges of the eyelids) suggests a

FIG. 8.16. Although clothes have augmented the epigamic function of hair in both men and women, hair styles still retain importance in the establishment of sexual dominance and in effecting sexual attraction in men and women, respectively. Both head and facial epigamic hair patches vary in form and appearance among the living races of man. The paintings were made of individuals from Eastern Europe (*top left*), West Africa (*top right*), New Guinea (*bottom left*) and North America (*bottom right*). (Courtesy Hans Friedenthal and Gustav Fischer).

more complex function that is not at present understood (Montagna 1965).

The sweat glands fall into two groups: the *apocrine* and *eccrine* glands. The apocrine glands secrete the odorous component of sweat and are primarily scent glands that respond to stress or sexual stimulation. Before the development of artificial scents and deodorants, they no doubt played an important role in human society. In modern man these glands occur only in certain areas of the body, in particular in the armpits, the navel, the anal and genital areas, the nipples, and the ears. Surprisingly enough, glands in the armpits of man are more numerous per unit area than in any other animal. There is no doubt that the function of scent in sexual encounter is of the greatest importance even in the higher primates and man.

The eccrine glands, which are the source of sweat itself, have two functions in primates. Their original function was probably to moisten friction surfaces, such as the volar pads of manus (hand) and pes (foot) to improve the grip, prevent flaking of the horny layer of the skin, and assist tactile sensitivity. Glands serving that function are also found on the hairless surface of the prehensile tail of New World monkeys and on the knuckles of gorilla and chimpanzee hands, which they use in quadrupedal walking. Glands in these positions are under the control of the brain and adrenal bodies, and even in modern man an experience of stress may produce sweaty palms.

The second and more recently evolved function of the eccrine glands is the lowering of body temperature through the evaporation of sweat on the surface of the body. The hairy skin of monkeys and apes carries eccrine glands, but they are neither so active nor so numerous as in man. Modern man is equipped with between two and five million active sweat glands, and they play a vital part in cooling the body. The heat loss that results from the evaporation of water from a surface is enormously greater than that which could be expected to occur as a result of simple radiation. The fact that sweat contains salt necessitates a constant supply of this mineral if man is to survive in a tropical climate.

It has been observed that like almost all mammals, primates sweat very little. Even hunting carnivores, such as dogs, lose heat by other means, such as panting. Sweating has evolved as a most important means of heat loss in man, a fact that is surely correlated with the loss of his body hair. The apparent importance in human evolution of achieving an effective means of heat loss indicates without doubt that early man was subject to intense muscular activity, with the production of much metabolic heat; he could not afford even the smallest variation in body temperature. With such a highly evolved brain, the maintenance of a really constant internal environment was a need of prime importance in human evolution.

Skin color is a rather striking human character, which attracts much attention. The basic racial differences in this character are slight; they are due not to a difference in the number of pigment-forming cells (*melanocytes*) but to the amount of pigment manufactured by these cells. The melanocytes inject pigment into the surrounding cells of the *epidermis* (the outer layer of skin), where it forms a shield to protect the cell nucleus from the harmful ultraviolet rays of the sun. Hair is pigmented by similar injection into the cells of the hair follicle. Active melanocytes may be selected for camouflage (as in the lower primates) or, in hairless man, for protection from the sun's rays. The differences of skin color in modern man are probably due to the advantage that fair skin offers in the temperate regions in allowing the sun's rays to activate the synthesis of vitamin D in the skin. The activity of the melanocytes is an example of a character subject to both developmental and genetic homeostasis.

The actual quality of the skin varies probably as much within a single population (if not in a single individual) as it does in the whole human species. Different kinds of skin occur in different parts of the body, and the form of the skin appears to be genetically determined. Modern man certainly appears to possess fine, smooth skin, but this effect is probably produced by its hairlessness and the protection that clothing and modern comforts offer. Again, a smooth skin may be subject to sexual selection, particularly among women.

The skin is a very important and complex organ of the body. Besides enveloping the body and maintaining an effective boundary and container for the body tissues, it is a strong waterproof membrane and a highly complex sense organ, responsive to pressure, temperature change, and damage. It is also an organ of thermoregulation. It is strong, hard-wearing, and develops claws, nails, and hair, as well as protective pigments. Man's skin has evolved with the rest of his body as an adaptation to his environment.

8.10 The human head

THE HEAD OF MAN can be seen to have been formed by the evolution of a number of separate functional complexes. How these complexes have influenced its visible and internal structure will now be summarized.

1. The evolution of the visual sense, accompanied by the expansion of the visual cortex, was the first factor in the evolution of the human head from that of an early primate. In particular, the large eyes, facing forward for stereoscopic vision, changed the appearance of the face and its bony architecture, which was modified to protect the delicate eyeballs.

2. Recession of the muzzle and reduction of the turbinal bones followed, with a resultant flattening and even hollowing of the face between orbits and jaws. The olfactory sense took second or even third place in the primate's perception of the environment.

3. Erect posture and later bipedalism brought with it a forward movement of the occipital condyles, which, together with the recession of the face as a whole, changed and improved the balance of the head on the spine, with the result that the nuchal crest and nuchal area were reduced.

4. At a late stage in human evolution came the recession of the masticatory apparatus and a reduction of the power and extent of the grinding surfaces involved in the mastication of food.

5. The brain had been increasing in size throughout primate evolution; with the reduction of the masticatory apparatus came a final great increase in brain size, which was doubled in about one million years. This final enlargement filled out the forehead and contributed to the vertical face of modern man.

6. Finally, hairlessness revealed a face that contained not only the speech apparatus but also a musculature that was increasingly used in visual communication by facial expression. With the loss of facial hair the face became an important means of visual communication and the seat of beauty.

In this chapter we have tried to subdivide the evolution of the human head into the evolution of a series of separate functional parts and then, as it were, to fit them all together again. It is important to emphasize that, since the head is so highly integrated a structure, the evolution of each functional part must have affected the evolution of every other part. A change in size of any part will have effected the balance of the head on the spine and so the development of the neck musculature. At the same time, the amount of development of any muscle (and in particular the masticatory muscles) will produce tensions and stresses in the bony architecture and in turn will affect its form.

In practice, the interactions of the different functional units of the head are very complex and can be fully grasped only by considerable familiarity with the skulls themselves. The basis of such interaction has, however, been presented here and should form a means of approaching a functional study of the cranial morphology of man's evolutionary lineage.

SUGGESTIONS FOR FURTHER READING

The most useful account of the structure and function of the mammalian sense organs and the brain is to be found in J. Z. Young, *The Life of Mammals* (Oxford: Oxford University Press, 1957). Beyond this, the reader is referred to the references in the text.

ᥰ9

Reproduction, the Family, and Social Structure

9.1 Reproduction and the placenta

TO WRITE A CHAPTER on the evolution of the human reproductive processes seems a project fraught with difficulty, for
fossil remains tell us nothing of this all-important aspect of our subject.
However, by comparing the reproductive processes of human and nonhuman primates, we can obtain valuable insight into the important
changes that must have occurred during the processes of human evolution and into their probable function. Because sexual reproduction is
the mechanism by which a species both survives and varies in evolution, the form of the mechanism is of special interest to us. In this
chapter we shall consider some large changes in the behavioral aspects
of the reproductive processes, changes that have influenced the form of
our society and the structure of our individual lives. Their study is a
fascinating aspect of human evolutionary biology.

Although the development of the human *embryo* (the individual
before birth) in the uterus, the process of *gestation,* is part of the
process of ontogenetic growth, it is convenient to treat it as part of

the reproductive processes. As we shall see, while the whole life-span of man has changed and lengthened during his evolution (9.7), this first phase of his growth is an exception. Table 9.1, which relates the

TABLE 9.1 PRENATAL AND POSTNATAL GROWTH PERIODS (FROM SCHULTZ 1956 AND OTHERS)

Primate	Gestation (in Weeks)	Menarche (Age)	Completion of Growth (Age)	Life-span (in Years)
Macaca	24	2	7	24
Hylobates	30	8.5	9	30
Pongo	39	?	11	30
Pan	33	8.8	11	35
Gorilla	36	9	11	40
Man	38	13.7	20	75

period of gestation to the total life-span of different primates, shows that man's gestation is relatively short compared with the period up to the completion of his growth. While his total growth period is twice as long as that of the great apes, his gestation is not significantly longer. However, the human infant is far more helpless than the infant ape or monkey, since he is born at an earlier stage in development; yet, at the same time, his growth rate during gestation is much faster. When we consider (in Table 9.1) the figures for man and, for example, *Pongo,* it is relevant that the average increase in weight of the human fetus is 12.5 grams per day, while in the orang it is only 5.7 grams per day. The evolution of the human placenta helps make possible this fast growth rate and needs consideration at this point.

Together with the monkeys, apes, and some few other mammals (insectivores and some rodents), man shares what would appear to be one of the most efficient types of placenta from the point of view of chemical interchange with the mother. In this *hemochorial* type of placenta, which may be compared with the lemur's more primitive *epitheliochorial* type (Fig. 9.1), there are no maternal tissues—only fetal tissues—separating the fetal and maternal bloodstreams. The blood vessels of the endometrium—the lining of the uterus—are actually penetrated by the fetal vessels, and the former break down to form a spongy, blood-filled tissue, with the result that the fetal vessels are bathed in blood and chemical interchange between the bloodstreams is maximal (Amoroso 1952).

As a result of this intimate association between maternal and fetal tissues, the placenta, at birth, carries with it a considerable part of the endometrial lining of the uterus. The placenta is for that reason termed *deciduate*.

The differentiation and elaboration of the primate placenta promotes optimum conditions for the developing embryo. Not only is the supply of food and oxygen enhanced, but waste products are rapidly removed. Another resultant advantage is the improved transmission of antibodies in the blood, which pass from the mother to the fetus and will immunize the new-born against disease. There is, however, the concomitant disadvantage that, when the blood proteins of the fetus are different from those of the mother, antibodies may develop in the mother's blood, "protecting" her from the alien blood of the fetus, but in turn passing into the fetal blood stream to cause clotting of the fetal blood. This dangerous effect, known as *isoimmunization,* probably tends to reduce genetic variability in blood proteins by removing variants from the breeding population.

A review of primate placentation from the primitive New World monkeys to the Hominoidea shows that the placenta develops at an

FIG. 9.1. Diagrams of two types of placentae found among the primates. *Left,* the lemur; *right,* the human type, showing the relationship between fetal blood (*above,* corpuscles with dark centers) and maternal blood (*below,* corpuscles with light centers). In the human placenta the fetal tissues are bathed in maternal blood with no intervening maternal tissues. The cell walls of the fetal epithelium have dissolved. (Redrawn from Amoroso, 1952.)

earlier stage in the course of gestation in the Hominoidea than in the monkeys. The human embryo does not begin its development in the *lumen* (open central space) of the uterus, but at a very early stage it enters the uterus wall and becomes implanted in the vascular tissue (densely filled with blood vessels) of the endometrium. This tissue is already being prepared for implantation from the time of ovulation (see 9.3), even though conception has not yet occurred. The human fetus is able to draw the maximum amount of nutriment from the mother as soon as the fetal circulation develops. In its early development the human fetus has a remarkably fast start and can grow at an exceedingly rapid rate.

9.2 Birth and infancy

THE OVERALL REPRODUCTIVE rate in any species or population is controlled by a large number of factors, but only one of them can be considered here: the birth rate itself. It is characteristic of almost all primates that they give birth to one young at a time. Among the higher primates only the South American marmosets regularly produce twins. The extremely low birth rate in man (one child per year is about the maximum) is the end point of a process of increased reproductive efficiency that leads to man from those forms of life, such as the salmon, that produce many millions of fertile eggs per year. Evolution has selected in man a reproductive process that enables him to maintain his numbers in a hostile environment, not by mass production but by prenatal protection and postnatal care.

Schultz (1948) demonstrates this development by the theoretical example shown in Table 9.2. This theoretical calculation of the reproductive potential of three primates is based on the assumption that man

TABLE 9.2 THE REPRODUCTIVE POTENTIAL OF HIGHER PRIMATES

Primate	Period of Fertility of Female (in Years)	Fertility Commences (Years from Birth)	Theoretical Maximum Number of Offspring after 45 Years
Marmoset	7	3	20 million
Chimpanzee	16	9	408
Man	28	17	64

and the chimpanzee produce one young every year and the marmoset three sets of twins every two years, with a sex ratio of one male to one female. It shows the very striking discrepancy between potential and actual in the marmoset compared with that in man. Of course, neither animal is able to utilize its full reproductive capacity, but it is clear that a human infant at conception starts out on a relatively safe journey. Its calculated chance of survival (in this example, with the population remaining constant) may be only 1 in 32, but in practice it is greater than that, since the birthrate is never maximal. There is no doubt that the human reproductive process is significantly more efficient than that of other animals.

We have stressed (see 1.3) that competition is a correlate of the evolutionary process and that it is far more marked within species than between species because members of one species require the same food and habitat, while members of different species generally do not. This intra-specific competition is found not only between adults but also between infants and embryos. In animals that produce several young at birth, competition exists among the different fetuses for a limited supply of nourishment and space. Rapid development of the growing organisms is favored for that reason, as well as for others that we shall discuss. The production of single offspring, typical of the higher primates, is a development of the greatest importance because it removes the intrauterine competition and allows a slowing-down of maturation in the fetal stages. In man the growth rate of the fetus is striking, as we have seen, but maturation is slow: an important evolutionary novelty is made possible by the absence of competition during the fetal stage of growth.

During human evolution, therefore, there has been a slowing-down of maturation or, to put it another way, a change in the stage at which birth occurs in *ontogeny* (the development of the individual from egg to maturity). There are a number of factors that affect this stage and require discussion. As a general rule, it is advantageous that the newborn animal be able to run about independently as soon as possible to fend for itself and escape predators, so a certain physical maturity at birth is essential. Operating against this important factor, however, there are two other factors.

In the first place, the fact that the birth canal passes through a bony ring in the mother's pelvis (see Figs. 5.3 and 5.10, pp. 112, 120) means that its maximum size is fixed in any mature female, and this maximum limits the size of the fetus' head (which is the largest part of the fetus' body in its cross-sectional area). Since the brain is the highly evolved controller of all homeostatic mechanisms, including behavior, considerable development of this organ is necessary for any degree of infant maturity. The size of the pelvic birth canal therefore limits the maturity of the newborn. The size of the birth canal itself is positively correlated with the overall size of the mother, so if its size is to increase in evolution (as it has), the overall size of the mature female will also be likely to increase, in spite of the competing advantages of small size (see 9.6). Whatever other factors are involved in the determination of the stage of birth in monkey or man, the close relationship between the size of the fetus' head and the birth canal is a strictly limiting factor.

We have mentioned that the baby is born at an earlier stage in ontogeny in modern man than in any other primate. It is helpless, and the bones of its body are very incompletely formed. The latter fact, however, proves to have its advantages, for the bones of the skull are not fused together and as a result can survive compression and distortion without damage to themselves or to the soft brain within them. The head is in fact flexible and can be somewhat elongated during birth; it will subsequently and spontaneously regain its characteristic shape.

Birth at an early stage in ontogeny therefore serves to provide a certain mechanical advantage, helping somewhat to overcome the limiting size of the birth canal. But it also serves to provide a more important physiological and psychological advantage, for the sooner the young animal has to face the outside world, the longer it will have in which to learn to cope with its environment before it reaches full maturity. When we turn from the higher primates to man, we find the latter advantage to be of predominant importance. The increased length of the learning period before physical maturity, and the earlier stage at which experience can influence brain function, are clearly of immense significance (see 9.7). The disadvantageous helplessness of the newborn (including imperfectly developed homeostatic mechanisms like body temperature control) has been overcome by the evolution of diligent parental care.

It is noteworthy that the helpless human infant could not have evolved without a mother able to carry it. The baby baboon, for instance, may be helped by its mother for the first day or two after birth but otherwise clings independently to its mother's body hair during the long daily trips to food and water. Only a bipedal animal is in a position to carry its infant everywhere for at least a year, with the infant unable to hang on by itself. During its period of helplessness the infant is being exposed to the vagaries of the environment—and in particular to the behavior of its parent—rather than remaining fully insulated in the constant environment of the water-filled fetal membranes within the uterus. In man, the environment will start to mold the developing creature at a relatively early stage in its growth, and so environmental influence will be greatly increased.

The influence of the environment upon the young animal begins with its relationship to its mother. The close proximity of the mother's body and the comfort of the milk supply stabilize the first affectional relationship of the young creature. Suckling establishes communication between mother and child; the tactile sense is first in this respect. Close dependence makes possible the transmission of learned behavior patterns. The longer the period of dependence, the longer the period available for such transmission and the greater the long-term effect of the affectional relationship on the family group (see 9.9). Only at sexual maturity does the bond begin to weaken and the young begin to assume adult functions. The lengthened period to *menarche* (puberty) and the completion of growth is shown in Table 9.1. As we shall see (9.7), this lengthened period of dependence on the mother is a factor of the utmost importance in human evolution.

9.3 Female sexuality

THE HUMAN *menstrual cycle* is of course the human version of the *estrous cycle* of other mammals. The two terms arise from two differences. In the menstrual cycle, the most notable event is the monthly discharge of blood from the uterus; in the estrous cycle, the most notable event is the period called estrus ("heat"), in which the female both desires to copulate and stimulates males for that purpose. Ovulation occurs during the phase of estrus. This period of great sexual activity is found in all mammals except man. *Menstruation* (loss of blood) occurs at the end of the cycle, long after ovulation. Slight bleeding occurs in many primates (Zuckerman 1930), but only in man does it amount to a heavy monthly loss of blood. The term "menstrual" means "monthly," and the cycle does occupy about thirty days in most primates, certainly in the higher primates.

The full cycle, which is properly called estrous (rather than menstrual), is shown in Figure 2.6 (p. 47) and occurs among all primates. Those which have a breeding season, rather than breeding the whole year round, may experience a period of *anestrus,* when the cycle subsides and sexual activity ceases. Only a few of the prosimians are reported definitely to have such nonbreeding seasons. The normal estrous cycle is interrupted in the mature female higher primate only by pregnancy and by a period for *lactation* (producing milk) following *parturition* (giving birth). The discharge of blood, that is so typical of *Homo sapiens,* follows the stage in the cycle that has quite reasonably been described as "pseudopregnancy." Immediately after ovulation, the wall of the uterus begins to develop its spongy blood-filled texture, which is in preparation for the implantation of the embryo. If implantation and pregnancy do not occur, this wall breaks down just as it does at birth, when the deciduate placenta is shed. The increased blood loss in women would appear to be correlated with the degree to which the endometrium is prematurely modified for implantation and the nourishment of the embryo. It indicates the speed with which the human endometrium responds to the hormone progesterone (see 2.4), and the speed with which the embryo will come to require nourishment from the mother and begin its growth.

An even more interesting evolutionary development in the human estrous cycle is the loss of the phenomenon of estrus itself. In many primates, estrus is accompanied by variation in the appearance of what has been termed the "sexual skin"—a specialized area of skin on the female, contiguous with the external genitalia. In these genera, the skin undergoes cyclic variation in its external form and color. The skin is thick and carries an unusually rich blood supply; at estrus the sexual skin swells and may assume bright-red coloration. The presence of sexual skin has not been reported among New World monkeys (except the marmoset) and varies a great deal among Old World forms, reaching its greatest development in baboons (Fig. 9.2). Among anthropoid apes it is much reduced, and only in the chimpanzee is it at all developed (Pocock 1925). The tumescence (swelling and thickening) and coloration of the sexual skin at ovulation is due to the increased level of the hormone estrogen in the blood. Its function apparently is to act as a visual sexual stimulant to males, thus insuring that copulation occurs at ovulation.

In modern man there is no sign of sexual skin, nor is there any clear evidence of estrus unless it be a very small rise in body temperature

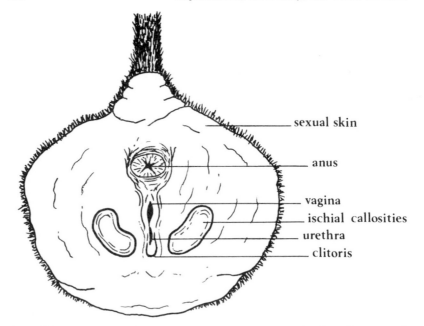

sexual skin

anus

vagina
ischial callosities
urethra
clitoris

Fig. 9.2. Rear view of a female *Macaca* at estrus, showing the great de
velopment of the hairless sexual skin. Note the position of the ischial
callosities in relation to the other anatomical landmarks.

that can be detected at ovulation. Though some evidence of a peak of
sexual response among women at estrus has been recorded by Benedek
(1952), Kinsey has concluded (1953, p. 609) that the available evidence suggests a maximum response just before menstruation, not
ovulation, so we must conclude that at present we cannot recognize
estrus in man. In mammals generally, the phenomenon of estrus interrupts normal behavior, with the result that the female, and in turn
the male or males, are almost totally preoccupied with sexual activity.
Among primates, estrus has been described as totally incompatible with
the nursing of infants, and a period of anestrus necessarily follows the
birth of young and accompanies lactation. The loss of estrus in human
evolution is a development of the highest importance, since there is no
period of sexual mania to interrupt normal social behavior. Following
are some of the many advantages that result.

1. A longer period of child-rearing without loss of reproductive capability.

2. The possibility of relatively permanent male-female relationships in a less competitive sexual atmosphere.
3. Sexual drives become more readily subject to social control.

The female sex organs do not otherwise vary a great deal among the higher primates. The protective *labia* (lips of the genitalia, see Fig. 2.4, p. 44) are rather more fully developed in women than in most other primates. On the other hand, the sensitive *clitoris* is larger in the nonhuman primates than in women, is exposed and often pendulous (except in the *Colobus* family), and even has a small *baculum* (stiffening bone) in *Cebus* (see 9.4). The small size of the clitoris in *Homo sapiens* is possibly due to one or both of the following factors.

1. The absence of any swelling of sexual skin, which would obscure the clitoris and protect it from stimulation.
2. A slight alteration in function due to a change in position in copulation (see 9.5). In particular, it is so effectively placed for stimulation during ventral copulation that excessive size is unnecessary and could be disadvantageous.

Finally, it is worth noting that the visual epigamic features that the female offers the male have moved in human evolution from the dorsal to the ventral side of her body. In place of the sexual skin, visible from behind, modern man responds to features upon the ventral surface of the female, and these epigamic features have spread from the genital region to the face. We find the development of pubic hair, of rounded breasts with their *areolae* (the sensitive skin surrounding the nipples), and of delicate facial features and lips (Goodhart 1960). From Upper Palaeolithic times, perhaps 20,000 years ago, we have definite evidence from rock art of man's interest in the epigamic sematic features of the human body (Fig. 9.3). While today many of these features are hidden by clothing, their use, like other aspects of human sexual behavior, comes under conscious control, which, indeed, may be one important reason for the development of clothes. These sematic features are positioned for face-to-face communication, and the tactile receptors they contain can establish cortical connection to effect erotic response.

9.4 *Male sexuality*

MALE PRIMATE GENITALIA have been described by Pocock (1925). The evolution of the male sex organs has not involved any remarkable changes, though there are some small differences. The human penis is more like that of the Old World monkeys than like that of the apes; only the gorilla among apes has a penis remotely approaching the size of man's. But the gorilla penis is still considerably smaller, which is surprising, considering that a gorilla is about three times the weight of a man.

A small bone or cartilage is found in the penis of all monkeys and apes, called the *os penis* or *baculum*. It extends from the body of the penis into the left side of the *glans* (the enlarged tip of the penis), which it stiffens. This bone has apparently been lost in human evolution, and it appears that the blood pressure in the glans during erection gives sufficient firmness for penetration without its support. This loss of the bone may be related to rather more gentle and careful copulatory behavior among humans.

In general, the length of the penis of Old World monkeys and apes seems to be related to the full thickness of the sexual skin at estrus, which would otherwise serve to keep a short penis out of the vagina. Among monkeys and apes the females of which do not have a developed sexual skin, the males have shorter penes. Man's long penis is possibly related to the long vagina in women, which with the labia protects the uterus from external infection.

Judging by the presence of a free-hanging scrotum and testes in most of the higher primates, the development of sperm cells is more efficient at a temperature lower than that of the rest of the body. This has been experimentally demonstrated in different mammals, including man. The testes are obviously vulnerable, but apparently this factor is of overriding importance only in the gibbon, which swings through the trees with folded legs (see Fig. 3.6, p. 68), whose testes are retained within the body wall.

9.5 Sexual behavior and copulation

THERE IS LITTLE doubt that the expansion in human evolution of the cerebral cortex and in particular of the frontal and parietal lobes has had as important an effect on human sexual behavior as on other activities. In mammals generally, sexual response depends on reflex behavior stimulated in the first place by hormones in the female and certain olfactory, visual, and tactile sensations in the male. In the evolution of man these subcortical mechanisms have become subject to excitation or inhibition by the cerebral cortex.

On the one hand, cortical excitation increases the range of stimuli that can effect response, so by association they may include many factors of no direct biological sexual significance. The rise of cortical control may also be seen in the behavior of immature individuals. As a rule, immature female animals indulge in no sexual play before the secretion of the appropriate hormones at approaching maturity; immature males occasionally do. The young female chimpanzee does show some interest in sex before maturity, but only among humans will young boys and girls (under the less rigorous repression of Polynesian society, for example) indulge in coital play involving nearly all the elements of adult behavior except ejaculation (Beach 1947).

On the other hand, the cortex may also inhibit sexual activity when a full range of valid biological stimuli is present; response to a real sexual situation may be totally inhibited. This inhibitory action of the cortex is so effective that in women sexual desire related to estrus has disappeared. The estrogen still flows as before, but its effect is no longer clearly apparent; instead of three days of sexual mania, sexual receptivity is effected by stimuli that may operate at almost any time.

It has been mentioned that the evolution of social hunting may have selected a lengthened period of sexual receptivity. It would, however, be more accurate to see the change as due to the stimulation of the female arising, not from internal factors (the hereditary hormone cycle) by a lengthening of estrus, but from external factors (such as the advances of men), which may occur at any time but which are associated in the cortex with the arousal and satisfaction of sexual desire. It is true that sexual response outside the estrous period has been observed in apes, but complete copulation is very rare indeed. However, in this feature, as in so many others, apes exhibit a shadow of the trend, which became fully evolved only in man.

A second factor requiring mention in the evolution of human sexual behavior is the adoption by man of the face-to-face position in coitus—the so-called "ventral" position, with the female supine, the male prone. An approximation to this position is found in all hominoids, whose mating positions are very variable, but, while the female gorilla or chimpanzee may lie on her back, the male will squat between her legs, not lie upon her body. When the ventral position became general among humans is quite uncertain. There are representations of human copulation dating from the late Pleistocene to Etruscan times (Fig. 9.3, C is possibly an example), and they seem to show humans behaving like animals in this respect, with entry from behind. However, pictures of animal copulations are equally common, and, in accordance with the magical interpretation of much early art, it seems possible that this animal behavior was specially adopted and represented by man to increase the fertility of the game animals. It would not be unreasonable to assume the adoption of the ventral position as man slowly became adapted to a terrestrial environment. A number of factors must have operated at that time:

1. The position is practical on the ground, while it was impractical in trees.
2. The development of the buttock (see 5.2), especially the steatopygous buttock (which contains large fat reserves and is found among Bushmen [see Fig. 11.10]), makes entry from the rear increasingly difficult.
3. The adoption of a prostrate resting position in a terrestrial animal would lead naturally to the ventral position in copulation.
4. The ventral position might have been associated with the invention of speech and the development of individual attachments between men and women and is surely associated with the ventral position of human epigamic features.

Consideration must also be given to the female orgasm, which has been claimed to be a uniquely human experience and which Ford and Beach (1951) suggest may be correlated with the extra stimulation that the clitoris receives in ventral copulation. There is, however, suggestive evidence of strong sexual response in female animals during *intromission* (full entrance of the penis) as well as before.

There is no doubt that in animals the function of the clitoris is to raise the level of sexual excitement to the point necessary for effective intromission. The gorilla is reported (Schaller 1963) to stimulate the female's genital areas both orally and digitally, and in one case even to stimulate the breast. The male chimpanzee has also been reported to

FIG. 9.3. Some of the most ancient known representations of the human figure, of paleolithic age. *A* from La Madeleine, *B* from Angles sur l'Anglin, *C* from Laussel, and *D* from Le Portel—all in France. (Drawn by Rosemary Powers.)

stimulate the clitoris orally, resulting in its erection (Ford and Beach 1951), but during copulation it receives no further direct stimulation.

However, by this point in copulation a high blood pressure has been developed in the female and the vulva and vagina are tumescent. This blood pressure has been measured in man and dog, and a high pressure subsists throughout coitus (but much longer in the bitch, in which intromission is maintained after ejaculation). Peaks of high pressure are identified by the woman as orgasm, which may be repeated: the experience is accompanied by contractions of the vagina and uterus, as well as many other subsidiary reactions.

Orgasm appears to be an intensification of the sexual response seen in other mammals, brought about by increased clitoral stimulation and associated sensations.

It appears that in human evolution the loss of the innate and predetermined urges of estrus is, as it were, balanced by the more effective but casual stimulation of the clitoris that occurs not only before but during intromission. In mammals generally, the estrus of the female initiates copulation; the male responds automatically. Among humans, copulation is brought about at any time by mutual interest and stimulation. This gives the human sexes a unique equality not found among other animals. It makes the sexual embrace a balanced experience, which may be an important factor in the structure of human society.

However, perhaps the most interesting result of this complex development was the individualization of sexual relations. Mate selection is of course common among mammals and birds, but in man the recognition of individual qualities goes much deeper. As a result of this and many other factors, more permanent bonds began to develop between man and woman. When female receptivity began to overlap the nursing of children, the man was brought into the mother-child relationship. Thus more permanent sexual ties underlie the structure of the family (but see 9.9).

9.6 Sexual dimorphism and secondary sexual characters

CHARACTERS PECULIAR TO the sexes but not directly part of the sex organs are present in the majority of animals. These differences usually develop at menarche and are called "secondary" sexual characters. Among primates, differences in size are common. In baboons, for example, males may have twice the weight of females, while in gibbons the females are the same weight or may be somewhat heavier (Schultz 1963b). When the males are larger than the females, they frequently have larger jaws, larger canines and associated structures, such as sagittal crests.

DeVore (1963) demonstrates that among Old World monkeys these morphological adaptations, which are correlates of large size and appear to serve for fighting and defense, occur primarily in terrestrial forms (such as the baboon and gorilla). The defense behavior of the male is less necessary in arboreal genera, since escape is so much easier in the trees and predators are fewer. These data suggest that sexual dimorphism has evolved with the male animal's role as defender of the primate troop as well as a result of sexual selection resulting from dominance (see 9.8).

There is, however, in this dimorphism more than survival value in the defense capability of a large male; it is equally advantageous to evolve a small female if food supplies are limited, and the limitation of food supplies is particularly apparent in the terrestrial environment. In the forest there appears to be no shortage of primate foodstuffs; the population is limited by other factors. DeVore and Washburn (1963) have shown that, with female baboons half the size of males, twice as many females can be maintained with a limited food supply than would otherwise be possible. Selection not only favors large males but favors females as small as is compatible with their social and maternal roles.

It might therefore be expected that man, as a terrestrial animal, would show considerable sexual dimorphism. In modern man, however, secondary sexual characters are somewhat limited and the difference in size between sexes is not nearly as great as in gorillas or baboons. Three factors appear to have operated to reduce sexual dimorphism:

1. In his role as defender, man has been able to turn to weapons. Size in man was not necessarily a condition of survival: a small but intelligent man would be able to outwit his enemy as well as would a more heavily built man. Although men generally are large primates, there is no longer any selective advantage in a heavy masticatory apparatus and large canines. Man's size gives him the strength necessary to use the weapons that he has developed for attack and defense and the ability to run fast when hunting.

2. Fossil evidence suggests that in human evolution individuals may have increased in size during the Middle Pleistocene. What perhaps is most noteworthy in this terrestrial genus is the large size of the females. The large size is perhaps due to two factors: first, the necessity for a large birth canal in an animal with such a large-headed fetus (with cranial capacity averaging 400 cc. at birth) and, second, the very demanding social role of the woman, who must be physically able to raise her large family as well as to undertake a certain amount of food-gathering.

3. As we shall see (9.9), there is reason to believe that something approaching a human family may have evolved quite early in human evolution. This development would have meant a considerable reduction in intermale rivalry. Under these circumstances we can posit a reduction in these secondary sexual characters that we believe may have arisen from such rivalry in the establishment of the dominance hierarchy (for example, the epigamic hair patches described in 8.9).

Evidence of sexual dimorphism in *Australopithecus* is not lacking and is of some interest. We have no reliable data about differences in stature, although they are likely to have existed, but we have some important variations in skull form. The variations are important not for their extent but for their slightness compared with those found in the terrestrial apes and baboons. In particular, there is no evidence of a large canine in any skull or of sexual difference in the size of any canines (Robinson 1956). What differences there are seem to be due to overall differences in size (and so weight) of the skull and dentition. Some skulls are somewhat larger than others from the same population, and the larger skulls have more strongly developed nuchal crests and larger temporal areas (as shown by the height of the temporal line). In about one in five individuals of *A. africanus* the beginnings of a sagittal crest can be seen, while it is present in all individuals of *A. robustus* (see Fig. 7.8, p. 184). Heavier musculature and heavier bone structure suggest a heavier male, which is hardly surprising. What is surprising is that the use of a heavy masticatory apparatus in defense was already a thing of the past. Surely *Australopithecus* must have already been adept at defending himself with weapons.

We do not know, of course, that the ancestor of *Australopithecus* showed sexual dimorphism equal to that of the modern apes—indeed, it is unlikely—but the reduction of the canine to a premolar-sized tooth must have occurred, for such a small canine is not found elsewhere among the higher primates. It is already becoming apparent in the possibly ancestral form *Ramapithecus*. We see, then, that reduction in the range of sexual dimorphism due to defense requirements is characteristic of evolving hominids. The dimorphism that remains seems to be almost entirely related to sexual functions.

Figures for average heights and weights of English men and women are given in Table 9.3 (see also Fig. 9.4). This size and weight differ-

TABLE 9.3 DIFFERENCES IN WEIGHT ASSOCIATED WITH SEX IN HIGHER PRIMATES

| Primate | MEAN WEIGHT IN POUNDS | |
	Male	Female
Baboon	75	30
Gibbon	13	13
Orang	165	80
Chimpanzee	110	88
Man (U.K.)	155	150
	(Height, 67.5 in.)	(Height, 62.5 in.)

The figures are approximate, since they are derived from small samples.

ence is the most obvious secondary sexual character that differentiates modern men and women. Besides this feature of sexual dimorphism, we find in modern man a number of minor differences, including such characters as shape of head, shape of pelvis, fat distribution, voice, body hair (8.9), growth rate, age at menarche, and many others. Some factors, such as the shape of the pelvis, are directly connected with the reproductive function; others, such as fat distribution and age at menarche, are more remotely related to sexual function. Some may be associated with sexual selection (reduction of body hair and retention of head hair), while others may be merely dependent on one of these factors (such as voice differences). Visible secondary sexual characteristics are certainly selected in modern societies, where a small proportion of individuals who do not satisfy the socially accepted requirements for sexual attraction do not succeed in finding sexual partners. The reproductive rate of such individuals is reduced by sexual selection.

This classic conception of sexual selection, introduced by Darwin, accounts for features selected by the opposite sex. Since in most primates, and traditionally among men, the choice of partner lies with the male, it follows that only the physical characteristics of the female are subject to sexual selection of this kind. In particular, we may mention under this heading the absence of facial and body hair and the overall form of the face and body. Head hair, together with well-rounded buttocks and breasts, have always been attractive to men and have no doubt been subject to sexual selection; if they did not increase the chances of a particular female's finding a mate, they did increase the chances of her mating with a genetically better-endowed male, so their joint descendents were perhaps more likely to transmit their genes to posterity (Goodhart 1960).

But there are other kinds of sexual selection: there is the selection of the "genetically better-endowed male" to consider. If this selection is not subject to female choice, it is due to the effect of intermale rivalry, which establishes the dominance hierarchy (see 9.8). As we have pointed out (in 8.9), the establishment of sexual dominance is

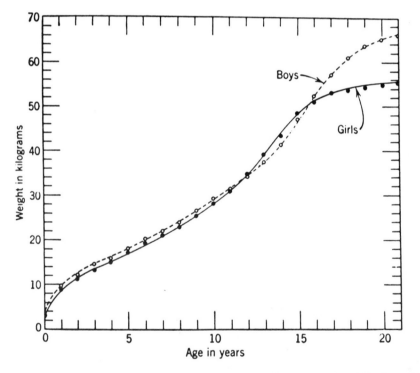

FIG. 9.4. Sexual dimorphism in man: the growth curve and adult size of males and females is clearly distinct. Growth is arrested by the hormones produced at puberty, so the smaller size of women is correlated with their earlier physical maturation. (From Shock, 1951.)

based on appearance rather than physical force, on threat rather than fight, the effect of which is that males with an impressive appearance (in the form of large teeth, epigamic hair, etc.) pass more genes to the next generation than do those less well-endowed. It is appearances that count. As a result, it is clear that male secondary sexual characters are selected not by females (except to some extent in our own society) but by intermale rivalry, which is reflected in the mating pattern.

Having discussed briefly the physiological and anatomical aspects of human sexuality in comparison with primate sexuality, we must now consider how the reproductive processes fit into the total life-span of the individual (9.7) and the structure of the society in which he lives (9.8–9.10). While sexual relationships are never, among higher primates, the main determinant of social structure, they are always important in that respect, and, at the same time, the socially controlled mating pattern affects the size and nature of the evolving deme.

9.7 The life-span of man

ONE OF THE MOST important and far-reaching differences between man and the nonhuman primates is their difference in growth rate. A slowing-down of the rate of growth and maturity is already apparent in the evolution of the primates as a whole, but the trend is greatly accentuated with the coming of man (Fig. 9.5). The period of infant dependency, which averages just a few months in most mammals, has already been extended to a year in monkeys and two years in apes. In man it is six to eight years. To these figures we must add a period of cultural dependency, which may continue even beyond sexual maturity.

At birth, the human infant is extremely helpless, as has been mentioned; in place of the rapid development of effective motor control common to most mammals, helplessness continues during a period of fast growth. The brain, which is only about one-quarter of its final size at birth, doubles in size within one year; in contrast, the brain of apes is already half-grown at birth. Compared with nonhuman primates, the human brain forms a very high percentage of total body weight in the developing infant.

The human mother must protect and nourish her infant during its period of helplessness and carry it about with her for two or three years; in contrast, the gorilla infant clings to its mother for only three or four months. The long period of contact between the human mother and child conditions the child to a need for a strong affectional relationship, which will ideally be satisfied in later life by the sexual and emotional bonds of marriage. This protracted immaturity of man provides a unique basis for socialization, intellectual development, and individualization. Retardation of growth so extreme is only possible in a social context, while in turn it is a central factor in the reinforcement of social structure and in the evolution of culture. This very slow growth rate is a unique and quite fundamental character of mankind.

Among girls, puberty arrives in two stages. The first stage is marked by the completed development of the sex organs and the appearance of the secondary sexual characters; it is termed menarche. The second stage is marked by the production of mature gametes (ova and spermatozoa) and is termed *nubility*. The ages of menarche are shown for some primates in Table 9.1. In girls nubility follows two or three

FIG. 9.5. Comparison of growth curves for man, rat, and cow, with the time scales and weight scales adjusted for equivalence. The curve for the cow is simple; for the rat it is an S-curve, and for man a double S. (From Shock, 1951.)

years later (about fifteen years of age), but in monkeys and apes it develops more rapidly.

Most mammals now enter upon their full reproductive life. Among primates, however, it seems that, while the female may begin her reproductive life at menarche, the male does not effectively do so. The mating pattern among baboons (which may be typical) is one in which the younger males are permitted by the older dominant males to copulate with the females when they first come into estrus, but after a few days one or other of the dominant males moves in and acts as consort to the female for the rest of estrus, when tumescence is maximal (Washburn and DeVore 1961). The relationship between estrus and ovulation is not known for certain in different primates, but, in general, ovulation occurs toward the end of estrus, so it appears that the older dominant male, not the younger males, will father the young. The young males appear able to satisfy their sexual drives without serious competition from the older males, but they do not contribute very much to the gene pool of the next generation until they too arrive at a position of seniority. It may be of only marginal importance, but this mating pattern also appears to reduce the incidence of son-mother matings that would result in conception, in the absence of any more direct mechanism for the avoidance of incest.

This delay in the assumption of full reproductive life among baboons is correlated with their sexual dimorphism. The females complete their growth and are sexually and socially mature at about four years, but the much larger males complete their growth and reach social maturity only about four years after reaching sexual maturity. For purposes of reproduction, therefore, there are in fact about twice as many females as males (although the actual sex ratio is 50:50). During the last four years of their growth, the young subdominant males live peripherally around the troop and protect it from predators. They are, suitably, its most expendable members. This trend is also detectable in modern man, for boys continue growth for a longer period after menarche than do girls (Fig. 9.4).

This social structure recalls in broad outline that of many African tribes, in which the young men must spend their early maturity as hunters and warriors, while the olders remain in the village. Among present-day polygamous peoples, the young men may have to wait many years to take wives, while the older men are taking their third and fourth. Though by no means universal, this kind of mating pattern allows natural selection a maximum opportunity to act through the males. Only a male who has survived a long apprenticeship both in society and in hunting will be in a position to father children. There is maximum opportunity for a weeding-out of less healthy and less intelligent males. It is possible that natural selection will in this way tend to maintain the evolution of a mating pattern most readily subject to its action, since groups with such a mating pattern will be most readily adapted to environmental change and so gain an increased probability of survival.

We can see, then, how natural selection, acting through society, can delay the full reproductive functions of adult male nonhuman primates as well as of man. Delay in the full reproductive function of adult females is, however, a uniquely human characteristic. It is primarily related to the evolution of culture, for, since one function of human parenthood is the transmission of learned behavior and culture, it is desirable that individuals themselves should have assimilated cultural traditions fully before they are called upon to pass them on to their heirs. This means that in advanced human society education (at home and in institutions) may delay marriage beyond the advent of nubility.

Traditions of learning and of culture are protected by specific (and particularly religious) institutions, and the possibility of cultural transmission is also assured in most societies by various other means. Such protection is assured widely by *rites de passage,* that is, social rites marking stages in the physical and social status of individuals. Initiation ceremonies are a case in point. Such ceremonies mark the attainment of sexual maturity and include a period of instruction in traditional tribal lore. In Western society, child education is enforced by law, while marriage is prevented by a rule of minimum age. In England, the minimum age has risen from twelve years in medieval times to sixteen years today. Those in our own society whose cultural heritage imposes the need for a long period of education experience a long delay between the coming of nubility and the onset of a full reproductive life.

It is noteworthy that from the standpoint of evolution this delay seems to be nothing new among men, for a period of activity directed to the immediate benefit of the social group has usually preceded a full reproductive role both in nonhuman primates and in humans. On the other hand, the longer period of education now offered girls makes the assumption of parenthood at nubility inappropriate. The delay between nubility and marriage is furthermore greatly extended by the recent startling increase in growth rate, which has brought the age of menarche from fifteen or sixteen years down to thirteen (Fig. 9.6). This trend, which is a complete reversal of the overall direction of human evolution toward a slower growth rate, is presumably due to changed ecological conditions associated with Western society and is perhaps an instance of genetic versatility rather than genetic change.

One clear trend in the evolution of man is the expansion in the actual amount of knowledge and skill that has to be transmitted from one generation to the next, an increase entailing an ever longer period of training and instruction. It follows then that, while the specialist aspect of this burden is taken from the parents' shoulders by the development of institutions of education, an immense responsibility

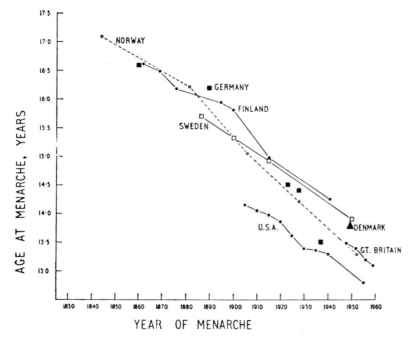

YEAR OF MENARCHE

FIG. 9.6. Age of girls at menarche, 1850–1950. This diagram shows clearly the remarkable change in the age at menarche that has occurred in Europe and North America during the last 100 years. The curious fact is that the rate of change is still constant at the present time (1965) and shows no sign of flattening out, yet there must surely be a limit in the near future to this downward progression. (From Tanner, 1962.)

still remains with the parents. The present trend toward earlier marriage in Western countries appears to be a solution neither to this problem nor to that arising from overpopulation. The age of marriage is a cultural trait of great biological importance.

Man's "three score years and ten" takes him through a slow period of development and growth and a long spell of child-rearing into an old age beyond his reproductive years. The end of woman's reproductive term of life comes with the menopause between the fortieth and fiftieth year; her survival beyond that age is an interesting and unique phenomenon of the animal world. Postreproductive primates have been recorded in zoos and very occasionally in nature but are certainly uncommon phenomena. It is not immediately easy to see how postreproductive life could be selected in evolution, since the fate of postreproductive individuals will not affect the composition of the next or future generations in terms of differences in the gene pool. However, there is one way in which a postreproductive individual could affect the birth rate, and that is by any cultural contribution (see 10.1) made to the descendant population in a social context. This possibility requires, however, a well integrated society, one in which old individuals can play a social role other than reproductive. While such conditions could conceivably apply to nonhumans, it is hard to see how a female nonhuman primate could fulfill a socially useful role in old age, since her adult social function lies almost entirely in her reproductive capacity.

There are two good reasons, however, why a postreproductive period of life can be of value to evolving man. In the first place, the slow growth of children means that they will require the presence of their parents until about fifteen years after their birth. Therefore the mother who bears her last child at forty-five will still be occupied in her function as a mother until she is at least sixty. In view of the slow maturing of the children, a postreproductive period will be essential for the survival of the last-born. There may be an advantage here in widening the gap between the average age of death and the menopause.

A second factor comes with the evolution of culture, and it applies to both men and women. The longer the period of life that must be spent learning, the more valuable to the deme will the adult individual be. Among lower animals, in which learning is not an important determinant of behavior, a quick turnover in population will make possible a faster rate of evolution, and so greater flexibility in the face of environmental change. When behavior is innate, it is known at birth, but when it is learned, it has to be laboriously acquired by each generation and cannot be lightly thrown away. Thus man's dependence on learned behavior is a reason for the selection of old age as well as for an extension in the overall life-span. The wise old man will be greatly valued in a social group for his knowledge of hunting, tool-making, and other masculine activities, and in particular for his experience of rare and occasional events, such as flood, drought, locust infestation, and so on. Similarly, the old woman will be valued for her knowledge and experience in childbirth, child-rearing, food-gathering and preparation, and other household arts. The old make a unique contribution to the survival of the cultural animal, for they are the storehouse of knowledge and wisdom.

9.8 Primate social life

THE HIGHER PRIMATES are social animals, and the adaptive advantages of a social way of life are manifold. The prime advantage probably lies in the fact that their social life facilitates learning (Washburn and Hamburg 1965). Clearly, infants can learn from their mother without the existence of social groups, or troops, as primate groups are usually called. But in social groups the amount of learning transmitted to the young can increase and broaden, and young individuals can benefit not only from their own mothers but from the experience of their peers as well as of the older members of the troop. The troop retains a pooled experience and knowledge, which exceeds that of any individual female, and it is available to the growing infant. For example, the identification of edible and inedible foods, the recognition of competitors and predators and what to fear in general, are valuable knowledge. Such knowledge can be gained secondhand from other members of the troop and does not require individual experience. Since disaster to one individual is felt as shock throughout the troop, all members may learn from such a disaster. Young troop members may even imitate behavior patterns that have been taken up by the troop in the past and that result from such vicarious experience (See Washburn and Hamburg 1965, p. 619). This socially learned behavior is the beginning of culture, and, since it is of great importance in human evolution it will be considered in chapter 10; for the present, we need only note its existence as a fundamental adaptive determinant of the social life of primates.

Beyond its facilitation of learning, social grouping must have been selected in evolution as an adaptation for mutual defense against predators (Chance 1961). The primate troop tends to be centered on the females and juveniles; the males live peripherally and, as we have seen, are equipped by their secondary sexual characters to defend the troop, and this fact especially applies to terrestrial species. At the approach of predators, such as lions or leopards, the males will always take up a position between the females and the danger and will act in concert to drive away enemies (Fig. 9.7).

FIG. 9.7. A baboon troop moving across country. Dominant adult males accompany the females with small infants and slightly older infants in the group's center. Some young juveniles are shown below the center, and older juveniles above. Other adult males and females precede and follow the group's center. Two estrous females (dark hindquarters) are in consort with adult males. (From DeVore, 1965.)

Another equally important characteristic of the social group is the maintenance of a territory of sufficient area to supply food for the troop, which is an adaptation to avoid overexploitation of food resources as well as to cut down intertroop conflict (Wynne-Edwards 1965). Owing to the richness of food supply in forested land, arboreal primate troops have quite small territories compared to terrestrial primates like the African baboons. It is interesting that territoriality is also found among certain hunting and food-gathering people, such as the Bushmen, and here the territory is even larger and may cover hundreds of square miles (Table 9.4). We shall return to a consideration of territory and food supply in the next section.

TABLE 9.4 SUMMARY OF DATA ON SOCIAL GROUPS OF PRIMATES (AFTER DEVORE 1963 AND ITANI 1965)

| | TROOP SIZE | | | Territory |
| | | | Density per | in Sq. |
Primate	Mean	Range	Sq. Mile	Miles
Langur	25	5–120	12	3
Papio (Africa)	61	12–185	10	15
Macaca (Japan)	90	4–700	—	6
Orangutan	3	2–5	—	—
Gibbon	4	2–6	11	0.1
Gorilla (mountain)	17	5–30	3	10–15
Homo sapiens				
Bushmen	20	—	0.03	440–1250
Australian	35	—	0.08	100–750

The primate troop is also characterized by an internal structure based on dominance, sex attraction, and mother-child relationships. To understand how dominance functions in effecting a stable social structure, it is necessary to consider briefly the part played by conflict in the creation of the dominance hierarchy. Conflict can take three forms: play conflict, threat, and open conflict. The controlled and harmless conflict of young animals at play gives them the opportunity to develop precise motor control and coordination and at the same time to establish their social status. In a similar way, a social structure will develop in a boy's school, both according to seniority and within a group of peers. A dominance hierarchy is established on the basis of strength, agility, and personality, and similar factors appear to operate among nonhuman primates. After completion of the period of play conflict, the structure will be maintained by threat, which alone is usually sufficient and is obviously adaptive, since it avoids the risks of wounds and diseases arising from open conflict within the troop. Every species has its own forms of threat signaling—an important form of communication in any social group. An example is shown in Figure 9.8.

Once established, the dominance hierarchy may remain stable for long periods but will of course be disturbed by the introduction to the troop of a strange animal, in which case open conflict may occur between adults to reestablish a modified social structure. Conflict, usually in the harmless form of threat, is very important in maintaining proper relations with other species and other troops. Territoriality is maintained by threat, and, for defense against a variety of enemies, sufficiently threatening gestures on the part of the males will usually scare away the intruder.

Founded on threat of conflict, the dominance hierarchy maintains

FIG. 9.8. Threat is an important means of establishing and maintaining social structure in primate groups. The actual form taken by the gesture varies among different species, but the "yawn" and lowered eyelids of the baboon are typical. (Courtesy Irven DeVore.)

the structure of the troop and orders its behavior and movement. The dominant males take precedence in the use of limited food supply, thus insuring that in a famine not all animals will starve equally but that the dominant will more probably survive (Wynne-Edwards 1965). The dominant males will also act as consort to the females at the height of estrus. The females get their status from the males with whom they associate, and the young in turn get their status from their mothers.

Any observer of primates will be struck by the amount of mutual grooming that takes place, and there is no doubt that it serves an important function in the removal of parasites and in the conservation of salt—both parasites and salt crystals are removed from the fur and eaten. But grooming serves another less obvious function: it seems to be a gesture of friendship between primates, for it is accompanied by a definite reduction in tension. On the one hand, grooming and sexual contacts sometimes intermingle, yet, on the other hand, many animals never seek grooming partners outside their own genealogies. Although our understanding of the function of grooming is as yet slight, it does appear to be a signal with a communicatory and bonding function within the troop. It acts in a positive way to hold members of the troop in affectionate interdependence (see Marler, in DeVore 1965, p. 550).

It has been said in the past that the troop is held together by sexual attraction, but that has been overstressed, since many species have birth seasons, when copulation does not occur, without loss of troop structure (Lancaster and Lee 1965). However, it would be wrong to assume that sex plays no part in social structure during pregnancy and lactation, even though it may not result in overt sexual behavior. Sexual behavior is, moreover, not merely dependent upon the estrous cycle; it has been reported from observation in Japan that the female monkeys that continue to menstruate, while the majority are pregnant, do not copulate, though sexual play and masturbation continue among males. This is an unusual situation and requires explanation. Do these females, like humans, continue to menstruate without the peak of estrus in the cycle to stimulate the males? Or is sexual activity directly inhibited by some climatic factor? It has been reported that chimpanzees have mating and nonmating seasons, and yet swelling of the sexual skin is observed at all times of the year. On the other hand, among the hamadryas baboons an increased swelling of the sexual skin was noted during the season of most frequent copulations (Lancaster and Lee 1965).

At the same time, Sade (1964) reports evidence among macaques of a seasonal cycle in the level of male sex hormones, which may determine the breeding season. We do not yet know how the cycle of birth and copulation is controlled in primates, though we do know it is related to the seasons. Investigation of this problem may throw important light on the evolution of human sexuality, with its absence of estrus.

Primate troops vary a great deal in size, from two to about five hundred, but the most common range is from ten to fifty (Table 9.4). Variation occurs even within a species in the same type of environment (Imanischi 1960). Two primates only, the gibbon and orang, adapted as they are to a fully arboreal life, exist in really small family-sized troops. Carpenter (1940) reports that the gibbon troop usually consists of a mature male and female, with one, two, or three growing young of both sexes. This troop has all the appearance of a human family, but, as we shall see, it bears no true relationship to the human family because its adaptive determinants are different. What similarities there are, however, are of considerable interest and require further consideration.

9.9 The nature and evolution of the human family

It is clear that any extrapolations that we may make from studies of primate sociology about the origins of human society are bound to be extremely tenuous and even perhaps misleading. Nevertheless, a comparative approach to this subject is the only one available to throw light on this fascinating problem. Because we believe that different human social structures are adaptations to particular environments, we cannot conclude that one is necessarily more primitive than another unless we have reason to suppose that one environment is more similar to the environment of early man than is another. For that reason we cannot recognize social survivals (that is, social vestigial characters) any more than we can recognize biological vestigial characters, so we cannot draw conclusions about the origin of human society merely on the basis of our knowledge of existing human societies.

We shall therefore use the comparative method with caution, and we shall lay special emphasis upon the equivalence of environmental conditions between the societies that we shall compare and from which we shall extrapolate.

Sociologists agree that the human family is an economic and political institution, and therefore we may suppose that it has arisen as an adaptation to economic and political demands rather than through the development of permanent sexual relationships or a particular form of territoriality, although the latter may strengthen the former. Miller has described marriage as a device "to check and regulate promiscuous behaviour in the interest of human economic schemes" (1931). We shall see that the rise of this economic unit may be an adaptation to a new ecological situation.

The relatively permanent economic group containing only one male is very unusual among primates, though in other vertebrates there are instances in which the father protects and supports the young if not also the mother. In many tropical species of birds, for example, male and female are permanently mated (Mayr 1963), while in some temperate-zone groups (geese and cranes), the young remain with their parents for a year, until they in turn reach sexual maturity in their first breeding season. A taboo on incest among these birds has been reported by some naturalists.

Such birds certainly appear to have evolved a family social group, and its basis is again economic. What is more, traditions of migratory routes, winter quarters and nesting areas, and other information appear to be transmitted from parents to young. However, the human family* has a uniquely complex structure, in that the young, of differing ages, remain with the parents because of the length of time the children take to reach maturity. So the human family develops as a result of slow ontogenetic growth, and as a correlate if not a consequence we find the incest taboo universally present (see 9.10); in turn, the family imprints behavior patterns on the growing young and forms their environment.

It is clear that the economic unit can easily be expanded to include

---

* It is well known that there are considerable variations in the modern form of the human family, but in almost all instances a nuclear family can be distinguished based on a one-male group. The one exception is that of *polyandry*—a rather rare phenomenon in which one woman is permanently united with more than one man. It appears to be an adaptation to limited food supplies and is associated with an artificial reduction in the proportion of nubile girls due to female infanticide—a most effective if brutal means of population control. See Keesing (1958) for discussion of the human family.

one man and many wives, if the man is able to support them. In modern African society the lobola (bride-price) might be interpreted as a token of wealth that makes the marriage contract economically justifiable, but, more important, it is part of a contract between two descent groups or lineages between which women can be exchanged. In modern Western society as well, marriage still retains its contractual economic basis. The more or less exclusive sexual services of the woman in marriage owe their origin in all probability to the need for the children to be the children of one man, who supports the family. Marriage in its present form must have arisen from the extended period of child-rearing, from the need to guarantee economic support for the woman even beyond her child-bearing years (see 9.7), and from the need to form strong political ties between different descent groups (see 9.10).

The human family unit is the simplest social unit in which we see a complete division of labor between adult individuals. It is to the fact that the roles of man and woman are fully complementary that the family owes its continuance and stability. Any interchange of roles, such as we see today in Western society, could threaten that stability. Economic independence for women is bound to have a fundamental effect on the economic basis of the family; its stability will then perhaps come to rest on sexual rather than economic ties.

It is not easy to see how the economically determined human family could have arisen from the primate troop. It is tempting to see the one-male groups of the gibbon as giving a clue to its origin. However, there are important differences. There is no division of labor between male and female gibbons, each being able to feed itself in the treetops. With more than sufficient food, the gibbon "family" is based on sexual and territorial considerations and can be derived from other primate troops by simple reduction. Such reduction, we may guess, might have occurred because the gibbon, being a highly mobile treetop dweller, has little difficulty avoiding predators. The larger organized troops are generally found among terrestrial species, and the smallest, like the gibbon, among the most completely arboreal species. On this basis we would expect the early terrestrial hominids to have a large, well-organized troop rather than anything approaching a family. Why should the latter arise in place of the more usual terrestrial pattern?

The solution to that problem was quite obscure until the results became available of a recent study of the hamadryas or desert baboons of Ethiopia (Kummer and Kurt 1963). These animals are described as sleeping on rocky cliffs in groups of as many as seven hundred. Baboons tend to sleep either in cliffs or in treetops (Fig. 9.9), and the shortage of sleeping accommodation in trees in eastern Ethiopia has been suggested as accounting for these very large groupings during the night, which give added protection against predators. In the morning, the large parties apparently break up into normal troops of fifty-odd animals and then further divide into family-sized one-male groups. These groups of one male, one or more females, and their young are the basic and stable groups of the hamadryas baboon, and they maintain their identity during the night gatherings. The sexual activity of the adult males is limited to their own females, even in the presence of other estrous females; only the junior males are sometimes promis-

FIG. 9.9. Baboon asleep in a tree, sitting upon his ischial callosities. (Drawn from a photograph in Washburn, 1957.)

cuous when the adult male is not guarding his partner. That this one-male group is an adaptation to food scarcity in a near-desert region is made clear by further observations (Hall 1963b) that, in time of grave food shortage, even the relatively rigid social structure of the common savanna (chacma) baboon may break down into one-male units.

We have here evidence of the formation of family groups in response to special ecological conditions—in particular, to food shortage over a wide area of open country—which is highly suggestive, for we have reason to believe that man evolved in the open plains and in ecological conditions that presented great problems in food-gathering. Before the evolution of social hunting, that is, in the early Pleistocene and before, man survived by scavenging and killing small animals (7.10) as well as by collecting roots and berries. To exploit such diffuse food resources requires a diffuse population in groups of minimum size: one-male family groups.

We do not know, and perhaps can never know for certain, the origin of the human family, but, if further research in primate behavior confirms the descriptions and deductions of Kummer and Kurt (1963), we shall have a hypothesis based on fact rather than imagination. The hypothesis shows the one-male human family to have arisen as an adaptation to the extreme terrestrial conditions of dry open plains at a time before man had developed the art of killing large mammals.

Only with the development of cooperative hunting in the Middle Pleistocene can we suppose females to have become finally and fully dependent on males for their food supply. The females would have continued to gather food, but together with their children they must have depended on the male for mammal meat. This development we may suppose also coincided more or less with the evolution of a longer life-span and a more dependent human infant, unable to cling to the hair of its mother's body. In the course of time, any mature female would have had to support two or three dependent young as well as another whose birth was imminent.

With the development of social hunting, therefore, we can see the one-male group bonded more closely, with division of labor and economic dependence. The woman reared the young and in return received meat and protection. With the necessity for cooperation between adult males, the unwritten contract of marriage between each man and woman became part of a political bond between descent groups, necessary for social stability when man could survive only through the existence of the social hunt and other concomitant social institutions (see 10.7). The social group was thus enlarged again, not this time as a promiscuous troop, but as a far-reaching political structure uniting descent groups broadly through intermarriage—all brought about by the phenomenon of *exogamy* (marriage outside the kin group).

This final stage in the evolution of the family was certainly dependent on the evolution of language and social institutions, which are discussed in the next chapter.

9.10 The evolution of exogamy

IT APPEARS THAT as a general rule different primate troops do not mix and there is limited movement of individuals between them. They are therefore said to be "closed," and since mating takes place between members of a troop they are described as *endogamous*. Inbreeding is the rule, and except among the females (in the Japanese monkey, at least), mother-child relationships are not recognized in later life; sexual behavior is believed to be wholly promiscuous.

The evolution of inbreeding among primates is remarkable, since it will tend to result in a decrease of genetic variation. Such a decrease is generally considered a disadvantageous condition because, although more genes are exposed to natural selection and nonadaptive variation is reduced, precious genetic variability is so depleted that the evolutionary potential of breeding populations is reduced. However, the social structure produces a large number of separate demes (for a troop can be nearly equated to a deme), and, at the same time, the troops are not quite closed, for there is some evidence that males leave their troop of origin and, after a period of living a solitary life, move into a new troop. In fact, a few genes probably do pass in this way between primate groups under natural conditions.

It is perhaps relevant that evolution of the monkeys appears to have been quite slow, at least since the beginning of the Miocene, for *Victoriapithecus*, a Miocene monkey, and *Mesopithecus,* from the Pliocene, are little different from living monkeys. One thing is certain: what the monkeys lost in morphological adaptability, they gained in versatility. Today the behavior of macaques is quite remarkably versatile (Kawai 1965). It also appears that monkeys can benefit from close adaptation to their environment, since they can easily follow the movement of the climatic and vegetative belts to which they are adapted across the world's surface; both their versatility and their mobility screen them from climatic and other environmental changes.

In contrast, the fast evolution of the Hominidae may prove to be correlated with the appearance of *exogamy* (outbreeding) and the resultant increase in genetic variability. The rather special conditions of primate social structure must have been broken down, the mating pattern changed, and an immense evolutionary potential released with the usual advantageous characters of *heterosis* (the selective superiority of genetic mixture in individuals).

In modern human society, exogamy is maintained by the evolution of the incest prohibition, which in turn is based on the recognition of kinship. Kinship, in turn, has probably arisen from the deepening and expansion of affectional relationships within the family. These relationships (father-son, mother-son, brother-sister, etc.), though derived from the sexual function of the parents, are reinforced by economic needs and services. The children are economically dependent on their parents for food, shelter, etc., and brothers and sisters have a subsidiary and complementary role to play in family affairs (food-gathering, baby-minding, etc.). Incestuous relations between members of the family would clearly upset the structure of the unit, since sexual and economic roles would be confused. They would also be genetically dangerous in such a closely related group as a family.

One of the simplest types of exogamy is found today among the food-gathering tribes of Africa and Australia. In these peoples, families are usually united by ties of kinship into small local groups of 20–50 individuals. A local group may "own" a well-defined area of land (comparable to the territory of primate groups) and the vegetables and game found upon it (Table 9.4). Members of the group live and hunt together and also have obligations toward one another in sickness and old age. Being kinsmen, members marry outside the group yet within the tribe, so the incest taboo usually applies throughout the group.

While this group of related families has superficial resemblances to a primate troop, the basis of its structure and breeding pattern is totally different, and, as we have seen in the previous section, it has probably arisen as a secondary development from the one-male group. Broadly speaking, it seems that the primate troop expanded into the tribe (an endogamous group), and smaller local exogamous groups developed within this wider structure. If so, we may see the appearance of exogamy as a direct development from the expansion of affectional relationships within a single descent group.

The existence of exogamy requires a social structure that stretches beyond the exogamous group. This factor results in another important difference between nonhuman and human society. Primate intergroup behavior is unfriendly and antagonistic; there is, so far as we know at present, no supergroup social structure. Human intergroup behavior can be considerably more friendly, and a social structure generally exists that relates social groups. This broad structure exists as a result of exogamy and the political relationships developed between descent groups that exchange marriage partners. It seems clear that human social life is based on kinship and intermarriage (though this is no longer very striking in modern Western society), for marriage is a contract not only between individuals but between different descent groups.

Thus a local descent group may stand in a certain relationship to other local groups of the same tribe for purposes of marriage (as well as *rites de passage*, where such ceremonies exist). Such a relationship involves periodic social gatherings, especially for potential marriage partners to meet. The gatherings commonly involve feasting and dancing, in which nubile girls and marriageable men are enabled to meet in an intimate manner under socially controlled conditions. In many peoples supergroup structures take the form of clans. In such circumstances, however, descent-group exogamy may in turn expand and enclose the whole clan, in which case the social structure will relate different clans within the tribe for purposes of marriage.

On the other hand, a reduction of the extent of the incest prohibition is characteristic of modern Western society as well as of Eskimo society. Because of the special conditions of modern life (a very dense mobile population) and of Eskimo life (a very sparse static population), a more extensive exogamy is either unnecessary or impractical.

9.11 The rise of human society

IN STUDYING the evolution of human reproduction, we have encountered a number of factors that are important in understanding the development of human society. These are now summarized.

1. Improved conditions for individual growth, both prenatal and postnatal, result in a speed-up in growth rate from conception to two years, followed by a slowing-down of growth to maturity. A long lifespan evolves with a postreproductive period, associated with the development of culture.

2. A reduction of sexual dimorphism results most probably from the use of weapons in defense and a reduction in intermale rivalry. Remaining sexual differences are of direct sexual function or arise through sexual selection.

3. Increase of cortical control of sexual behavior is accompanied by an increase in the range of effective sexual stimuli, as a result of response by association. The phenomenon of estrus is lost, and sexual behavior comes under more conscious control.

4. Evolution of a long, dependent infancy conditions a need for sexual and affectional relationships in adult life. This factor, together with the frontal position in coitus, emphasizes individualization in adult sexual relationships, which come to have powerful affectional overtones.

5. Mutual defense and the search for mates are replaced as a prime determinant of social grouping by the search for food. Social grouping is therefore in man primarily economic and only secondarily defensive and sexual in origin.

6. The human family evolves as a one-male group in response to economic needs, reinforced later by kinship structure and the incest taboo. Division of labor arises by age and sex.

7. Economic competition is replaced by economic cooperation, and marriage is an instance of such cooperation. Food competition is replaced by food-sharing, and status is not so much maintained by greed as by generosity. These changes arise from the move into a new terrestrial environment with the later, concomitant dependence on mammal meat. Hunting necessitates cooperative group activity, which stabilizes a new, broader social structure.

8. Conflict for dominance is replaced by kinship as a mechanism of social organization (though the dominance hierarchy may persist in all-male institutions). Recognition of kinship is accompanied by prohibition of incest, a universal characteristic of human society; local descent groups are exogamous.

9. Broader social groups develop with an economic and territorial

basis, and, with the further expansion of exogamy, social structures spread beyond the immediate descent group to clan and tribe.

The biological needs of living organisms are, broadly, food, sex, and safety. Among primates, these needs are satisfied within the organization of the troop. In the evolution of man we see a new social grouping arise according to this hierarchy, in response to the difficult environment of the open savanna plains, where the need for food was satisfied first by dispersion and later by teamwork. Therefore we find that economic needs determine a new kind of social structure, which is reinforced by political and sexual relations. Modern human society has evolved out of this economic-political-sexual structure, but it has been strengthened still further by other developments. The basic framework that has been outlined in this chapter was enriched and controlled by the rapid development of culture, which has brought man to his present state. A consideration of culture now follows.

SUGGESTIONS FOR FURTHER READING

A recent review of work and progress in studies of primate social life (with references) is S. L. Washburn, Phyllis C. Jay, and Jane B. Lancaster, "Field Studies of Old World Monkeys and Apes," *Science* 150 (1965): 1541-47. Some classic papers have recently been republished; C. R. Carpenter *Naturalistic Behavior of Nonhuman Primates* (University Park, Pennsylvania: Pennsylvania State University Press, 1964). A recent selection of original research on this matter is to be found in I. DeVore, *Primate Behavior* (New York: Holt, Rinehart and Winston, 1965). For a well-illustrated article comparing human and nonhuman societies see M. D. Sahlins, "The Origin of Society," *Scient. Amer.* 203 (1960): 76-87. On the social structure of tribal society see (for example) R. Linton, *The Study of Man* (New York: Appleton-Century Co., Inc.; London: Peter Owen, 1964). Examples of tribal kinship structure can be found in A. R. Radcliffe-Brown and D. Forde, *African Systems of Kinship and Marriage* (London: Oxford University Press, 1950).

$\mathcal{L}10$

Culture and Society

10.1 Culture

CULTURE HAS BEEN described, discussed, and defined at great length by social and cultural anthropologists. On the other hand, it has received very scant consideration by biologists, for it has been generally assumed to be a uniquely human phenomenon and thus outside the field of biology. But human biologists cannot avoid at least some consideration of the origin and function of this most all-pervading human attribute.

When we try to discover what culture is, we find it almost always defined as a purely human possession; Dobzhansky calls it a species character of *Homo sapiens* (1963). Most cultural anthropologists define culture as specifically human and at the same time dependent on symbolic thought or language. Kroeber and Kluckhohn (1952, p. 181) define culture as consisting of "patterns explicit and implicit of and for behavior acquired and transmitted by symbols, constituting the distinctive achievement of human groups, including their embodiments as artifacts." L. A. White, too, in a fascinating discussion, states culture to be "dependent upon symboling . . . trafficking in meanings . . . which cannot be comprehended by the senses alone" (1959).

Evolutionary biologists must approach the definition of culture differently. Our definition must not be designed *a priori* to distinguish modern human society from nonhuman primate society; it must try to define in its very simplest form that phenomenon which today is recognized to be what we call culture so that we can then see whether it can be found elsewhere in the animal kingdom and what function it performs. Let us turn first to E. B. Tylor, the father of cultural anthropologists, who, as one of the first investigators, defined man's culture as "capabilities and habits acquired by man as a member of society" (1871). More recently, Keesing (1958) has defined culture as "the totality of learned socially transmitted behavior" and Oakley (1963) has defined it as "the sum total of what a particular society practises,, produces and thinks." These definitions may seem very broad, yet at the same time they are more precise. We are not concerned, like White, with defining a discipline or, like Kroeber and Kluckhohn, with trying to grasp an abstraction. We are concerned first with what men and animals do and how they come to do it. Secondly, we must examine how human behavior and human society differ from animal behavior and animal society, so as to discover what social novelties, if any, appeared during the evolution of man.

For us, culture must be defined along these lines, as a kind of behavior acquired in a particular way: as the totality of behavior patterns of a social group of men or animals that are passed from generation to generation by learning. Thus culture is socially determined, learned behavior, and it clearly is not a specifically human phenomenon. Cultural behavior patterns are the outcome of versatility; they arise from behavioral flexibility and a capacity for imitative learning. It seems clear that behavior patterns that become part of the culture of a group must be adaptive, though in what way is often not clearly apparent. But there is no doubt that cultural behavior is an evolutionary development of the greatest importance, since a new adaptive behavior pattern developed by one member of a group may be quickly taken up by others through imitation, and such a behavioral response to the environment on the part of the deme is much faster than that made possible by genetic mutation.

From the reports of Japanese monkey behavior already referred to (Imanischi 1960, Kawai 1965), there is no doubt that cultural behavior patterns can be easily developed by social primates. During the period of careful observation of these monkeys since 1952, they have been observed to adopt a number of quite novel kinds of behavior, which have been invented by one individual, imitated by other members of the group, and then passed from generation to generation (with, interestingly enough, varying degrees of success). Food-washing and swimming in the sea are both patterns of behavior that were invented and became part of the troop's culture during the period under study. Similarly, it seems very probable that the use by chimpanzees of sticks to extract termites from their nests, reported by Goodall (1965), is a cultural behavior pattern. Haldane (1956) has reviewed the considerable evidence for cultural behavior among other mammals and among birds.

Culture has also been described as a "non-genetic adaptation," and as "an organ of human behavior" (Huxley 1958). But the first description will apply to all learned behavior, the second to material culture only. Culture is more accurately to be seen as a set of behavior patterns that are learned by members of society from members of society and that are adaptations of their society to the environment. Culture is a product of society and a property or character of society. Through culture, "behavior has reached a supraorganismal level" (Huxley 1958).

If cultural behavior is to be passed around a social group, its spread must depend on imitative learning if not instruction (1.5). It follows, then, that culture will be limited to social animals that can learn imitatively; but, given this possibility, any novel behavior pattern with a selective advantage will, under appropriate circumstances, be incorporated into the behavior of the social group in which it arises. Culture will spread by diffusion.

It is characteristic of culture that cultural techniques or traditions are passed down within an evolving group, and during their passage through time they may also change in accordance with the needs of the social group that possesses them and with their changing environment. Cultures, in fact, "evolve," not according to the mechanism of organic evolution, but independently of it. The reason for the speed of cultural change, or "evolution," should be clear. While adaptive organic mutations (that is, new genes and gene combinations) may take generations to become established and spread through a deme, new cultural adaptations may spread in one generation; they may be acquired very quickly and passed on by learning. Cultural adaptation, being fast, is also flexible and will allow numerous specializations for different ecological niches.

Huxley (1958) recognizes three aspects of culture (though they are not clearly distinct), as follows.

1. Overt acts of behavior, such as rituals (*socifacts*)
2. Material results of overt acts of behavior (*artifacts*)

3. Potential behavior, in the form of assumptions, ideas, values, intentions, etc. (*mentifacts*)

"Socifacts" are certainly the simplest and are the kind of culture not uncommonly found among animals, as has been described. We must also include here a considerable amount of primate behavior, including some elements of social structure that we know to be subject to modification. It is clear, too, that there is no hard and fast line between socifacts and artifacts. The manufacture of artifacts is only a particular sort of behavior, involving objects taken from the environment and an appropriate organ of manipulation. Birds use thorns, stones, and twigs as tools, and so do primates. Chimpanzees prepare their sticks for termite extraction. Men fashion objects with great skill to achieve a particular end. Such objects are termed "artifacts" and are indeed a clear-cut and remarkable product of human cultural behavior. Man is often defined as a toolmaker and therefore as the cultural animal, but toolmaking is really only one sophisticated kind of behavior. It is not really different in kind from other overt behavior except in its material product.

Evolution is opportunistic, and any novel behavior pattern with a selective advantage will, under appropriate circumstances, be incorporated into the behavior of the evolving deme. Such behavior is necessary to develop and maintain material culture, for the use of external objects as tools increases the effective exploitation of the environment and decreases the danger of predators. The beginnings of material culture arose when objects were fashioned from raw materials—when sticks were intentionally sharpened and stones carefully shaped.

Techniques of toolmaking are not typically learned by trial and error at different times but are invented by intelligent behavior and then transmitted as imitative learned behavior from one generation to another. Children learn from their parents not merely by imitation but also by instruction involving speech. Very simple cultural traits were certainly evolved without speech, but the real cultural advances that we associate with the Hominidae must almost certainly have awaited an adequate language. Speech alone made possible levels of abstraction that were necessary for the development of material culture and human society, for it is an accomplished kind of communication between individuals that makes possible a material culture and a complex economic social structure and maintains its integration.

Man's immense capacity for culture, which is dependent on his increasing educability (Dobzhansky and Montagu 1947), is clearly a character of great selective value, and it is surprising that its extensive development is unique in the animal world. Capacity for culture is, of course, a character that is as much a part of man and as much a part of his heritage as his hand or his pelvis, and its evolution is interdependent with all his other attributes. It is, however, possible to see how man's capacity for culture may have arisen and to examine the essential prerequisite for its evolution.

Since the transmission of culture depends upon the facilitation of learning in a social context, we can deduce that such learning, which is typical of the social primates and which in turn maintains social integration, is a *sine qua non* of culture. Behavior patterns transmitted in the social context of early primate society were the forerunners of the human behavior patterns that we call culture and, surely, were the origin of man's capacity for culture. Culture itself was a product of man's inventive genius, which was in turn the product of intelligence. We find the clear traces of culture arising in the tightly integrated societies of primates, where what has been described by Etkin (1963) as "social sensitivity" is very well developed, for social cues are cues to behavior, and social stimuli control individual response. It is in these tightly knit social groups, in which there is ample opportunity for imitative learning, that the transmission of acquired cultural behavior grows, and in which more complex behavior only awaits man's inventive genius.

It is a very important characteristic of material culture that in relation to its creator it is not only an extra-bodily organ but also part of the environment, and it is a part of the environment that affects man closely. When man's culture "evolves," therefore, his environment changes, and a new adaptation of the organic body will be selected (see chart on next page).

We therefore find man living in a fast-changing environment and adapting to it with a fast-changing culture. No sooner does the culture adapt than the environment has changed, and further adaptation is selected. In face of this ever increasing rate of environmental change, man's physical evolution runs far behind (Dobzhansky 1963), which suggests that man is ill-adapted genetically to his environment. In at least one sense that is true: without the barrier that his material culture forms between man and his environment, he would be unable to sur-

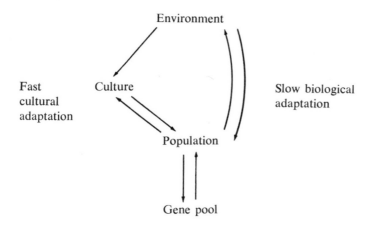

vive. But it is also open to question whether man is fully adapted in any sense, for the rate of change in his environment may appear to be outstripping even his cultural adaptations (see 11.10).

Huxley cites "mentifacts" as an aspect of culture; they are the assumptions, ideas, and values that determine man's conscious behavior. Belief in God, belief in the desirability of moral rectitude, belief in the value of the individual, are the kinds of ideas that form the basis of modern society. Ideas, which form the basis of religion and ethics, are the most sophisticated aspect of culture, for they involve conscious intelligent thought, a uniquely human capacity. This unique characteristic of mankind is of course adaptive, and it too must evolve, like other cultural traits. In general, mentifacts are by nature rather static and stabilizing in their effect; on the other hand, they can be lethal if they do not retain some degree of flexibility.

Surprisingly, one aspect of the subject of this section is well documented in geological deposits. While the remains of early man are rarely preserved, at least one kind of cultural product almost invariably survives: stone tools. The development of stone tools, which have been described as "petrified ideas," while not necessarily correlated with the the development of man's culture as a whole, does give us at least some guide to his cultural progress. And this progress is very astonishing, for it is not constant, nor is it irregular, but it is exponential: the rate of change is not constant but increases regularly.

The ever increasing speed of technological progress is evident. Developments during the three hundred years since the beginning of the industrial revolution have altered the face of the earth. Some six thousand years ago the use of metals, and before that the development of agriculture, had already changed man's environment. Even the rate of progress in agriculture and metals, though slow, was very rapid compared with the evolution of the stone-using cultures that occupied perhaps two million years. The increase of man's cultural resources was at first exceedingly slow, a painful growth of idea and technique. But, unlike evolutionary progress, cultural progress was cumulative, and both the quality and quantity of man's cultural assets have grown and have now surpassed the understanding of any single man.

Man's culture is, however, not a thing apart. It is dependent on the evolution of both speech and society itself. I shall attempt in this chapter to discuss both the internal psychological correlates of culture, such as conceptual thought, memory, intelligence, and speech, and the external correlates, such as social structure. Finally, some of the determinants of human behavior can be summarized.

10.2 Percepts and concepts

IN OUR CONSIDERATION of the evolution of man and his culture, it is necessary to refer to what has been described as man's unique mental characteristic: conceptual thought. Treatment of this subject is difficult because it involves the discussion of perception, and neither the formation of percept nor that of concept is yet well understood. What follows, therefore, is a personal and immensely simplified account of a very difficult subject, but one that cannot be omitted in any treatment of human evolution.

A *percept* may be considered to be the mental image of the external environment. Just how this mental image comes into existence is not yet known, but it is clear that it is based on two kinds of information; one is the input from the senses, and the other is the memory of previous experience. It can be shown with ease that a given percept is not necessarily a true if limited interpretation of the present environment but that it is strongly influenced by previous experience. It seems clear that in the growth and development of each individual mammal, motor investigation of the environment plays an essential part in building up its appropriate perceptual interpretation. There is no doubt that the content of perception varies beyond our understanding among the different kinds of animals, and we cannot conceive the world of a dog, for example, or of a nocturnal prosimian. Our own perception of the outside world has evolved with the primates, to which the motor component is of fundamental importance in understanding the environment. Spatial relationships must be first experienced to be later perceived, and we inherit from our primate ancestors a very spatial—a very three-dimensional—perception of our environment.

From these considerations follow two conclusions:

1. If primate perception depends so much on motor investigation, the quality of perception will depend on the extent and refinement of the motor investigation. Primates, more than all other mammals (except bats), live in a three-dimensional world; their eyes are stereoscopic, and their movements are in all three planes of space. They must have very precise ideas of spatial relationships, for arboreal locomotion involves a knowledge of space far greater than that which may be necessary to ground-living forms. The prosimians as well as the higher primates have no doubt come to perceive the environment as a three-dimensional rather than a two-dimensional pattern. The integration of spatial data from the senses to form a composite perception of the environment has clearly gone further among primates than among other groups of animals. Visual, somatic sensory, and auditory inputs will be analyzed and integrated with the motor and proprioceptive patterns. Such integration appears to take place, at least in part, among the association areas of these different sensory inputs on the parietal lobe of the brain (see 8.6).

2. Our second conclusion is that the memory component of perception is of fundamental importance and must almost inevitably come to include not merely an experiential record of events but some generalizations about spatial relationships. These generalizations are immeasurably expanded and deepened by the information obtained about the environment as a result of the manipulation of objects (see 6.6). By manipulation, the higher primate can extract an object from the environment, free it, as it were, from spatial implication, and build up a perception of it as a discrete object, not merely as part of a pattern. In time, the primate will come to perceive the environment not only as a three-dimensional pattern but also as an assemblage of objects.

Man, though a primate, is no longer an arboreal herbivore, a fact that has played an important part in the evolution of his perception.

Kortlandt (1965) records that if food or any other familiar object is given to zoo chimpanzees at a place where they are not accustomed to receive it, the apes are inclined to react to it as though it were something entirely strange, and they may even refuse to consume their meal. For apes, things tend to lose their identity when they are displaced. Among carnivores, on the other hand, a displaced food tray or other object usually causes no problem, as every dog or cat owner knows. As Kortlandt puts it, the perception of apes carries a certain quality of "thereness," that is, its position in relation to other things, for among these primarily visual creatures the patterning of the environment is still the basis of their perception. Carnivores, on the other hand, identify food primarily by scent, and no strong visual pattern contributes to their perception of it. Visual perception in primates functions to identify static objects that comprise their food; in carnivores olfactory perception functions to identify mobile objects that comprise their prey.

When man began to hunt, his perception evolved accordingly. Using his prime sense, vision, man evolved the ability to identify objects on the move without reference to their relationship to the fixed part of the environment; he saw them as totally separate from their environment. Here was a fundamental improvement in perception and something novel among land animals: a carnivore that hunted by sight.

It is clear that, first, manipulation and, later, hunting came to make man's perceptual world different from that of other primates; indeed, different from that of all other animals. Man's analytic perception, more than any other factor, opened the door to the development of conceptual thought and eventually to his remarkable culture.

Let us now turn to concepts. A *concept,* as generally defined, is an abstraction from the particular to the class. The concept "bird," for example, must be abstracted from the perception of, first, "this flying object" and, later, "that flying object." The concept "bird" does not apply to "many birds" or "all the birds I have seen" but to all birds possible in space and time. Similarly, the concept "food" applies not to "this food" but to all possible and potential food—fruit not yet plucked, animals not yet hunted. Consideration of the evolution of perception, such as we have attempted, seems to imply some degree of abstraction from experience, from the particular to the class. The abstraction may not have gone far, and it may not be complete as a concept, for intermediate stages of abstraction can exist. Nor is such abstraction conscious, for perception is not a conscious activity. But it does seem likely that conceptual thought may perhaps have had its origin in the classification of experience that was necessary for the sophisticated interpretation of the environment involved in perception. It seems likely, then, that concepts form part of the mental activity of animals, but there may still be an important distinction in the mental activity of man, for thinking is a conscious process, and so, it follows, is conceptual thought. Apes can deal intelligently with objects here and now—objects they can see and the function of which is clear. They can be trained to carry out activities that appear to show foresight, and they can learn appropriate behavior for future needs. For example, chimpanzees will select straws and prepare vines (by stripping off side shoots), even when they are out of sight of any termite hills, and then set out to visit a known but distant group of hills to obtain termites (Goodall 1965). Apes in zoos will use sticks to reach bananas too high above them to be plucked by hand and will pile up boxes for that purpose; yet they have limited creative and imaginative ability. An experiment was performed by Köhler (1925) to demonstrate the limitations of ape mentality. He constructed a box loosely out of sticks, so that they looked like boards. When the chimpanzees were presented with bananas out of reach, they were unable to see, within the structure of the box, the sticks they needed to get the fruit. Thus, an ape is unable to make a tool out of a natural object; he is able only to use a natural object as a tool with, perhaps, slight modification. An ape cannot conceive the tool without seeing it. He cannot see the stick in the plank or a hand-axe within a piece of rock. This man alone can do.

Freedman and Roe (1958) have suggested that frustration may well be one prerequisite in the development of conceptual thought; it is certainly a component of it. If a biological need arises and is not quickly satisfied, the requirement for such satisfaction will appear in the mind, not as a particular object, perhaps, but as a generalized one. Thus frustration may bring with it imagination, and imagination is the consciousness of sets of concepts, which are the classification of experience. Man, having in his possession the concept of a small cutting stone, can look for it in a rock. He can see the possibility if its manufacture in future time, even though he may not have it at present. Abstraction means escape from the present, escape for man's mind from the immediacy of life. It has been said that what distinguishes man from animals is the length of time through which his consciousness extends. In animals, this dimension is small, stretching a little way into past and future; in man, it grows both qualitatively and quantitatively. The evolution of conceptual thought gives man greater power to live in the past and in the future by abstraction from the past.

To summarize, we find in mammals evidence for a classification of experience, which might be called unconscious conceptualization. This sort of classification, at even a very low level, seems to be necessary for the development of perception. As perception improves and incorporates more data from sensory investigation, especially in the higher primates, we find the probability that certain associational patterns of such data are crystallizing as concepts that might be equated with "things" and perhaps with relationships. Human conceptual thought appears to be characterized particularly by its conscious nature, but it is no doubt the result of a steady process of evolution from less conscious and indeed unconscious concepts in primates. Man's achievement was the fully conscious concept of things he does not possess but needs; the recognition of game, weapons, women, or children as classes brought with it the classification of more and more of man's environment and the possibility of foresight of future needs. Man, leaving behind the narrow limits of present time experienced, entered the broad expanse of past memory and future concepts. His foresight depends upon abstraction from the past in a manner that is termed intelligent (see 10.4).

But the conscious concept did not appear unaided. It seems probable that it was finally evoked by the use of symbols, gestures perhaps, but more often words, which make up language. The concept "bird" could be brought into full consciousness only by its identification with the word symbol "BIRD". The word symbol was the twin of the conscious concept, and it seems probable that they were born together and grew together.

As we find language in man today, it is not an inborn reflex, but the capacity for speech and conceptual thought is certainly innate; only the symbols themselves must be learned. From the kind of vocal signaling discussed later in this chapter has evolved a totally new structure of complex sounds to express not only perceptions and emotions, which animal signaling expresses, but finally concepts, and with them speech was established.

What, finally, are the neurological correlates of conceptual thought? We cannot expect to find a concept in the brain, for the brain is a living system, not a collection of bits. We can, however, point to one fascinating principle, which may in time become more clearly established than it is at present. As we have seen, the brain is a spatially organized and oriented organ in which the two sides are related by contralateral connections to the opposite sides of the body, and in turn by sensory input to the two halves of the spatial environment. Thus sensory input and motor elaboration within the brain are spatially organized. There are, however, some brain functions that are non-spatial, and they include all physiological homeostatic control mechanisms (such as body temperature, heartbeat, breathing, etc., controlled by the hypothalamus). In primates, we can add perception of depth derived from stereoscopic integration (see 3.7) and, in man, concept and word memory (see 10.3). Spatial relationships involving depth and distance may appear to be predominantly spatial concepts, but they are not *of* space, they are about space; in themselves they are spaceless and concerned with dimensions rather than patterns.

We do not know accurately the site in the brain of concept and word memory, but we do know that the so-called "primary speech area" is concerned with both these things and that it is to be found on one side of the brain only (see 10.6 and Fig. 10.3). It is shown by Penfield and Roberts (1959) to occur on the left parietal lobe only, in what has been called "the association cortex of association cortexes" (see 8.6). On the other side of the brain, in the same area, notions of space appear to be elaborated, and damage here often leads to disturbances of form and space recognition, body image movement, and spatial interactions.

We have seen that an object that can be manipulated is in some way freed from complete spatial implication and can be "handled" mentally, apart from its environment, as a concept. Such a concept does not need spatial representation in both hemispheres of the brain; representation on one side is sufficient. Equally, concepts of spatial relationships are not in themselves spatial representations, and they too require representation on only one hemisphere. It therefore appears that the neurological correlate of conceptual thought may prove to be unilateral representation in the cerebral cortex. Concepts based on objects, and other abstractions that can be symbolized, are possibly represented on one parietal lobe; spatial relationships (less conscious and not symbolized) appear on the other. If this correlation proves to be correct, it is a valuable insight into one aspect of brain function.

10.3 Memory

MEMORY IS A PSYCHOLOGICAL and neurological attribute of fundamental importance in the evolution of animals. By this term I do not refer to the information recorded in the DNA molecule, which is passed from generation to generation, though this might be termed "racial memory" (see 1.3). I refer rather to information recorded in the brain during the life-span of an individual. Penfield and Roberts (1959) distinguish in man three levels of memory, and they will form a useful basis for our discussion. In the brain, however, they may not be neurologically distinct from one another.

1. *Experiential memory.* Experiential memory is a neuronal record of the stream of experience. This remarkable property of the brain appears to preserve *in sequence* all the experiences of which an organism is aware (not necessarily consciously) during its life. The extent of development of this phylogenetically old memory cannot be precisely established in animals, but its existence can be postulated as a necessary basis of learned behavior. Learning necessitates recording the sequence of events of any action and its accompanying experience, and such a record must be available for comparison with future sequences of experienced events. This memory operates at the subconscious level, and, even in man, learning can be and often is wholly unconscious. Thus, when one meets a person, the degree of familiarity of his face will be instantly known, and an appropriate greeting will follow.

Every experience is automatically compared in an instant of time with all other equivalent experiences, every new face with all other known faces. Normally it will not be possible to recall the previous experience at will; familiarity will not necessarily be accompanied by a full conscious knowledge of the previous circumstances of the meeting. However, it is interesting that ease of recall, both conscious and subconscious, will depend on the amount of emotion that accompanied the original experience. This is a fascinating device, which speeds up the learning process in all animals. Biologically important experience is accompanied by emotion—fear, pain, pleasure. In some way, such emotion (typically accompanied by the release of certain hormones) impresses the neuronal record of the experience more deeply in the brain. Thus, the learning of biologically useful behavior is facilitated at the expense of biologically useless behavior. Man, however, has to face the problem of learning facts that are not in a context of emotion; he has evolved further levels of memory record.

2. *Conceptual memory*. Conceptual memory may be considered to be the accumulation of abstract concepts about experience. It is the record of classified experience in no time sequence rather than a full sequence of particular *referents* (that is, individual events and objects). At its simplest level it is little different from experiential memory, for in the recognition of a face the mind will "present" known faces as a class, ready for comparison. In a dog's experience of rat-catching, the dog will already have all rat-catching experience, as it were, classified for reference, and he will draw on this experience as he tackles his dangerous task (for rats have sharp teeth). But I do not suppose any abstraction is fully made. If a dog is told "rat," he will look excited and ready to spring, but we may guess that he will experience the emotion and sequence of his last, or his most emotional, rat hunt. The abstract concept "rat" is of no biological value to him, but it is interesting that if it was developed it probably resulted from his master's use of the linguistic symbol "rat." For a dog, the meaning of the word is learned by hearing it at different rat-catching experiences, and, if an abstraction is to be made, it is made with the use of that symbol.

But, in man, conceptual memory goes much further. We can record classes of objects and our experience with them (cars, car-driving), and we can also record emotions without attached objects (love and hate) and classes of experience, such as emotion itself. Beyond this, we can continue to abstract and classify indefinitely to such a point as that of the concept "entropy." Second-order abstractions and others even more remote from direct personal experience are certainly confined to humans, and in view of the importance of symbols in the handling of abstractions (such as $e = mc^2$), it seems unlikely that even the lowest level of abstractions are commonly extant in animal psychology.

3. *Word memory*. The distinction between conceptual memory and word memory is made by Penfield and Roberts on the basis of both clinical and everyday experience. It is not uncommon to recall a concept (for example "stork") but to forget the word symbol, so that one is forced to describe the concept ("you know, those white birds, the kind that nest on rooftops, steeples, etc. What are they called?"). It is even possible to learn the concept without ever knowing its word symbol. ("I have often wondered what those large black birds that nest

in groups in treetops are called"). Equally, it is easy to forget the meaning of a word that was once known ("I have forgotten the meaning of 'solipsism' "). Words can be learned that have no conceptual basis ("abracadabra"). The distinction seems clear. In clinical studies, electrical stimulation may result in the recall of words without concepts or, on the other hand, concepts without their word symbols (described with much difficulty), a condition known as aphasia. Evidence strongly suggests that concept and word memory are closely interconnected and evolved together but are nevertheless distinct.

It appears that concept-word facilitory circuits develop and become fixed as in a conditioned reflex; the nerve cells are quickly habituated to the passage of impulses through a repeated pattern. As Penfield and Roberts (1959) point out:

> A man listening to a speaker may follow the man's words, ignoring the concepts: or he may attend only to the concepts of which the words are symbols, ignoring the words. If this listener is bilingual, he may fail to notice what language the speaker had used.

Word symbols may be learned with immense speed by a human child; every normal child learns virtually an entire language by the age of five, and in a bilingual household a child can learn two languages by the age of six. A nine-year-old boy has been known to understand, read, and write nine languages fairly fluently; a mature man many more. It is noteworthy that the units of language are words, not letters; words are heard, and words are read. Chinese writing, which, like ancient Egyptian, is based on ideograms—that is, discrete concept symbols— runs closer to brain function than does Indo-European writing, with its limited alphabet. The basis of reading is word recognition, not word analysis.

The relationship between these different kinds of memory and the sensory input from the environment, which has been discussed in chapter 7, is summarized in the simple diagram on p. 301. It will form the basis for our further discussion of brain function.

10.4 Intelligence

A VERY USEFUL DISCUSSION of the distinction between learning and intelligence has been published by Herrick (1956, p. 354). We may define learning as a pattern of constructive activity performed unconsciously or consciously; the act of learning may be a purely empirical process without any end in view, but its outcome will be a kind of knowledge—an adaptive behavior pattern. The capacity to learn has evolved steadily throughout the animal kingdom, and Rensch (1956) has shown that it has evolved with the increase in brain size. The processes of learning and intelligence are closely connected and have something in common, but there is certainly some distinct feature of human mental activity that it is convenient to define as "intelligence" and that can be distinguished from a highly developed capacity to learn.

Intelligence has been defined as the relating activity of mind—the ability to realize the connection between discrete objects and events. It clearly involves imagination, which may be considered to be the presentation from the experiential memory of memory traces—knowledge—not obviously directly connected with the immediate experience. It may involve conscious recall of memory, but the significant feature of imaginative thought is that a much broader range of memory traces is brought to the interpretation of day-to-day experience than in the process of simple unconscious learning, for only thus could the imaginative connection between events be realized.

In man, the everyday distinction between intelligence and the capacity to learn is not always immediately clear. For example, expert linguists or stenographers have learned complex skills without necessarily being unusually intelligent, and even professors may be famous for their learning rather than for their native brilliance. In contrast, a comparatively ill-educated man may be highly intelligent. But intelligence cannot exist alone, it is a capacity that interacts with knowledge (which in man may be considered to be the accumulation of experiential and conceptual memory). Acquired knowledge is the fuel with which intelligence burns, without which intelligent action is impossible. "Intelligence integrates knowledge and gives it direction"; it is a conscious and "purposively directed mental process with awareness of means and ends" (Herrick 1956, p. 367).

The neurological seat of intelligence cannot be defined, for it is not a specific activity but a very generalized facilitory system. It is a method of handling knowledge as a whole. Its evolution is correlated with the evolution of the cerebral cortex, but that does not mean that the cortex is necessarily the seat of intelligence. On the other hand, the function of the cortex is necessary for intelligent activity because of its essential role as input analyzer and memory bank.

In the accompanying diagram, an attempt has been made to develop our diagram of memory structure (see 10.3) to indicate very simply the part played by mediating mechanisms in mental activity, and in particular the part played by intelligence. Mental activity means, broadly, the neuronal mechanisms that operate between stimulus and response. It effects response according to the stimulus offered by the environment, and such response may be behavioral or physiological. Physiological responses are automatic and inborn (adjustment of body temperature, salivation, etc.) and do not concern us here (see 1.4). Behavioral responses are often learned and may even follow intelligent thought.

From the diagram we see that we can consider behavior to be motivated in three ways, by three levels of mediating mechanism. Phylogenetically the most ancient is the innate kind of mediation. This is believed to involve the transmission of the impulse between stimulus and response through an inherited pattern of nerve paths. The response can be modified only by inhibition.

The second type of mechanism is already found in lowly invertebrates (such as the flatworm), and here we have the beginnings of the capacity to learn by the conditioned reflex. In this second kind of mediating mechanism, the relevant cerebral facilitory circuits are activated by the process of learning, the circuits are conditioned by habituation, until the appropriate response follows automatically upon the stimulus (Sperry 1955).

In the most advanced organisms, conscious thought can determine the response according to what amounts on each occasion to an original assessment of the environmental situation. Unconscious habit (conditioned reflex) can now be superseded by the phylogenetically new and flexible approach that we call intelligent. Of course, men do not always act intelligently; a vast amount of our behavior springs from unconscious conditioned reflexes, but, while activity that was originally intelligent may eventually tend to condition our behavior, it is in its origin at least partially free from previous patterns of activity. Truly intelligent thinking (if such a thing is possible) may be considered to be free from the direct influence of any existing cerebral facilitory activity. When, therefore, intelligence mediates our behavior, it carries our response far beyond that of the conditioned reflex into a totally new realm of flexibility and adaptability. For, on the basis of the refined input analysis that the human brain can provide, a much more precise and delicate assessment of the environment is available, and, in turn, intelligence makes possible a much more exactly and delicately appropriate response. With the considerable development of intelligence that man possesses, the possibilities of novel behavior are practically infinite, and from this remarkable development of the human mind has come man's culture and his genius for invention.

10.5 Communication and speech

SOME FORM OF COMMUNICATION is almost invariably found among sexually reproducing animals both vertebrate and invertebrate. As might be expected, it reaches its greatest development among social animals (such as bees or prairie dogs), but, even among solitary animals, some signaling devices are used. Those which precede mating and are termed "courtship" are particularly striking.

In our study of human evolution, however, we have to consider in particular the kinds of communication that have evolved in human society and make social intercourse possible. Among primates we have to recognize the existence of olfactory signals (see 8.4), especially during estrus, as well as tactile and visual signals. The development of the sexual skin in baboons is a clear instance of a visual signal, as are the bright markings on the face of the male mandrill. As a gesture of aggression, the male will also display small areas of pale skin above his eyelids and open his mouth wide to demonstrate his magnificent and frightening dentition (Fig. 9.8). It is significant that dogs have evolved a fairly complex visual system of communication, which depends not only on facial expression but also on the position and movement of the tail and indeed on the whole body (Fig. 10.1).

But facial movements have in fact probably evolved further as a means of communication among primates than among other groups of animals. Figure 8.14 (p. 237) shows that the chimpanzee has a range of facial expression that is not very far short of our own. Perhaps among humans slight changes of expression are both more readily made and more easily perceived than they are among apes, but there is no doubt that facial expression has evolved as an advanced form of primate communication.

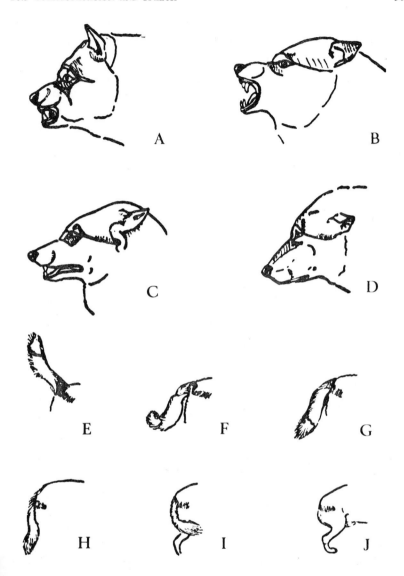

FIG. 10.1. Examples of visual communication in dogs. *Above,* some facial expressions: (*A*) confident threat, (*B*) threat with some uncertainty, (*C*) very weak threat, (*D*) uncertainty and suspicion. *Below,* some caudal expressions: (*E*) self-confidence in social group, (*F*) uncertain threat, (*G*) normal carriage (in a situation without special tension), (*H*), depressed mood, (*I*) and (*J*) complete submission. (From Schenkel, 1948.)

We must consider here in much more detail the so-called vocal-auditory signaling, which does not depend on visual behavior and so can be used over distances or when an individual is visually occupied in some other way. This type of signaling has evolved into speech, which has made possible man's greatest cultural achievements. Such a system of signaling by sounds, which among animals is termed a "call system," is widespread among birds and mammals and is usually concerned with one of five behavior factors (Hediger 1961), as follows.

1. A warning signal in the presence of an enemy
2. Signals concerned with mating and territorial possession
3. Signals relating to mother-child contact
4. Signals concerned with maintaining social structure
5. Signals announcing food

In any integrated social animal group the importance of such calls will be immense. Monkeys and apes are known to be the most continuously noisy animals extant—only the barking of a pack of hunting dogs might be comparable but is not such a continuous phenomenon. Schultz (1961) has written:

> The orgies of noise, indulged in especially by howlers, guerezas, gibbons, siamangs, and chimpanzees, seemingly so repetitious and meaningless, are probably at least as informative to the respective species as most after-dinner speaking is to *Homo sapiens*.

He comments:

> Without the hearing of sounds, produced by their own kind, monkeys and apes would never have become the intensely social animals that they are. Sounds of a surprising variety serve continually for the contact between members of the group, for the orientation of mother and young, for the information of the entire group about possible danger, and, last but not least, for scaring enemies of different or the same species and even for warning rival groups away from the territories already occupied.

Although monkeys make a lot of noise, the amount of information transmitted by their calls is not necessarily greater than among other mammals, for a great proportion of it falls into Hediger's fourth category above, dealing with social structure. In particular, Kortlandt (1965) claims that, relative to brain weight, signaling ability is greater among dogs and wolves than among any apes. No one will deny the remarkable ability of sheepdogs to respond to a wide variety of auditory signals, and, since dogs are social carnivores, their signaling system almost entirely falls under Hediger's fifth heading—food. This function also applies to the visual signaling system of bees (discussed in 1.5). Signaling is closely related to food-getting, and it reaches a peak among social carnivores.

Dogs, like men, sometimes hunt animals bigger than themselves, and, as we have seen (7.11), social hunting requires cooperation, endurance, intelligence, foresight, and a system of communication. If apes do not talk, it is not so much that their speech apparatus is very different from our own (the differences are slight, as we shall see in 10.6) but that, being browsers, not hunters, they have nothing so essential to say. Speech is part of man's behavioral adaptation to his new life as a social carnivore. As among dogs and wolves, human communication came to serve an absolutely essential function, and for the quite complex organization of the hunt, sounds came to carry very precise meanings. It is not a coincidence that dogs and men understand each other so well today; until recently they both led the same kind of life, that of the social carnivore. As we shall see (10.8), advanced communication is not the only psychological attribute that they have developed in common.

However, though a call system and a language are both means of communication, they are quite distinct. Hockett and Ascher (1964) have shown that there are very significant differences between them, so many in fact that it is difficult to trace the possible course of the evolution of one into the other. These differences may be summarized as follows.

1. Calls are mutually exclusive. That is, an animal cannot emit a complex double call with some features of one call and some of another. Only one call can be emitted at a time. This situation is described as "closed"; language, in contrast, is "open," in the sense that we can freely emit utterances that are entirely novel combinations of sounds.

2. A call is emitted only in the presence of the appropriate stimulus; a call system does not show temporal or spatial displacement. Speech, on the other hand, does; we speak freely of things out of sight, in the past, future, or even nonexistent. This capacity of speech is based on thought processes discussed in the preceding sections.

3. The differences between the sounds of any two calls are total. Speech, on the other hand, is the elaboration of a limited number of components of sound that in themselves have no meaning but, according to their pattern, may have an infinite number of meanings.

4. The call system is probably to a great extent inborn, so the relationship between stimulus and response is genetically determined and somewhat inflexible. Language, on the other hand, is learned, and its transmission must depend on man's capacity to memorize and vocalize. However, this capacity for speech is a genetic endowment, for no amount of effort will teach a nonhuman primate to speak. The actual process by which the primate call system might have evolved into human speech has been discussed by Hockett and Ascher (1964) and falls outside the field of this book.

10.6 The evolution of speech

THE ACT OF SPEAKING uses a set of body parts of quite diverse primary function. They have been taken over for this new secondary function more or less without modification and without interfering with their previous function. The speech apparatus includes the *larynx,* tongue, and lips, and while these organs must work closely together they are controlled by motor nerve supplies of very different origin in the brain. At the same time, as Spuhler (1959) has pointed out, while such coordinated muscular movement usually requires adjustments from proprioceptors, they are absent from the important laryngeal muscles, and feedback control comes by way of the ear. The only place where the different motor organs and steering apparatus of speech could be connected is in the cerebral cortex. This suggests that the corticocortical connections that make speech possible are phylogenetically new and their appearance is probably correlated with the evolution of the human cerebral cortex.

But before further consideration of the cortical speech areas, it is necessary to understand how the larynx, tongue, and lips came to effect speech. The few slight evolutionary changes that are believed to have effected the speech apparatus of evolving hominids have been described by DuBrul (1958) and can be summarized as follows.

1. As we have already seen (7.5), the chin has been formed in such a way as to avoid any further decrease in the space that forms the floor of the mouth. This floor is effectively sealed (Fig. 10.2) by a hammock-like diaphragm of the *geniohyoid muscle,* which lies be-

neath the tongue and can raise and lower it, aided by the tongue musculature.

2. The relative shortening and broadening of the jaw has brought with it a shortening of the tongue. The *genial* (anterior) and *hyoid* insertions of the tongue are brought closer together, and the base of the tongue is thrown back into the pharyngeal area; the whole is quite thick and bulbous.

3. The *hyoid bone* and larynx have also retreated a little down the neck, so the *epiglottis* and *soft palate* are separated by a small space called the *pharynx.*

4. The *digastric muscles* have been slightly rearranged, so that they disturb the stability of the hyoid bone as little as possible, and have

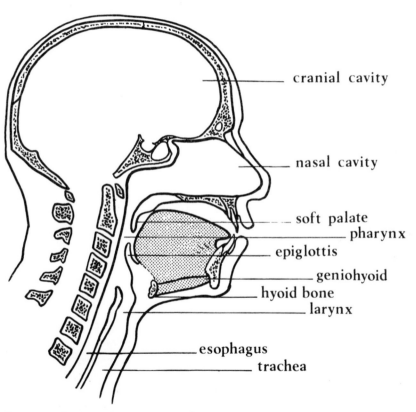

Fɪɢ. 10.2. Section of human head showing structures concerned with speech production. The tongue and its musculature are shaded.

moved apart to allow up-and-down movement of the floor of the mouth (Fig. 10.3).

The result of these small changes is that the nasal cavity can be closed off completely so that expelled air can be shunted through the mouth and the tongue and lips can move freely to interrupt this flow of air. The actual sounds of speech are formed by the voice box, or vocal cords, in the larynx. Here vibrations are set up in the expelled air and are modified in the mouth. The shape of the tube formed by the larynx, pharynx, and mouth determines the vowel sounds upon which the consonants are imposed by the tongue and lips.

It seems that the really important physical human character is the possession of the pharynx—the short space between the epiglottis and the soft palate. Here is the tube that make possible resonant human *phonation* (articulation of sounds). The distinction between man and apes lies not in man's ability to make sounds but in the kinds of sounds he makes and the remarkable way in which he interrupts his resonant

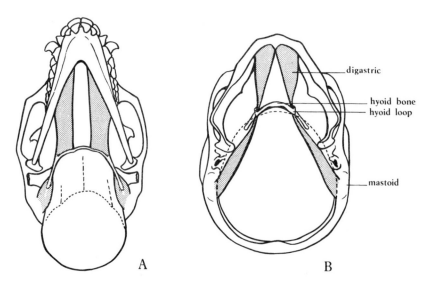

FIG. 10.3. Diagrammatic basal views of the skull of a monkey (*A*) and of man (*B*). In the monkey, the digastric muscles are attached to the hyoid bone; in man, two fibrous loops are formed on the bone through which the muscles pass. In man, the posterior parts of the two muscles are also farther apart to make room for the neck (which has moved forward) and the tongue. The dotted line shows the approximate extent of the brain in each animal. (Redrawn after DuBrul, 1958.)

notes with the consonants of speech. Movements of the mouth concerned with speech are not greatly different from those concerned with sucking or swallowing. Just as the sucking reflex concerns the lips and tongue, so the consonants are formed: *p, b, m* at the lips; *d, 1, n, t* at the tip of the tongue; *g, k* at the tongue base. The proximity of the tongue to the larynx and sides of the mouth may also form gutturals and clicks in certain languages.

As Andrew has demonstrated (1965), the baboons show us how this production of speech sounds may have arisen. In baboons a common form of communication is lip-smacking—a display derived from movements of the lips and tongue that they use in grooming. Lip-smacking is a not uncommon greeting among higher primates, but the baboons alone emit a grunt at the same moment. These grunts, modulated by the tongue and lip movements, sound very much like human vowels and are produced in exactly the same way. The plains-dwelling baboons and the plains-dwelling ancestors of man shared a way of life that depended on group cohesion and structure. It is perhaps not a coincidence, therefore, that baboons share with man the ability to make vowel sounds modulated by tongue and lip as an aid to within-group communication.

Speech, however, is more than complex sound. It is the act of codifying thought in sets of controlled and connected sounds, and such codification occurs in the cerebral cortex. The primary motor area for speech, which controls movements of the lips, tongue, etc., lies in the *motor gyrus,* as shown in Figure 8.10 (p. 226). In speech and writing, impulses must pass from these areas through the different nerves to the speech apparatus or hand. The resulting movements of the speech apparatus musculature in vocalization and the precise movement of the hand in writing are conditioned reflexes. But the motor gyrus itself is not, of course, concerned with associating words and concepts.

Evidence from cortical excision and electrical stimulation experiments has shown, according to Penfield and Roberts (1959), that the parts of the cortex concerned with the source of speech symbols and concepts lie (as we have seen) for the most part on one side of the brain only, the so-called "dominant" hemisphere, usually the left. (Damage to that hemisphere in early life will result in displacement of the so-called speech areas to the right hemisphere). These speech areas are shown in Figure 10.4. They consist of the parietal area, which appears to be most important, and *Broca's area* on the frontal lobe.

FIG. 10.4. The three speech areas of the cerebral cortex. The parietal-temporal (*1*) is the most important; the frontal (*2*) "Broca's area" is the next most important but has been found to be dispensable in some patients; the superior frontal (*3*) is dispensable and lies in the supplementary motor area. The first two are found in the dominant hemisphere only; the third is duplicated on both sides. (Redrawn from Penfield and Roberts, 1959.)

(The parietal area on the right [nondominant] side is concerned with awareness of body scheme and spatial relationships; see 10.2) It is of great interest that this parietal speech area overlaps the parietal association area (see 8.6), which has been claimed to be found only in man, as well as the interpretive cortex of the temporal lobe.

In modern man there appears to be a high negative correlation between the side of the dominant hemisphere and left- and right-handedness. The majority of people are right-handed and have left cerebral dominance, while at least half the left-handed people have right cerebral dominance. The evidence suggests that this hemispheric dominance with preferential use of limbs is a character found only in man. It is also interesting that it is not found at birth but emerges in the course of growth, coinciding with the development of speech from about two to twelve years of age.

Sperry (1965) has done some remarkable experiments with the help of two patients in which the *corpus callosum*—the nerve tracts connecting the two hemispheres—have been surgically severed. These experiments show that in the patients only the activities of the right side of the body (with nerve supplies to the dominant left cerebral hemisphere) are reported to be conscious; the left side of the body can be shown to behave quite independently, and the patient is not able to report such activity as conscious experience. We also have confirmation that speech and writing are unique correlates of the dominant hemisphere and that speech is necessary to express consciousness. Unfortunately, the experiments do not show whether consciousness is also a correlate of the nondominant hemisphere and therefore whether or not it is confined to animals with a means of symbolic representation.

All this evidence points strongly to the fact that speech is a genetically determined character of modern man. The importance in this respect of the inferior posterior parietal area of the cortex, which is absent or at best rudimentary in other primates, makes it highly probable that this character was selected and evolved in the Middle Pleistocene, at which time we know that man's cranial capacity very quickly increased. It seems equally probable that the slowing-down of the postnatal growth rate occurred at that time, with the result that, in each individual, speech could develop during the slow maturation of the brain. Language, the actual words we use, is part of culture; this remarkable and uniquely human kind of behavior rests on man's peculiar genetic endowment, which gives him his large, slowly maturing brain and his ability to verbalize.

10.7 *Social stability and social institutions*

THE EVOLUTION AND SURVIVAL of a cultural society depends, as does that of a deme without culture, on factors of variability and stability. Just as a population of animals evolves by the stabilizing action of natural selection upon a random source of genetic variability to produce a controlled and more or less steady evolution, so society evolves by a process of variation channeled by stabilizing factors. The source of variation lies in the infinite variety of human behavior and invention, and the factors that stabilize this variation are just as important to the survival of society as are those effecting it. The individualistic and imaginative nature of man makes possible an immense variety of behavior patterns, and it is characteristic of social institutions both among higher primates (the dominance hierarchy) and among humans (one-male grouping) that they promote stability in these patterns and in effect protect society from anarchy. Thus the potential plasticity and flexibility of individual behavior, although precious sources of novelty, are controlled in man by social sanctions and other properties of religious and legal institutions. Such institutions protect and transmit both sanctions and knowledge, which are necessary to integrate and maintain social structure and the onward life of the social group.

Some of the most important ways in which social stability may be maintained will be briefly considered, for, although the variety of human customs and beliefs is endless, social behavior and situations are everywhere basically the same. The following stabilizing factors have been selected in cultural evolution because they have helped to insure the survival of human societies.

1. In preliterate societies, traditional knowledge (folklore) is preserved in ritual form by, for example, religious institutions. This function of religious and similar institutions is also carried through into literate society.
2. The integration of the social group, its cohesion, is maintained by the direction of certain sentiments toward a symbolic center.
3. Cohesion may also be maintained by economic bonds of a ritualistic kind as well as by the real economic bonds that are its basis.
4. Individual behavior is controlled and oriented toward social integration by a system of religious and legal sanctions.

Each of these stabilizing factors will be discussed.

1. The preservation of a body of knowledge essential to the social group is an important factor in maintaining continuity in social life and is the basis of tradition, which helps to promote regularity in behavior patterns. Not only knowledge about how to behave but also more abstract knowledge about the supposed bases of human existence are preserved in preliterate societies in the form of ritual (a verbal and behavioral statement) or myth (a verbal statement). Both ritual and myth are means of condensing and encoding knowledge; both are, characteristically, regularly enacted in public as a means of maintaining their power and integrity.

Ritual is a kind of behavior that has been described as typical of both humans and animals, and it is necessary to be clear about the distinction between the two. Although the two forms of ritual, human and animal, have superficial characters in common, their function is really different. Both human and animal rituals are stereotyped behavior patterns used as means of communication; well-known examples among animals are the dance of the bee, which communicates the direciton and distance of a source of honey, and the courtship dances of birds. The complexity of these animal rituals has only one aim, to transmit an unambiguous communication signal relating, in these instances, to the whereabouts of food and the prospect of copulation. The signal is related to immediate biological needs. Human rituals may be distinguished insofar as they rarely relate to immediate biological needs, are concerned with social rather than individual communication, and are more than unambiguous signals; in fact, they might better be described as ambiguous statements.

Of course, man himself has predictable courtship patterns that can be described as ritualistic and relate (for example) to the prospect of copulation (drinks, dinner, dancing, kissing, petting, etc.), but there is a flexibility here not found in birds. In a discussion of human rituals we are concerned with stereotyped behavior patterns normally associated with set words, patterns that gain their power by being carried out in an exact form and that are consciously enacted. Ritualistic signaling that precedes copulation in animals and humans is an unconscious behavior pattern with an immediate biological end. By human rituals, we refer here to behavior consciously enacted with a meaning both deep and abstract, relating to no simple biological need. Human ritual serves to perpetuate knowledge necessary for survival and, by combining speech and action, constitutes a much more compact form of social memory than words alone (Leach 1966). Compared with speech, the language of ritual is enormously condensed; a great variety of different meanings are implicit in the same category sets (also an attribute of mathematics). Ritual is a special form of language with a very high information content, but, unlike language, the meaning of ritual depends upon its social context. A ritual act is a social act—it is society's meditation of behavior and memory.

The analysis of a human ritual is complex and cannot concern us here. In its remarkable way ritual records knowledge about social origins, about social structure, kinship, and obligations. It records behavior patterns of a fundamental nature, such as hunting, toolmaking, and food preparation. Ritual is, as it were, the DNA of society, the encoded informational basis of culture; it is the memory core of human social achievement.

Myth is the verbal derivative of ritual, and, with the evolution of writing, the informational content of ritual has to some extent taken a verbal form. The written early Sumerian myths are probably only the verbal part of a ritual and as such are only half the language, but, with the development of writing, myth came to incorporate much of the informational content of ritual in its typically condensed form. As literate peoples, we feel more at home with the creation myth of the Book of Genesis than with what seem to us meaningless rituals, but the character of this myth, as that of others, is to have many meanings (only one of which is discussed below, in 10.8).

It is impossible to extrapolate to the origins of social behavior from a study of primitive society today, but nevertheless it seems a reasonable postulate that ritual behavior was an early and effective means of recording cultural achievement in the absence of a developed language. With the evolution of language, the trend may have been from ritual to myth, from a more to a less compact means of encoding knowledge necessary for the survival of society. Such knowledge will contribute to the continuity of social norms and the stability of behavior, with its recognition by individuals as tradition worthy of respect.

2. Claim has been made that the word *religion* is derived from the Latin verb *religare* (to bind). If correct, it is not merely a coincidence that an important function of religious institutions is to bind society together, even if it is done by binding men at the same time to God. In primitive societies a personal religion, such as some varieties of Western Christianity, is very weakly developed, and public ritual forms the basis of religious activity. In fact, all rituals may be described as religious, for they not only bind individuals to a core of social knowledge, but, by performing them, individuals are bound to each other in a common activity often requiring much effort and skill.

The binding function of religious ritual is, then, its second important function. Not only are traditions ritualized, but many important social activities appear to take on a sacred and ritual quality. An element in the common life of a society may come to have a special significance and in time become an act of religious observance. Especially important in this respect are the *rites de passage* (birth rites, puberty rites, marriage rites, death rites), which consolidate social roles and social structure, as well as bind members of the society together. But religion does more than that: it directs social sentiments toward one stable and symbolic center.

In many primitive societies, this further binding property of religion takes the form of ancestor worship, which creates, as it were, a continuum between the living and the dead. The transition from contemporary to ancestor is believed to be a gradual one; the ancestor's identification with the next world is only slowly completed. In time, the sacredness of the deceased increases until in due course great reverence is paid to one common ancestor. Thus worship of one common ancestor binds the members of descent groups together and gives them a common center for their sentiments. Archeologists have given us evidence of burial customs of prehistoric man of perhaps some 40,000 years ago. Skeletal remains of the large-jawed men from western Europe and Asia have been discovered within stone circles, with implements and the remains of a food supply (for example La Chapelle). These people buried their dead with great ceremony, and certainly believed in their survival after death.

In clans, the totem may fulfill the same function as the ancestor, and in tribes or nations, the ancestor/god may be personified by the living king or queen. Like the ancestor, the king or queen, although alive, is invested with a sacred quality, which enhances the social effectiveness of the institution. Divine kings are known in Africa, and the divinity of the monarch was still recognized in England until the end of Stuart times (1688). The English monarch today, though not explicitly divine, still fulfills a religious function and acts as a symbolic center, especially in times of national danger. Society needs both ritual and symbol to give it form and continuity.

3. Another device that appears to stabilize and maintain social structure is artificial economic interdependence. We have already seen (9.10) that human society is bonded by economics and kinship. What we have to note in this section is that the bonding is sometimes strengthened and channeled by ritualized economic exchange. In societies with a subsistence economy, in which an economic super-structure does not "naturally" exist, we often find a network of economic bonds superimposed in the form of the bride-price or, more generally, in the form of "tribute" or "royalties." The goods thus accumulated by a king or chief priest are in practice redistributed to the members of the society who supplied them; nevertheless the ritual economic

transaction serves to bind the society together in a common act and at the same time enhances the role of the king or priest. The modern system of taxes can be seen as a redistribution of goods for the common good and is, in fact, one of very few transactions in which the individual is directly and personally associated with the state.

4. These different means of binding and stabilizing society are clearly factors of overriding importance in the evolution of man. It remains to point out that religious and legal institutions help control human behavior at an individual level for the benefit of the society. What "is done" and "is not done" is a powerful determinant of human behavior; it is dictated by tradition, religion, and law, through each individual's peers and his elders. Religious and legal sanctions control human behavior at its most fundamental level, and the two kinds of sanctions are often so closely allied as to be indistinguishable, as in the Ten Commandments. Among these vital functions of religious and legal institutions falls the control of man's biological needs, by means of sanctions against theft, aggression, adultery, and so on. From the need for such social control of human behavior arises in turn the mechanism whereby an individual directs his own behavior toward social ends—that is, the evolution of ethics.

10.8 The evolution of ethics

MAN HAS BEEN described as the ethical animal, which is undeniably one striking characteristic that distinguishes him from the rest of the animal kingdom. Its early recognition is recorded in the Book of Genesis, where the story of Adam and Eve describes man's acquisition of the knowledge of good and evil, and how possession of this knowledge resulted in expulsion of man from paradise into the world that we know.

This ancient myth embodies one of the most important events in the evolution of man—the evolution of ethics. Ethics arose as a direct result of the appearance of self-awareness in the growing human consciousness. Cortical control of motor activity slowly came to give evolving man consciousness of his actions and, beyond that, consciousness of himself as an individual being. As has often been said, the animal knows, but only man knows that he knows. Man could see, as a result of his self-consciousness, how many of his activities were directed to satisfy his needs, his basic requirements for life; but he could also see that certain of his actions satisfied only social needs, that they led not to personal satisfaction but to frustration.

It is significant that socially oriented learned behavior is probably most highly developed, not in nonhuman primates, but in dogs and wolves. When a pack of dogs hunts, it performs a cooperative activity that requires considerable discipline. In rounding up their prey, the members of the pack may have to show remarkable self-control in the interest of the group. As social carnivores, dogs have evolved the possibility of self-discipline, which can be learned from and imposed by their peers and elders. As a result, as Kortlandt (1965) has pointed out, dogs are the only creatures besides man that appear to experience guilt—the only creatures to have evolved a recognizable superego, or conscience. Domesticated dogs can be quite easily taught not to touch meat left on the kitchen table. They can generally be relied upon in their master's absence, and they can certainly feel guilt if they disobey, as any dog owner will know. Man and dog understand self-discipline, and that is one reason why they understand each other.

If dogs have a social conscience, as members of a social group, they are certainly not far from being ethical animals, but, as we have seen, ethics is more than this, for it is the resultant of social conscience *and* self-awareness. Without the latter the dog will not consciously make an ethical decision. This is not to deny altogether the possibility of self-awareness in dogs; a certain degree of self-awareness may exist in dogs, as it may in monkeys and apes. It seems likely that it does, for, as we know from our own experience, consciousness is not an all-or-none phenomenon; it varies by degree. However, it seems unlikely that a dog would experience an agony of indecision as to whether or not to succumb to strong temptation. Because guilt follows the act, we need not assume that foresight of guilt necessarily precedes it.

Ethics as we know it may have arisen, then, from the full development of self-consciousness in a demanding social context. The key to man's nature lies in his evolution of social hunting; like the dog, man was a social carnivore. In such circumstances, the actions of every individual affected others in the social group, and what is important is that it was of course the social group (as part of the deme) that was evolving, not the individual. In gaining awareness of his own needs and activities, man also gained awareness of the needs of the society in which he lived. It is the conflict between the two needs, those of the individual and those of the society, that makes necessary some device for directing a choice between possible actions. Among men as among dogs, natural selection insured that such choices be made on the basis of their survival value to the social group, so the right choice will more often prove to be altruistic, the wrong choice antisocial.

Ethics therefore arise when man finds that he has to make conscious choices in a social context. That is why the story of Adam and Eve has been described by religious teachers as the "fall of man" and by psychologists as the coming of self-consciousness and self-awareness. Many unself-conscious social animals appear to behave altruistically and to suffer or die for the benefit of their social group or their young. The agony of the human condition arises from man's self-consciousness and his knowledge of the price he pays as an individual for his social life. The evolution of the human condition is described as "the fall" because the author of Genesis describes the coming of human self-awareness as alienation from a state of holiness and the entry of evil into mankind. Clearly, the evolution of self-awareness brought with it a totally new and terrible situation: that human activity was to be directed, not by the straightforward operations of an unthinking brain that was a self-sufficient and integrated whole, but by the conscious functioning of the human mind, which can foresee the pleasant and unpleasant, good and evil, results of its actions. Self-consciousness and foresight therefore brought discord to the mind of man.

Freedman and Roe (1958) have accordingly described the emergence of *Homo sapiens* as the beginning of the age of anxiety. The need for values can be seen to arise from his neurological situation—from the fact of man's possessing an "archaic neurological and endocrinological system partially but not completely under cortical control." On the one hand, the internal and unconscious homeostatic system of needs and satisfactions affects the motor system and physiological structures in a broad and relatively imprecise manner, while, on the other hand, the cortical analysis of sensory data responds relatively accurately to fine distinctions and social cues of no obvious physiological significance. In practice, there is a dislocation and delay between biological needs and their satisfaction that is due to social demands. Conscious frustration of biological needs, then, becomes the condition of man and leads to internal conflict and anxiety.

Only in man is there simultaneously such a rigidity of social channeling, and such a degree of potential plasticity and flexibility for the individual. Incompatible aims and choices which are desirable but mutually exclusive are inevitable conditions of human development. This discrepancy between possibility and restriction, stimulation and interdiction, range and constriction, underlies that quantitatively unique characteristic of the human being: conflict [Freedman and Roe 1958].

Internal conflict and frustration may, however, be among the most important stimuli of cultural progress, of the development of adaptive behavior and technology.

We can see, then, that with the evolution of self-awareness man stands quite suddenly in possession of conscious knowledge, purpose, choice, and values, and, as Simpson (1949) has pointed out, these possessions involve reponsibility. Responsibility is man's special burden, and though society supports the individual at every turn, it is the individual who must make the final choice and upon whom the social group always depends. This, however, was not the only way in which the individual assumed a new and magnified importance in human society.

10.9 The rise of the individual

THE THEORY of evolution makes it clear that the functional unit in this dynamic process is not the individual but the population. It is therefore of some interest to consider how it comes about that in human society the individual assumes a value that among animals it does not possess. The answer appears to lie in some special feature of human evolution.

The division of labor between the sexes, which we presume must have developed among the ancestors of man, is the beginning of the process of individualization. The fact that particular males and females are interdependent means that one individual is ultimately important to another, if only at an economic level. With the appearance of one-male groups, the interdependence became sexual and it expanded still further with the evolution of the family. The wife and husband recognized each other as economic and sexual partners. The frontal position in coitus enhanced this recognition; role names, such as "wife," "husband," "father," "mother," appeared and reflected the division of labor within the family. At this simple level, individuals came to depend on each other more and more, and perhaps that inter- dependence within the family was the basis of love. Individualization appears to have grown through the recognition of an individual's dependence on other particular individuals both within and beyond the family.

At a later stage in human evolution we find a diversity of occu- pation stretching beyond the family. The important function of the elders, the priest, or the king made these individuals of immense importance to the society that recognized them and their vital role. In Neolithic times we find a new diversity of occupation; individuals made different contributions to social needs, some made tools and weapons and some produced food. Different goods and services were produced by different people in the more tightly knit urban communi- ties that evolved. More people came to depend on more individuals to satisfy their different needs, and individualization developed with the increased complexity of society.

But besides the division of labor there was possibly a more funda- mental reason for the individualization of *Homo sapiens.* The more behavior depends on learning and the more complex it becomes, the more behavior will vary among individuals. Variation in competence in performing tasks is a commonplace in the animal world and is striking among the Japanese monkeys (Itani 1965). It is a very important factor in man's evolution because, the more behavior patterns vary, the more important is individual action—individual achievement—to the population as a whole. By his behavior, an individual can determine the fate of the social group of which he is part, for better or for worse. Society comes to care about the behavior of individuals, especially when they perform their more socially oriented activities, and, as we have seen, society comes to control these activities.

What is especially important in this thesis is that behavior in man is to a great extent intelligently directed, and the application of intelli- gence is a character of the individual, not of the deme. Intelligence itself is genetically determined, and genes for intelligence are selected as are any other genes, but intelligence, as we have seen, is a general- ized faculty, and its varied application in problem-solving (and prob- lem-setting) is the property of the individual. The evolution of intelligence will therefore by its nature result in the evolution of the individual as an important factor in the survival of the species because the evolution of culture is due not only to natural selection within a varying gene pool but also to selection of a series of imaginative cultural novelties that arise from the intelligent activities of individuals. At the cultural level, therefore, the society looks to the individual, never the reverse. The individual, as the source of invention, is the source of culture.

It is relevant that intelligence and intelligent activity are not directly correlated with ability to learn (see 10.4) or with good citizenship, sociability, or a strict adherence to social norms. As a result, society must attempt to preserve individuals, even if they are not socially well-adapted. Society must value an individual as a person, for upon individual people the evolution of society depends. In a cultural society the contribution of each individual to the deme is no longer only via the gene pool but may be direct and immediate, as a result of intelligent behavior. Cultural evolution finds its sources of variability, its "mutations," in individual behavior, and they can spread through the deme, if they prove of value, within one generation.

10.10 Human behavior

WE HAVE ATTEMPTED briefly to describe and understand the origin and function of culture. Culture appears to comprise behavior and ideas that are the property of a society rather than an individual and are learned by social animals from each other. Human culture has developed from some basic primate characteristics that have been rapidly evolved. In particular, primate visual three-dimensional color perception has evolved into typically human "carnivore" perception, without loss of acuity, and with it have appeared conceptual thought, self-consciousness, and intelligence.

Among primates, culture evolved in tightly knit social groups. Social groups, though of modified structure, remained the necessary basis of human culture and made possible the extensive transmission of this kind of learned behavior. The modifications involved the evolution of the family and of exogamy, which, respectively, improved cultural transmission within the social group and improved cultural diffusion between groups.

Culture must have come at an early stage to contain its own means of transmission. Imitation was reinforced by instruction, which was made possible by the evolution of speech. Man had something to communicate that could not be transmitted by gesture, facial expressions, or simple sound signals; the development of human culture depended on the development of a language that was adequate to transmit it in all its complexity.

The newly evolved flexibility of human behavior that arose from the cortical control of behavior patterns might have tended to weaken social bonding, and it seems clear that one of the functions of religious and other social institutions was to stabilize individual behavior for social ends. Social bonding was maintained by these institutions in various ways so that the newly evolved versatility of man's behavior would not disrupt his social group and endanger its survival, yet was available as a source of new cultural invention. Tradition and convention in this way served to control human behavior, especially in the biologically important realms of food, sex, and defense; man became conscious of the different motives of his behavior, and the human condition of internal conflict and mixed motives was present.

Culture now controls every item of human behavior. It is clear that even the simplest basic biological activities (such as blinking or defecation) can be at least partly culturally controlled and that the socially important activities, like feeding and copulating, are under very strict cultural control. In our work we fulfill roles in society determined by society for the benefit of society; at the same time, society aims at arresting the activities of such anticultural and antisocial individuals as thieves and gangsters. Only a very stable and secure society can afford much deviation from the social norm, valuable though it may be. Man is a social animal, so his survival as a species depends on the maintenance of his society: as a result, individual behavior must be controlled and directed by social needs. Though man invented culture, it has in turn made man.

Man is a cultural animal, therefore, not because he alone has culture but because culture has come to condition his every act. Man owes his nature to an evolutionary trend in which cultural adaptations have been selected and have maintained on the earth this organism that perceived so clearly the nature of the environment that it learned to change it for its own advantage.

SUGGESTIONS FOR FURTHER READING

For a cultural anthropologist's view of culture see R. Linton, *The Tree of Culture* (New York: A. A. Knopf, 1955), and B. Malinowski, *A Scientific Theory of Culture, and Other Essays* (Chapel Hill: University of North Carolina Press, 1944).

A recent publication deals with an aspect of primate behavior that has received scant attention up to the present: S. A. Altmann (ed.), *Social Communication among Primates* (Chicago: Chicago University Press, 1966).

Social institutions have not in general been described as evolutionary adaptations: their immediate social function has been investigated rather than their long-term adaptive function. Some current ideas on the social and psychological function of ritual in an African tribe may be gained from R. G. Lienhardt, *Divinity and Experience, the Religion of the Dinka* (Oxford: Oxford University Press, 1961).

$\mathcal{L}11$

The Origin of Man

11.1 Ape or Monkey?

$\mathcal{Q}$ IN THE PRECEDING seven chapters we have reviewed what is known of the evolution of the different great functional complexes of man. We have drawn on the evidence of living and fossil primates in order to gain insight into the evolution of man's functional and behavioral adaptations.

We have seen that both modern man and his closely related and probably ancestral genus *Australopithecus* have clear affinity with the semibrachiating higher primates (see 6.7). This fact seems well established on the basis of the present evidence, but the semibrachiating complex alone does not suggest whether man is more ape-like or more monkey-like, whether he evolved from a brachiating ape or a brachiating monkey. In certain characters man seems to resemble most closely the living semibrachiating monkeys, and we have noted in particular the high index of cephalization of these primates. Man's hand and penis also show close similarities to those of certain Old World monkeys. In contrast, the apes have hands that have undergone specialization for brachiation, so they have to a great extent lost their manipulative power.

This situation is typical of many characters of man when they are compared with apes; we find that man is less specialized in many of his brachiating features and shares, instead, more generalized features with the Old World monkeys. The generalized nature of modern man was stressed in a famous paper by Straus (1949) and is of the utmost importance. It used to be accepted without question that man shared a common ancestor with the apes, but, since we recognize that many Old World monkeys brachiate quite extensively, we do not need to postulate that man was descended from an ape simply for that reason. As we have seen in the earlier chapters of this book, there are other characters besides those connected with the forelimb skeleton which suggest that man is more ape-like than monkey-like.

Of course, we can always postulate parallel evolution to account for similarities between two groups of living organisms, but, if we do so without evidence, we are going to arrive at a more complex hypothesis than that postulated on the basis of no parallel evolution. A principle of scientific method known as Occam's razor states that "plurality is never to be posited without need" (*essentia non sunt multiplicanda praeter necessitatem*); in other words, the phylogenetic hypothesis should be such that it requires a minimum number of postulates or ancillary hypotheses. For that reason, we cannot postulate parallel evolution without certain evidence for its existence.

Therefore, we can accept man's ape-like characters (other than in the forelimb) as suggesting common ancestry with the African apes; in particular we should recall the absence of a tail, the form of the foot, and the presence of a vermiform appendix. Other characters that man shares with the living apes are less striking but are probably relevant; they include the form of the thorax and abdomen, the absence of sexual skin, a retarded growth rate, and great flexibility of behavior. But it is clear that these characters are not so strikingly ape-like as to lead us to postulate a recent common ancestry with the African apes (theory *T5,* Fig. 3.11, p. 79) but merely to deduce that the ancestral hominid was probably slightly more ape-like than monkey-like. If, therefore, such an ancestor bore some characters of monkeys and some of apes, and if we discount extensive parallel evolution, this evidence suggests an early differentiation of the Hominidae from creatures themselves not much differentiated from the common stock of monkeys and apes. Insofar as they were differentiated from such an ancestor, they were beginning to be recognizable apes and so are classified in the subfamily Dryopithecinae.

Such a conclusion, based on the study of living and Pleistocene primates, is of course extremely hypothetical, yet it does seem consistent with the fossil evidence available from the Oligocene, Miocene, and Pliocene (36–3 million years ago), which now requires some consideration.

11.2 The earliest hominids

THE HUMAN FAMILY, the Hominidae, includes those living and fossil forms that are more like modern man than like other living primates. This assessment of similarity is the general basis upon which the classification of fossil remains must be made. However, we know enough of the processes of organic evolution to realize that, by convention, families should be differentiated not by slight anatomical differences but by a distinct complex of adaptations. The adaptations that distinguish the hominids, apes, and monkeys are primarily locomotor and were discussed in chapter 3; the Hominidae are quite strikingly distinct from all other primate families as a result of their terrestrial bipedalism. They have accordingly been defined by Le Gros Clark on the basis of their total morphological pattern, and the following has been modified from his summary definition (1964, p. 119).

Family Hominidae: a subsidiary radiation of the Hominoidea distinguished from the Pongidae by the following evolutionary trends.
Progressive skeletal modifications in adaptation to erect bipedalism, shown particularly in a proportionate lengthening of the lower extremity, and changes in the proportions and morphological details of the pelvis, femur, and foot skeleton related to mechanical requirements of erect posture and gait and to the muscular development associated therewith.
Preservation of well-developed pollex, ultimate loss of opposability of hallux.
Relative displacement forward of the occipital condyles and restriction of nuchal area.
Consistent and early ontogenetic development of a pyramidal mastoid process.
Diminution of canines in phylogeny to a spatulate form interlocking

slightly or not at all and showing no pronounced sexual dimorphism with disappearance of diastemata.

Replacement of sectorial first lower premolars by bicuspid teeth (with later secondary reduction of lingual cusp).

Alteration in occlusal relationships, with the result that in later forms, at any rate, all the teeth tend to become worn down to a relatively flat, even surface at an early stage of attrition.

Development of an evenly rounded dental arcade.

Marked tendency in later stages of evolution to a reduction in size of the molar teeth and in subnasal prognathism.

Progressive acceleration in the replacement of deciduous teeth in relation to the eruption of permanent molars.

Marked and rapid expansion (in some of the terminal products of the hominid sequence of evolution) of the cranial capacity, associated with reduction in size of jaws and area of attachment of masticatory muscles and the development of a chin.

In the interpretation of fossil remains, the limitations caused by scarcity are particularly apparent in our knowledge of the early hominid *Ramapithecus*, of which only jawbones and teeth are known. Nevertheless, as far as they go these fragments satisfy the definition given above, and, indeed, the material is not only quite close to that of *Australopithecus* but has much in common with the mandibles of *Homo erectus* from Swartkrans in South Africa (orginally named *Telanthropus capensis*) (Fig. 11.1).

The earliest specimens of *Ramapithecus* come from the late Miocene (about 12–15 million years ago) of the Siwalik Hills in northern India and were collected by Lewis in 1932 (Lewis 1934). Since then the fragments have been studied by Simons (1964), and with them he has placed other fragments previously believed to belong to fossil apes. We can now recognize *Ramapithecus punjabicus* from India and from Fort Ternan, Kenya (Pilbeam and Simons 1965): the African forms appear to date from approximately 14 million years ago (Evernden and Curtis 1965).

The following diagnosis, adapted from Simons (1964), serves to distinguish *Ramapithecus* from other hominid genera.

Ramapithecus: a genus of the Hominidae distinguished by the following characters:

Masticatory apparatus absolutely smaller and mandible shallower than that of *Australopithecus.*

Face shorter than in *Australopithecus* but not so short as in *Homo.*

Incisors and canines less reduced compared with cheek teeth than in *Australopithecus.*

Incisor procumbency considerable; maxillary canine morphologically resembling the smallest of the Indian species of *Dryopithecus,* but in size no bigger than the canine of *Australopithecus.*

We have compared a fragment of *Ramapithecus* both with a species of *Dryopithecus* (see Fig. 7.7, p. 183) and with an early specimen of *Homo* (Fig. 11.1). There seems every reason to accept *Ramapithecus* as a hominid, as Lewis originally suggested, on the basis of the present evidence. If so, we can suppose that the Hominidae may have become separated from their dryopithecine ancestors in the Middle Miocene (possibly 20 million years ago) at the latest. This is

FIG. 11.1. Mandibular fragment of *Ramapithecus* (*A*) and mandible of *Homo erectus* (*Telanthropus*) from Swartkrans (reconstructed) (*B*). Note the similarity in size and shape of teeth. (After Simons, 1964, and Robinson, 1953.)

about the time when the various species of *Proconsul* were flourishing in East Africa (again about 20 million years ago according to Bishop [1964]), and, as we have seen from the forelimb skeleton, *Proconsul* could very well be the semibrachiating ancestor of the Hominidae that we are looking for (theory T3, Fig. 3.11, p. 79). Yet those who have studied the teeth of *Proconsul* (Clark and Leakey 1951, Simons and Pilbeam 1965) proclaim it to be clearly pongid in its dentition, and it has recently been placed squarely in the genus of fossil apes, *Dryopithecus,* with the result that *Proconsul* is now used as a sub-generic name by the latter two authors. It seems clear that while *Proconsul* is close to our hypothetical ancestor, especially in the limbs, it is already too ape-like in its teeth to be that ancestor himself.

We must therefore look elsewhere, perhaps to an earlier age. Simons (1965) has suggested that the Oligocene genus *Propliopithecus,* which has a short face, is more what one would expect to see as a forerunner of the family Hominidae than as an early dryopithecine or gibbon (Fig. 11.2). As we might expect, the further back we pass in time, the more difficult it is to distinguish members of the different families of higher primates, and there is certainly as yet no clear demonstration that *Propliopithecus* should be classed as a hominid. However, this genus, discovered by Markgraf early in this century, may be considered as a possible hominid ancestor from the Oligocene, some 30 million years ago, when the main groups of higher primates were only just becoming clearly differentiated.

As we turn now to the diagram of hominid ascent (see Fig. 3.11, p. 79), it seems that the most reasonable course would be to accept theory T2, which leads from an early ape-like dryopithecine form in the Oligocene, rather than the other theories, which suggest a more recent origin for the Hominidae.

11.3 Leaving the forest

AT SOME TIME the early ancestral Hominidae left the tropical forest. We have no direct evidence as to when they left or why. In the absence of such evidence, we can only make suggestions on the basis of our knowledge of the general processes of organic evolution.

It is clear that the total morphological pattern of the Hominidae is

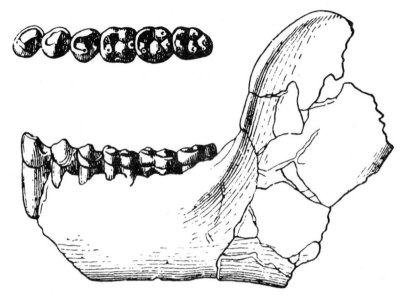

FIG. 11.2. View of left side of the mandible of *Propliopithecus;* above are the crowns of the teeth. Although the tip of the canine is broken, it is smaller than in the *Proconsul* species of similar size. Claimed by many to be an ancestor of the gibbons, a recent study has shown the unlikelihood of this claim, and Simons (1965) has suggested that *Propliopithecus* has characters commensurate with hominid ancestry. (From Schlosser, 1912.) Approximately twice natural size.

associated primarily with bipedalism. If the interpretation of this pattern that has been placed upon the fossils of *Ramapithecus* is correct, we must suppose that *Ramapithecus* may have moved bipedally more often than living apes do, though clearly the associated adaptations of the pelvis and hindlimbs would be less striking in this animal than those we see in *Australopithecus*. If *Ramapithecus* was bipedal, which hominid status implies, he was most probably living in fairly open country, since bipedalism is not a very useful adaptation in the tropical rain forest, with its dense ground cover. For the present, therefore, it is reasonable to suppose that the Hominidae first became established in open country in the Miocene (15-20 million years ago), though just why it happened is not known.

We do not have to postulate a sudden climatic change to account for a new adaptive radiation, though there is some evidence of a reduction in the total area of forest in central Africa soon after that time as the result of a more arid climate. By Pliocene times many plains-living forms, such as the giraffes, gazelles, and baboons, were evolving under new selection pressures.

As we have seen (1.3), competition is of the nature of organic life, and pressure to radiate is always present in organic evolution. Any character, therefore, that proves to be preadapted to a neighboring environment will allow radiation into that environment if other adaptations do not forbid it (see 3.9). It seems clear that a degree of preadaptation is essential to account for this process, which is the first stage of speciation in evolution. The more striking the contrast in environment, the greater the degree of preadaptation that we must postulate.

We know that the baboons as well as the hominids have made this move from forest to plain, and, in the case of the baboons, their arboreal quadrupedal locomotor adaptation was fully preadaptive to plains life. It seems correspondingly clear that the early hominids must have evolved a degree of bipedalism in the forest; this improbable suggestion is acceptable only in the face of the evidence we have of semibrachiation in hominid ancestry. Interestingly enough, the great paleontologist W. K. Gregory postulated in 1928 that some brachiating would have been essential for the hominid ancestors of man before they could have become habitual bipeds. We would much less readily be able to accept the possibility of a change in adaptation from quadruped to biped. The present evidence for semibrachiation gives us a happy solution to the problem of the origin of bipedalism, since it involves an erect posture and the direct vertical transmission of weight from body to feet. It is well known that chimpanzees, gorillas, and especially gibbons can walk for some distance on two legs. Although their posture is stooping rather than man-like, the possibility of bipedalism is present and is due to adaptation to the changing mechanics of body weight and stress that result from regular brachiation (Napier 1964).

We can suppose, then, that in the early Miocene (or earlier) there were some dryopithecine apes already evolved as semibrachiators; their arms were lengthening, their spine was stiffening, and their feet showed adaptation to standing upon branches (see Fig. 5.18, p. 132). Perhaps some of them were already occupying more open country, such as that occupied by the (mainly terrestrial) mountain gorilla today. But, unlike the mountain gorilla, they were small, light creatures, perhaps no more than four feet high, so an upright posture presented fewer mechanical problems. At the same time, in the bamboo-covered mountainsides inhabited by the mountain gorilla today, visibility is very limited, and standing up does not improve the view. But in more open country standing erect would have afforded a good view, and bipedalism would also have had other striking advantages. Sometimes a modern baboon (or a patas monkey) will stand erect to get a view over the grasslands, and the protection against predators thus offered to an animal with already excellent sight must be very considerable.

The early hominids were in fact probably preadapted for plains life in a number of ways. Not only could they walk or run short distances, but since they were not very large or heavy they could hold themselves erect without much fatigue and see a long way with great acuity. They had hands, and they possibly could already carry and use objects as tools as well as throw weapons for defense. With an omnivorous taste for food, they could live on anything from foliage and herbage to termites, lizards, and small mammals. Pilbeam and Simons (1965) claim that the reduced incisors and canines of *Ramapithecus* suggest that tool-using may have become established by the late Miocene, since smaller front teeth require the use of other means to strip bark and prepare both animal and vegetable food, and there is certainly no reason why *Ramapithecus* should not have been equipped with a very dexterous hand even at that early date, even if tools themselves were not used.

The pelvis of the early forms may have been far less ape-like than we might suppose from our knowledge of living apes (for example, the chimpanzee pelvis in Fig. 4.7, p. 93). We have a fossil primate from the early Pliocene, *Oreopithecus*, perhaps 10 or 12 million years old, which is less specialized than the living apes and appears to have a number of hominid-like characters in its pelvis; but so far as we know it was not bipedal (Straus 1963). It seems from such evidence that, as we go back in the evolution of the Hominoidea, we find not only that the hominids get more ape-like but that the apes get more hominid-like; both families are more generalized and more alike.

For the same reason, we need not suppose that the early hominids had either a heavy masticatory apparatus or a large muzzle. Many monkeys have quite short snouts and no sexual dimorphism in that region. Both *Oreopithecus* and *Proconsul* were short-faced, and we have pointed out the mechanical relationship between cranial balance and erect posture, another important preadaptation to the hominid way of life.

Our only early hominid, *Ramapithecus,* had a wide distribution, which suggests success, for it is a common evolutionary pattern that the successful exploitation of a new ecological niche will result (where geographically possible) in extensive spatial radiation. Such a successful radiation clearly occurred in the case of *Ramapithecus,* for the specimens from India and Kenya are extremely similar, though widely dispersed. It is interesting that their dispersion is paralleled by that of the early ape genus *Dryopithecus* (Simons and Pilbeam 1965).

We need not think, therefore, of a descent from the trees as involving a sudden and revolutionary adaptation resulting, perhaps, from some startling mutation. Nothing so drastic is involved. Evolution is the slow unfolding of new forms. Semibrachiation is preadaptive to bipedalism; its advantages can have been realized only in fairly open or scattered woodland. Bipedalism is preadaptive to plains living; our hominid ancestors had some startling advantages for plains life, in terms of their sensory acuity, powers of prediction, and manipulative ability. The opportunistic nature of the evolutionary process allowed the exploitation of an ecological situation with great possibilities. Early hominids no longer used their eyes mostly for locomotion, as they had done in the forest; they could now use them largely for the more productive activities of food-finding, defense, and intraspecific communication.

One other adaptation, however, seems necessary as a postulate. Baboons have survived in open country to a great extent as a result of their highly evolved social structure. If early hominids were not fully preadapted in this respect, they almost certainly were partially preadapted. At any rate, it seems that plains life for such a defenseless creature as a primate necessitates the rapid evolution of a means of cooperative defense and a binding social structure. This social structure made possible the remarkable changes we see in the Pleistocene phase of human evolution.

11.4 *The origin of man*

APART FROM *Ramapithecus,* the earliest hominid fossils of which we know the age with any certainty are those of *Australopithecus,* found at Olduvai, Tanzania. They are now believed to date from about 1.9 million years ago (Evernden and Curtis 1965). In the lowest levels at this site (Bed I) we find remains not only of *Australopithecus robustus* (previously known as *Zii janthropus*) but also of an advanced form of *A. africanus* (originally named *Homo habilis*). The interpretation of these important fossil remains has recently been discussed by Tobias and others (Tobias *et al.* 1965) and the interpretation placed upon them in these pages is approximately in line with the published views of Clark Howell and Robinson (Howell, in Tobias *et al.* 1965, Robinson 1965). These two species of *Australopithecus* have already been discussed, and we have distinguished the heavy-jawed, probably herbivorous *A. robustus* from the light-jawed, omnivorous *A. africanus* (chapter 7).

The fact that both species lived in the same area and over the same considerable period of time (in eastern and southern Africa for at least one million years; see Appendix) suggests that they must have occupied different ecological niches, since apparently they did not compete directly for food, shelter, or space. If they had so competed, only one species would have survived. Furthermore, they must have originally evolved in isolation. While there is now reason to believe that genetic isolating mechanisms may arise within a population, it is a highly improbable event. In the absence of evidence to the contrary, we can safely postulate that two species like those of *Australopithecus* must have evolved in isolation and only much later (when they were full species, so interbreeding did not occur) could they have survived as distinct populations in the same area. It has been suggested by Napier (1964) that *A. robustus* remained on the forest floor long after *A. africanus* had entered the more open savanna country. This history of two divergent forms suggests, then, that the first members of the genus *Australopithecus* appeared some considerable time previously, which takes us well back into the Pliocene.

A summary definition of the genus *Australopithecus,* which is modified from that published by Le Gros Clark (1964, p. 168), is given below.

Australopithecus: A genus of the Hominidae distinguished by the following characters:
Cranial capacity ranging from about 450 to 700 cc.
Strongly built supraorbital ridges.

A low sagittal crest in species with heavy masticatory apparatus.
Occipital condyles well behind the midpoint of the cranial length but on a transverse level with the auditory apertures.
Nuchal area of occipital bone restricted, as in *Homo*.
Consistent development of pyramidal mastoid process less striking than in *Homo*.
Jaws variable in size but often massive.
Chin absent but inner symphyseal surface relatively straight and vertical.
Dental arcade parabolic in form with no diastema.
Spatulate canines wearing down from the tip only.
Relatively large premolars and molars.
Anterior lower premolar bicuspid with subequal cusps.
Pronounced molarization of first deciduous molar.
Progressive increase in size of permanent lower molars from first to third.
Limb skeleton (so far as is known) conforming in its main features to that of modern man but differing in a number of details, such as smaller sacroiliac articulation and generally smaller size.
Ischial tuberosity lower than the acetabulum, unlike modern man, and oriented differently in relation to the ilium.

This summary of characters of *Australopithecus* takes us in one direction close to *Ramapithecus* and in another direction close to *Homo*. It may be that *Ramapithecus* gave rise directly to *Homo,* without the intermediate *Australopithecus* stage, but on the basis of the present evidence it seems improbable. What is possible is that the two earlier genera will prove to be so alike that we shall transfer the species *Ramapithecus punjabicus* into the genus *Australopithecus* and call it *Australopithecus punjabicus*. But for that we must await further discoveries of fossils of the important genus *Ramapithecus*.

In the early Pleistocene, therefore, we can recognize these two species of *Australopithecus,* well established in eastern and southern Africa and clearly distinct. As we have seen, that called *A. africanus* is the more *Homo*-like, and at Olduvai it approaches very closely the early forms of *Homo erectus* (Tobias and von Koenigswald 1964).

While it is possible and relatively simple to separate two contemporaneous species (such as those of *Australopithecus*) by a study of their morphology, it is not so simple a matter in the case of two sequent species or genera, one of which evolved out of the other (Campbell 1963). Because the genus *Australopithecus* gave rise to the genus *Homo* somewhere, at some time, intermediate forms will have existed that form a continuous series from an easily recognizable *Australopithecus* to an easily recognizable *Homo*. Therefore, while we can use definitions such as those quoted here as a general guide to elucidate fossil remains, they will not help us with fossils that fall near the boundary between two sequent species or genera. Somewhere, we have to admit, an *Australopithecus* gave birth to a *Homo*, and they were, from our point of view, indistinguishable.

In view of the difficulty of recognizing such a boundary, and because of its supposed lack of reality and meaning, some authors (notably Robinson 1965 and Pilbeam and Simons 1965) have suggested dropping the generic distinction and calling the two early Pleistocene species *Homo africanus* and *Homo robustus*. There is, however, good reason for retaining the generic distinction: with the appearance of *Homo erectus*, at the beginning of the Middle Pleistocene, we have a period of relatively rapid evolution, which resulted in an organism occupying an ecological niche different from that of its predecessors. It was with the change from scavenging to organized hunting of big game that we believe *Homo* evolved out of *Australopithecus*.

Change in diet and food-getting techniques may seem relatively superficial as a reason for distinguishing two genera, but, throughout our review of human evolution, it has become clear that this change was closely correlated with many others of a fundamental genetic nature, including the vast expansion of the brain. It was in the Middle Pleistocene that man evolved, not before. *Australopithecus* was a clever, bipedal, tool-using, plains-living hominid; *Homo erectus* was a primitive human being. He was more than an ape, more than just another primate; he was the animal with the greatest all-around sensory acuity, the greatest intelligence, the greatest manipulative ability, and the most complex culture in the world.

Of course, the change was gradual and continuous, yet in evolutionary terms it was rapid and unique. In fact, the distinction between *Australopithecus* and *Homo* is understated even by a generic boundary, for it marks the difference between animal and man, a difference that cannot be neglected.

11.5 The first men

THERE IS NO DOUBT that throughout the Pliocene the evolving hominids survived as a result of their social structure as much as of their intelligence, for social life is one of the primates' most important adaptations. By the early Pleistocene, therefore, we would expect *Australopithecus* to have a stable and well-adapted social system. We have evidence of the kind of food remains this hominid was leaving (see 7.11) and the climatic conditions in which he lived (Evernden and Curtis 1965, p. 383), which appear to have been much like those of the present day. From this we have deduced that the hamadryas baboon might suggest a possible model for his evolving social structure (see 9.9). Although the evidence is limited, this hypothesis seems the best available at present for the origin of human society. We have noted, too (see 9.6), the absence of great sexual dimorphism in *Australopithecus* and have suggested that this lack might be correlated with the reduction in the importance of the dominance hierarchy in a social structure based on one-male groups.

But the analogy between hamadryas and *Australopithecus* must not be pressed; the two genera are very different, and their behavior and society may be quite distinct. If, however, *Australopithecus* did evolve one-male grouping as an ecological adaptation, there is little doubt that he must have retained a wider troop structure as an interbreeding unit and as a basis for cooperation in defense against predators.

Cooperative hunting cannot have arisen out of a vacuum, but must have come gradually from another related cultural adaptation. In the same way that a physical structure may prove preadaptive for different functions, so cultural structures may equally serve a novel purpose. From what we know of the behavior of baboons, it is not unreasonable to suppose that behavioral adaptations for cooperative defense gave rise to cooperative offense. There is, in fact, considerable evidence of cooperative hunting among baboons. One eyewitness has, during twenty years, repeatedly observed, in South Africa,

> apparently organized hunts which often result in the death of the intended victim. The baboons, usually led by a veteran of the troop, surround an unsuspecting three-parts grown Mountain Reedbuck, or Duiker, as the case may be, and on one occasion, a young Reedbuck doe was the victim. It would appear that on a given signal the baboons close in on their quarry, catch it and tear it asunder. . . . In nine cases out of ten,

the game animal is devoured limb by limb, and after the affair is all over all that is to be found is the skull and leg bones [Oakley 1951].

Such behavior may be unusual for baboons, but it does suggest that the difference between cooperative defense and cooperative offense is not very great. Many primates use signals for troop control: what is interesting here is that the baboons show the sort of discipline that we associate with dogs, when they act as cooperative hunters. It appears that primates are sufficiently versatile in their behavior to develop this particular pattern when it proves to be adaptive.

It is clear, however, that, unlike the baboon with its powerful jaws and canines, neither *Australopithecus* nor *Ramapithecus* would have been able to hunt and kill large animals without weapons. It is possible to stun animals by accurate stone-throwing, and some African peoples today will corner a large hippopotamus by throwing sand in its eyes. But it is hard to cut up any large mammal without tools; the skin and tissues are extremely tough. However advanced the tools of *Australopithecus* were, it does appear on the basis of the present evidence that they were not enough advanced to kill or to cut up large mammals.

We can surmise little else about the behavior of *Australopithecus,* but we know a great deal more about *Homo erectus.* From the fossil evidence, we can see that early man had the skill and endurance to catch and kill large mammals—a skill and endurance that would be hard for any reader of this book to develop. Besides a variety of stone tools (Fig. 11.3), *Homo erectus* probably used clubs of wood and bone, and perhaps even simple spears. With only stone tools preserved, together with an occasional shaped bone, it is hard for us to know just how extensive the development of non-stone culture must have been, but we can guess that, with large mammals at their disposal, early men were not slow to utilize the skins, sinews, and bones for a number of purposes. Bolas stones linked by leather thongs were a case in point. All this required manual dexterity of a high order; a dexterity evolved in the forest as a locomotor adaptation was preadaptive for the creation of a material culture.

It has been pointed out that motor control depends on feedback from proprioceptors (see 3.6). The muscle proprioceptors make possible precise motor control of limbs for locomotion, especially important in arboreal locomotion. More precise human motor activity requires other sensory feedback as well; manipulation requires visual and tactile feedback, and speech requires aural feedback. It is possible to write with one's eyes closed but difficult to maintain legibility; it is not possible for a totally deaf child to learn to speak and sing normally. The evolution of manipulation and the evolution of speech seem to have gone hand in hand, and they appear to involve extensive cross-connections in the cerebral cortex between the different sensory receiving areas (visual, somesthetic, and auditory cortexes) and the motor cortex. It is

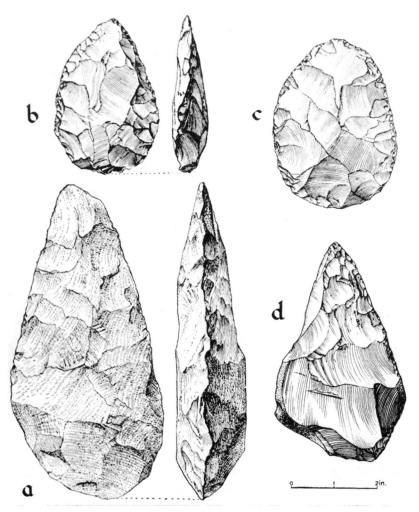

FIG. 11.3. Acheulian tools of the Middle Pleistocene, from Olorgesailie, Kenya (*A*), St. Acheul, France (*B*), Wady Sidr, Palestine (*C*), and Hoxne, England (*D*). (By permission of the trustees of the British Museum [Natural History].)

these corticocortical connections that are such a striking character of the human brain and that are a necessary correlate of manipulation and speech.

This integration of sensory input and motor experience has, of course, occurred in respect to both action and memory. Both manipulative skill and speech require memory of neuronal motor patterns; words are as much a pattern of motor activity as they are sounds, and the motor pattern and the sound are memorized together. This motor-sound pattern is linked by reflex learning to a concept, and the concept to a percept. The total capacity of human memory, of percept and motor pattern, with complete cross-referencing, is almost beyond our imagination. Hypnosis reveals that an enormous amount of experience is recorded in the brain—even experience of the most trifling kind. Pfeiffer concludes that during one lifetime, a man can store about ten times more information than is contained in the nine million volumes of the Library of Congress (Pfeiffer 1955, p. 85).

We must finally note that the evolution of man has been characterized not only by an enlarged brain, though such enlargement is a striking correlate of corticocortical nerve tracts and this vastly increased memory store, but also by an enormous expansion of its computing properties. We have seen (in 2.6) the relationship between input, memory, and the ability to predict, and, of course, it is this ability to make increasingly valid prediction that characterizes human evolution. The more experience (the bigger the input) and the more detailed the sensory analysis, the more knowledge gained of the environment (the bigger the memory); and the more knowledge, the greater the possibility of correct prediction. Rosenblueth et al. (1943) point out that predictions of a high order are limited to organisms with evolved spatial receptors. Input relating to all three dimensions of space must be integrated to some kind of timing mechanism to make possible human perception of events as they follow each other; and human perception is unique.

Intelligent thought is the conscious prediction of events made on each occasion on the basis of the totality of experience. Because man can put more data into his computer, his prediction can be more accurate than that of any other creature. This is man's great strength: action mediated by accurate prediction, activity based on reason.

G. G. Simpson has written:

It is important to realize that man is an animal, but it is even more important to realize that the essence of his unique nature lies precisely in those characteristics that are not shared with any other animal. His place in nature and its supreme significance to man are not defined by his animality but by his humanity [1949, p. 284].

Although there are many other characteristics of humanity, perhaps the most fundamental is his enhanced ability to predict, which we recognize as reason. Reason was no doubt poorly developed in the first *Homo erectus,* but it made possible his survival by the development of new cultural adaptations, and its value is today reflected in man's dominance over other forms of life.

11.6 The genus Homo

ONE OF THE MOST STRIKING FACTS about *Homo,* as compared with *Australopithecus,* is its relatively wide distribution. At present, *Australopithecus* is known only from Africa, and, although some teeth from China and one of the earliest hominid fragments from Java have been tentatively identified as of this genus, the evidence is at present too slight to warrant any certainty in the matter (Tobias and von Koenigswald 1964). There are, in fact, no hominid fossils from Europe or Asia between *Ramapithecus* from India and the earliest Pleistocene fossils from Java; there is a gap of perhaps 12 million years. This gap does not mean that the intervening forms did not exist in Asia or Europe, but merely that we have no present evidence for their existence. Up to the present, the paleontological research carried out in the Pliocene of India and China is very limited, and it would be rash indeed to assume that Africa was the only area in which *Australopithecus* evolved.

It is striking, however, that we have fossils of early *Homo erectus**
from Java and China as well as from Africa. It could be that the evolution of cooperative hunting and its associated behavioral and anatomical adaptations enabled early *Homo* to spread from central Africa north up the Nile Valley into Asia and east through the tropical zones of India and Southeastern Asia. In the absence of a constant

---

* Until recently, the fossils described here as *Homo erectus* were placed in the genus *Pithecanthropus* and termed *Pithecanthropus erectus.*

environment throughout that area, the spread would have been made possible only by the evolution of a degree of versatility unique in the primate order, together with a very rapid assimilation of novel cultural adaptations. Man had arisen from nomadic scavenging bands, and his tendency to keep moving may have eventually led him into Asia, which was a vast area ready for occupation and exploitation, an area in which human evolution would further accelerate.

Possibly the earliest Asian fragment of man comes from Sangiran, Java (see Fig. 11.4). It was originally named *Meganthropus* but is probably best considered a very early form of *Homo erectus*. It is a mandibular fragment containing three teeth and is therefore considerably less meaningful to us than the fragmentary skulls of about the same age from Sangiran and from Chenchiawo in China (see Appendix, p. 368). The first, described by Weidenreich (1945), has a cranial capacity of 900 cc.; the second, described by Woo (1965), has a cranial capacity of only 780 cc. From Africa we have one skull from the early part of the Middle Pleistocene that has not yet been described, but it appears to have a very small cranial capacity (Leakey *et al.* 1964, p. 8, skull No. 13). Some interesting fragments of jaws and teeth are also known from Olduvai, and they closely resemble the Javanese forms (Tobias and von Koenigswald 1964). It should be added that we have no reliable absolute dates for the Asian fossils, though the range 700,000–500,000 years B.P. is a likely approximation. In Africa, the earliest forms that might be attibuted to *Homo erectus* come from Olduvai Bed II and may date from nearly 1 million years B.P. (Tobias *et al.* 1965).

There are very close similarities between many of the Olduvai and Javanese fossils, a fact that need not surprise us. It is indeed encouraging that at this period the fossil record is relatively complete and that we can trace so well the transition from *Australopithecus* to *Homo erectus* at Olduvai (Howell, in Evernden and Curtis 1965). The morphological and chronological relationships between the different individual fossils require much more analysis than is at present available before we can establish their classification with any certainty. There is reason to hope, however, that with so much material for study the picture will be greatly clarified in the not too distant future. We can only generalize at present that at the beginning of the Middle Pleistocene (say, about 1 million years ago), an early form of *Homo* became slowly established throughout the tropical regions of Africa

FIG. 11.4. Map of the Old World showing the locality of some of the important sites mentioned in the text and listed in the Appendix.

and Asia. While we have at Olduvai a unique record of the evolution of *Homo* from *Australopithecus* in stratigraphical sequence, we have no reason to suppose that the evolving populations did not in fact cover a much wider area.

The genus *Homo* has been compared with the genus *Australopithecus* by Le Gros Clark (1964), and the following is based on his definition and that of Leakey *et al.* (1964, p. 6).

Homo: a genus of the Hominidae distinguished by the following characters:

A large cranial capacity with a mean value of more than 1,100 cc. but with a considerable range of variation, from about 700 cc. to almost 2,000 cc.

Masticatory apparatus variable in size but relatively smaller than the neurocranium when compared with *Australopithecus* and much reduced in modern *H. sapiens;* accompanying changes involve flattening of face.

Forward movement of occipital condyles in relation to skull as a whole.

Reduced masticatory musculature with temporal ridges never reaching the midline of the cranial vault, their height being variable.

Nuchal area relatively smaller than in *Australopithecus,* variable, and in *Homo sapiens* much reduced.

Skull more rounded, and muscular attachment areas in general variable in size but less well marked than in *Australopithecus,* and in modern man almost imperceptible.

Supraorbital torus variably developed, being enlarged in *Homo erectus,* though with reduced postorbital constriction compared with *Australopithecus;* torus much reduced in some subspecies of *Homo sapiens.*

Dental arcade evenly rounded, usually with no diastema.

Mandible less deep than in *Australopithecus* but variable in its horizontal stressing, from an internal torus in *Homo erectus* to an external chin in many subspecies of *Homo sapiens.*

Canines relatively small, with no overlapping after the initial stages of wear.

First lower premolar bicuspid with a reduced lingual cusp.

Molar teeth variable in size, with a relative reduction of M3.

Forelimb shorter than hindlimb.

Pollex well developed and fully opposable, so the hand is capable of
a precision grip.

Hindlimb skeleton seems not to be very variable and is fully adapted
to bipedal locomotion, as in modern man.

Following the early *Homo erectus* fossils from Java, China, and
Tanzania, we have some more skulls or jaws of slightly more modern
appearance from many sites in the Old World. These date from approximately 550,000 to 350,000 years B.P., and the most valuable come
from Tanzania (Olduvai), Algeria (Ternifine), Germany (Heidelberg),
Hungary (Vértesszöllös), Java (Trinil), and China (Choukoutien)
(Fig. 11.4). In these specimens we find cranial capacities of around
1,000 cc., yet the heavy brow ridges are retained (see Fig. 3.13, *A,*
p. 81). Though the brain is expanding, the jaws are not yet reduced.
All these fossils may be classified as *Homo erectus,* but they clearly
represent later and more *sapiens*-like populations than those we have
discussed so far (Howell 1960). Their distribution is broader, and
they reach the most northerly points occupied by any hominid so far,
latitude 41° in China and 49° in Germany. As has been stated, from
the Chinese site near Peking we have evidence of fire as well as of

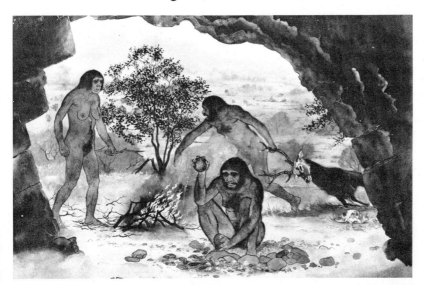

Fig. 11.5. Imaginative reconstruction of the life of *Homo erectus* from
Peking. (By permission of the trustees of the British Museum [Natural
History].)

large mammals in the diet (Fig. 11.5). We find man cave-dwelling in these colder climates, with a hearth and a home base; no doubt his hunting activities supplied him with skins for clothes as well as other byproducts that could be utilized in the development of a growing material culture.

The distribution of the known fossils of *Homo erectus* is indicated on the map, Figure 11.4. For convenience, the different geographical groups of populations that the fossils represent may be classified as subspecies, and that has been done in Table 11.1.

TABLE 11.1 SUBSPECIES OF HOMO ERECTUS

Approx. Time-span (Years B.P.)	Europe	N. Africa	E. and S. Africa	E. Asia
350,000– 550,000	—	mauritanicus	leakeyi	erectus and pekinensis
550,000– 900,000	heidelbergensis	—	habilis*	modjokertensis

* Specimens from Tanzania (Olduvai, lower Bed II) and South Africa (Swartkrans).

11.7 The rise of modern man

THE EARLIEST FOSSILS that can be classified as *Homo sapiens* are those from Swanscombe in England and Steinheim in Germany (Fig. 11.4). The former consists of the parietal and occipital bones only, the latter of a skull without a mandible. But there is enough here to demonstrate the presence (at 52° latitude) of a hominid far more like modern man than *Homo erectus,* yet still quite distinct from ourselves (Fig. 11.6). The date of these skulls, which come from the Mindel-Riss interglacial period, is still uncertain, but they are unlikely to be more than 200,000 years B.P. and may be as little as 150,000 years B.P. There is, then, a considerable chronological gap between these fossils and those of *Homo erectus* that we have been considering. Although 150,000 years is not a long time in the process of evolution, during this period *Homo erectus* evolved into *Homo sapiens,* and the brain increased from about 1,100 to 1,300 cc. For the present, however, the gap makes a convenient boundary between the earlier and the later species of *Homo.*

FIG. 11.6. Imaginative reconstruction of the life of early *Homo sapiens* from Swanscombe. (By permission of the trustees of the British Museum [Natural History].)

Similar in both age and form the Swanscombe and Steinheim skulls represent a population that spread across the plains of northern Europe during a warm period of the Pleistocene (Howell 1960, Ovey 1964). Though their cranial capacity was nearly as great as that of modern man, their masticatory apparatus (as seen in the Steinheim skull) was still not yet fully reduced, and the supraorbital torus was still more pronounced than in modern man (Fig. 11.7). What reduction had occurred, however, was not a world-wide phenomenon, for the Stein-

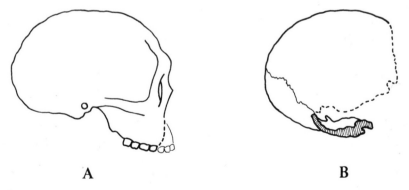

A   B

FIG. 11.7. Skull of early *Homo sapiens* from Steinheim (*A*) and skull bones from Swanscombe (*B*).

heim-Swanscombe population in Europe was replaced, after a period of extreme climatic conditions accompanied by glaciation, by another population, which, although it had an equally large cranial capacity, had at the same time retained a heavy masticatory apparatus only slightly smaller than that of *Homo erectus.* This large-jawed population, with its heavy supraorbital torus and large nuchal area, is known by the name of *Neandertal,* where the first fossil human skull to be so described was found in 1858. This Neandertal population, so much more primitive in appearance than its predecessor, remained in western Europe until the final glaciation of the Pleistocene, when it was replaced by a modern population, some 35,000–50,000 years ago (see Figs. 3.12, *N* and *M,* p. 81).

These three successive European occupations are related to the succession of cold glacial and warm interglacial periods that we associate with the Pleistocene in the Northern Hemisphere. Rapidly changing climatic conditions there caused frequent migrations and rapid adaptation among the plants and animals of Europe and Asia. Only the southernmost part of the continent avoided very drastic climatic modifications—the Arabian peninsula, India, and southeastern Asia. Under these variable conditions, the nomadic hunting populations of *Homo* must have moved north and south, east and west, following the game and vegetable zones. In this way, we can account for the changing populations of Europe, variable in facial morphology but all big-brained.

We have discussed Europe in this section because more is known of early *Homo sapiens* from that area than from elsewhere. We have, however, evidence of the big-jawed forms both from southern Africa and from western and southeastern Asia, so they were certainly widely spread at one time. However, interestingly enough, all the fossils we know are quite late in time (about 50,000 years B.P.), and, while we know nothing of their immediate predecessors, we know that all were replaced very suddenly by modern forms. This means that modern man was evolving elsewhere: in central and northern Africa or southern Asia.

Although we have no relevant fossil evidence from those other areas, there is no reason to suppose that the evolution of man did not occur over a wide area; *Homo* was nomadic, and gene flow was accordingly rapid and extensive. The most satisfactory hypothesis on the basis of the present evidence is that his evolution occurred over a wide area in Africa, Europe, and Asia but that relict populations survived in certain marginal areas, where they may have been temporarily isolated by desert, glaciers, or sea. Whether at a later date they were reabsorbed by hybridization is an open question, but, in spite of man's tendency to kill any competitors in his ecological niche, it seems likely that at least some genes from these populations may have become incorporated into our modern populations.

It is of interest that the big-jawed fossils recovered from western Asia (Israel and Iraq) are in some cases more modern in appearance than their contemporaries in Europe, Africa, and southeastern Asia, though the distinction is not very clear (McCown and Keith 1939). Only further discoveries from the central areas of the Old World of fossils that are at least 100,000 years old can tell us whether the advanced Steinheim-like forms evolved in Asia and Africa as well as in Europe.

Our ignorance about the evolution of *Homo* is still great, but for convenience it is helpful to use subspecific designations for the different populations we have mentioned. They are listed in Table 11.2 in spatial and temporal sequence.

TABLE 11.2 SUBSPECIES OF HOMO SAPIENS

Approx. Time-span (Years B.P.)	Europe	Asia	Africa	S. E. Asia
0–35,000	Modern subspecies of *Homo sapiens**			
35,000–100,000	neanderthalensis	palestinus	rhodesiensis	soloensis
100,000–200,000	steinheimensis	—	†	—

* Modern man probably entered Australia and America about 20,000 years B.P.
† Undescribed fossils from Olduvai may fill this gap.

11.8 Modern man as a zoological species

THE FINAL SCENES in this story of human evolution show the replacement of the large-jawed forms by the small-jawed people—ourselves. In the continuously evolving organic world, what we see around us today is, as it were, one frame in the continuing motion picture of human evolution; "mankind evolving" is the subject of Dobzhansky's important book (1962). We find man to be as we are today, living in the places we occupy, doing the things we are doing.

Our genes and our environment together have created us as we find ourselves; our physical nature and our behavior are so determined. Our society and culture have brought about the situation in which we read this book now; it is all part of our complex process of adaptation to each other and to the planet on which we live.

But much has happened in these most recent phases of human evolution. Since the appearance of man indistinguishable from ourselves, which is recorded in the fossil record in France (Cro-Magnon) and other sites (Fig. 3.12, *M*, p. 81), in Kenya (Kanjera), and in southeastern Asia (Niah in Sarawak), about 40,000-50,000 years ago, he has spread throughout the land masses of the Old and the New World and now occupies a vast range of environments. Stable populations are adapted for life in the arctic and in the desert. Man's adaptations are of course both physical and cultural: variations in body form and body chemistry are adaptations to the environment, as are variations in culture.

We are not yet able to account for all such variations in terms of their functions, but we can understand a certain number, especially the most obvious ones, such as the ratio of surface area to weight (Fig. 11.8), which is correlated with temperature and relative humidity, or skin and eye color, which is correlated with solar radiation (see 8.9), or nose shape, which is correlated with absolute humidity (see 8.4). These kinds of bodily adaptations are clear enough to make recognizable the sorts of differences that zoologists would classify as subspecific, and, as a result, anthropologists recognize between six and nine different subspecies that have arisen as modern man's adaptations to different ecological situations (Garn 1961) (Table 11.3 and Fig. 11.9). Of course, their isolation is incomplete, and gene flow continues be-

TABLE 11.3 SUBSPECIES OR GEOGRAPHICAL RACES OF MODERN MAN (AFTER GARN 1961) (SEE FIG. 11.9)

	Notes
1. Amerindian	
2. Polynesian	Polynesians, Melanesians, and Micronesians
3. Melanesian	are combined by some authors
4. Australian	as a single group.
5. Asiatic	
6. Indian	Indians and Europeans are combined
7. European	by some authors as Caucasians.
8. African	
9. Micronesian	

Fig. 11.8. Two neighboring tribes in East Africa show very different physical adaptations. On the left is one of the pygmies from the rain forests of the Congo; on the right, one of the Dinka, a tribe that lives in the desert regions of the upper Nile. They represent the tallest and shortest people in the world. (Courtesy British Museum [Natural History].)

tween them; otherwise they would be defined as distinct species. Man is a single widely dispersed polytypic species, showing adaptation to a wide range of environments.

One of the difficulties in understanding the adaptations that distinguish the different subspecies of modern man lies in his nomadic nature. Evolution is a slow process, but migration can be rapid, and, as a result, populations originally genetically adapted to climate A are now, as a result of the high adaptive value of culture, living in climate B. As we recognized earlier (see 10.1), organic adaptation in man therefore lags far behind environmental change. The problems intro-

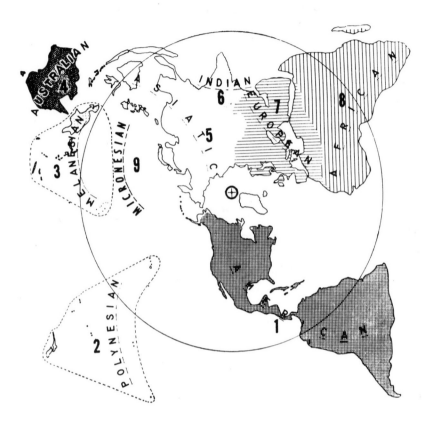

FIG. 11.9. Distribution of nine surviving geographical subspecies of *Homo sapiens*. Each is bounded by natural barriers in the form of sea, ice, mountains, or desert. (From Garn, 1961.)

duced by migration in understanding racial differentiation and characterization are very great. To understand the relationship between the present pattern of *Homo sapiens* populations and their environment must involve, in practice, a consideration of their cultural adaptations as well as their anatomical and physiological characters.

The recent phases in human evolution are striking at both an organic and a cultural level. As Washburn has pointed out in an important paper on the study of race (1963a), there were perhaps from three to five times as many Bushmen as there were Europeans only

15,000 years ago, when the ice sheets of the last glaciation reduced the habitable area of Europe to half that available to the Bushmen in eastern and southern Africa (Fig. 11.10). Since that time, differential population growth has changed the whole pattern of *Homo sapiens* on the face of the earth, so, as a result, although the majority of racial elements have probably survived, their proportions have changed out of all recognition.

As we all know, one after another population has undergone the so-called "cultural revolutions" that marked the beginnings of the ages of agriculture, of metallurgy, and of industrialization. Each revolution

FIG. 11.10. On the right is shown a sketch of a Bushwoman from the Kalahari Desert in South Africa. She shows well the remarkable and characteristic steatopygia, which is found in this extreme form among only two tribes (Bushmen and Hottentots). On the left is a drawing of a figurine (8 inches high) recovered from Savignano in Italy, which is possibly over 20,000 years old. Relics of this kind suggest that steatopygia was widespread in Europe in prehistoric times.

has brought with it improved adaptation and has resulted in population growth. Today we find industrialized countries supporting an immensely greater population per square mile in comparison with those at an earlier stage of cultural development. This increased population has been made possible by a whole range of adaptations, including the organization of a greater food supply and, recently, advances in medical science. Life expectancy has improved beyond all recognition. Even today, in South Africa, a white woman can expect twenty-five more years of life than can a black woman (Washburn 1963a). Changes in life expectancy are readily subject to cultural adjustment; they can rapidly change the distribution pattern of *Homo sapiens* and will probably do so again as they have in the past.

As we find him today, *Homo sapiens* is in a state of rapid change, change that is due, not so much perhaps to an increase in rate of evolution (such a rate cannot at present be satisfactorily measured), as to an increase in rate of cultural change, which has brought with it fast migration and very fast adaptation. These developments in culture place man in an unusual situation, which requires some further elucidation.

11.9 Tools and technology— man's material culture

FROM WHAT has been said in the preceding pages, it seems not unreasonable to trace the origins of man's material culture to two of his special mental attributes: his perception and his intelligence.

We have discussed the importance of the evolution of human perception at some length (see 10.2), and its significance as a correlate and determinant of culture cannot be overrated. Man came to see his environment in a unique manner, one that carried a greater informational content about the nature of the environment than any other. We now know that the real structure of our environment is beyond our perception, for it is an emptiness sparsely occupied by electric charges moving at great speed. There is no world corresponding to the world of our common experience. But the way the human organism came to perceive the average effect of these electrical phenomena has fashioned his world. His senses enabled him to form in his mind the percepts of objects, solid, colored, and textured; these objects lie in his mind, not in the environment, and what other animals make of these electric charges, which constitute the environment, we cannot tell. One special character of human perception was, however, that since it depended so much on manipulation it came in turn to facilitate manipulation; because it evolved to a great extent from the motor investigation of texture and form through effectance motivation, it came in time to increase the motor investigation of the objective world as it was perceived.

The evolution of manipulation for the manufacture of tools, and eventually for the advance of technology, has come to depend, appropriately, on the development of perception. Man has used his tools to increase his sensory awareness and to reveal still further the nature of matter and organic life. By the beginning of the seventeenth century man had invented the telescope, which enabled him to see more clearly the form of the universe, and the microscope, which enabled him to perceive the minute structure of matter and organisms. Today, powerful telescopes and electron microscopes have vastly increased our visual perception, just as amplifiers, thermometers, and chemical analysis have effectively increased the range and sensitivity of our other senses.

Modern technology appears to be based on this expanding knowledge of our environment, which springs from our increased powers of perception. There is a limit to this increase, however, because we find that at the microcosmic level we are dealing with electric phenomena that can no longer be termed objects, since they do not have simultaneously a position and a velocity. It follows that, while there is much to be done in developing these aids to perception, the development of technology may in the future receive its impetus from the mechanization of other mental processes that characterize the brain, and, in particular, the processes of computation and prediction. The computer, another superorganic extension of the human brain, will in turn come to modify man's relationship with his environment.

The second factor that is complementary to man's unique perception is, of course, his intelligence: his ability to make conscious deductions on the basis of his experience, his power to reason. We have mentioned the conscious nature of intelligent thought, and the hypothesis springs to mind that it was the adaptive value of reason that brought the evolution of self-awareness (see 10.8). Whether or not this was so, it seems that human perception and human reason, interacting under the competitive conditions of organic life, are the twin bases from which we may suppose the growth of human material culture to have developed.

We must also recall that human culture has one essential character: it embodies a complex means of communication. Just as sexual reproduction allows a more rapid spread of novel genetic information within the gene pool than would be possible by asexual heredity, so the aspects of cultural behavior that form systems of communication (speech and writing) allow cultural diffusion within an "idea pool" at a fast rate. Writing is, at the same time, culture's own memory, another attribute previously known only in organic life. Today, machines can sense, analyze, and record; memory of percepts and experience are a commonplace, stored in books or on videotape. Man has learned to project into a cultural form most of the activities of his own brain. Man's unique achievement was, therefore, in the first place, the extension of his motor function and, in the second place, the extension of his sensory and neural functions, all by means of a material culture.

The "brain-like" nature of culture, so obvious in its store of knowledge and ability to compute probabilities, is derived from the abilities not of one man but of a whole society. No one man, without education, could build a computer or write an encyclopedia. Culture is the long-accumulated experience and knowledge of the whole society. The basis of the idea of involution is that cooperation replaces evolutionary radiation and that by cooperation man is creating machines of a superhuman kind. Culture is in one sense the group mind of *Homo sapiens*, and it depends on cooperation.

The advantages of cooperation have of course resulted in the evolution of society not only among men but among many different kinds of animals. As we have seen, these societies have in turn evolved quite sophisticated means of communication, yet only among men have the material products of cooperation been preserved as an external record of experience. It is the development of human society's high-speed communication systems, its sensory and motor machines, and its memories and computors that differentiates it from any other. Soon, as a result of the development of "multiple access," we shall be able to dial our problems to the state computor by telephone. When we can do that, our function will no longer be to solve problems but to invent them. As Herrick has written, "the most significant characteristic of intelligence is the ability to invent problems. This capacity for imaginative or creative thinking marks the highest level of integration in the organic realm" (1956, p. 359).

11.10 The function of modern culture

WE HAVE TRIED to understand the adaptive nature of the three aspects of culture: mentifacts and socifacts (10.7, 10.8) as well as artifacts (11.9). Yet when we turn to consider the present state of man, it looks as though culture is failing as an adaptive mechanism —as though it may lead to destruction rather than preservation of the species. In this connection there are three features of modern culture that may throw some light on the complexity of our cultural adaptation and help us understand it.

In the first place, modern culture makes a very effective barrier between man and the external environment that is outside his cultural adaptations. The result is that under the shield of culture man is able to survive and breed with a genetic endowment that in the absence of culture would not allow him to survive (the survival of diabetics is an obvious case in point). The dangers of this situation have been repeatedly stressed and have been recently discussed by Dobzhansky (1962). They will not, therefore, be pursued here; instead, let us consider another aspect of this cultural barrier.

The present acceleration of cultural development may in practice be due not to a primary failure in adaptation but to an imprecision in cultural adaptation. Thus, a particular novel cultural trait that arises in response to a particular environmental condition may also alter a second environmental condition as a by-product. While such imprecision may also occur in organic adaptation, the speed and novelty of cultural change renders it more significant. For example, clothes are developed (perhaps) to cut down heat loss from the body, and, although they are most effective, they also have far-reaching effects on humidity, solar radiation, abrasion, external parasites, and many characters of a sematic kind, especially epigamic features. The original equilibrium is adjusted only to result in a new imbalance; yet, while this imbalance may seem continually to increase, the power to adjust that is allowed us by modern culture can increase too. Human evolution is characterized by a great increase both in immediate environmental variability (through culture) and in cultural adjustment to it. Every development may be an attempt at adaptation, yet it may in turn bring with it a new factor requiring adaptation.

Second, it is clear that one of the central problems of the modern world arises from the fact that cultural adaptation has gone further in some social groups than in others and in any case is of a different nature in different places. Nations that have steadily evolved cultural adaptations find themselves today (in the absence of war) in a relatively stable environment. Nations with different and more limited cultural adaptations may as a result of modern communications and transport receive culture "secondhand" from culturally more "advanced" nations, which may amount to a gross change in the environment and in turn cause a biologically unstable period, requiring considerable cultural adjustment on the part of the native population. To give a simple example: in England the increase in the means of production that resulted in an increased food supply occurred at the same time as (if not before) the developments in medical science that raised the life expectancy from about forty to about sixty-five years of age. There was, in fact, enough food available for the vastly increasing population. Today, in many countries we see the results of medical science as an improvement in life expectancy, without its accompanying and necessary improvement in food supply; the result is intermittent famine. Culture contact, by its nature, introduces instability into the environment of human populations insofar as such populations absorb behavior patterns that for them are nonadaptive. They must then adapt to these patterns. In fact, it is a remarkable sign of the adaptive efficiency of culture that contact is not always disastrous. On occasions it has been fatal (the Tasmanians could not survive it), and it has often been nearly fatal (as for the North American Indians), but in most instances adaptation rapidly follows.

Third, we must recognize that cultural adaptations are not always directed toward the impact of the external environment. They also serve to protect society against the individual, for man's survival depends on the integrity of his society, and, as we have seen (10.7), cultural behavior is directed toward maintaining that integrity. The problem is particularly acute in the large social groups that characterize modern man. Possibly we may come to see that national enterprises, such as war-making (almost certainly unique to modern man) and, more recently, space exploration, are adaptations to maintain the bonding of the societies that undertake them. Equally, the occupations they afford keep individuals from facing an excess of leisure, which is another phenomenon that Western society must face and to which it must adapt.

When man is not engaged in work that occupies him totally, he can look into his own mind with intelligent self-awareness, and he will find there something more intractable than the external environment. As Eiseley has written (1958), "ancestral man entered his own head, and he has been adapting ever since to what he finds there." There is no doubt that a great deal of human behavior that appears to be non-adaptive, often termed religious and frequently (though not necessarily) ritualized, arises in response to some form of projection into the environment of mental experience that is not rationally understood. With his increase in leisure, Western man turns from his society's god to a personal god, as well as to his psychiatrist; he must come to terms with the phenomenon of his own consciousness.

We see then that human culture springs in some very general sense from the projection into the environment of human neural attributes and mental experience. Man extends his means of perception, his means of computation and of memory, into the outside world. He uses these extensions as adaptations to his environment. In understanding his needs, in using his reason, man comes finally to look into himself, and he must in turn adapt to what he finds in his own consciousness. Man has to live not only with his environment and with his fellows but also with himself, and his behavior is an adaptation to all three.

11.11 The dream animal

APART FROM our great ignorance of biological organization that is the structure of life, the supreme problem for the biologist lies in the evolution of consciousness and its relationship to matter. Because consciousness is often believed to be a specially human character and because of the difficulties of any attempt to study a phenomenon so subjective, this mysterious problem has received scant attention from biologists. Hinshelwood (1959) is one of the few distinguished scientists who have drawn attention to it and discussed the form of the problem. As he said, "the question of the relation of the internal and external worlds cannot and should not be ignored by men of science."

Both he and Thorpe (1965) argue that human behavior is not machine-like, and it is clear that the mind-matter relation should not be totally ignored in any text on the evolution of man. The difficulty for the scientist arises from the fact that he is used to dealing with observable data, and, apart from one's own subjective experience, the existence of consciousness in others can only be inferred. But, as Hinshelwood points out, somewhat the same comment could apply to the existence of the atomic nucleus; in the absence of direct observation, we can regard its existence only on the basis of inference as in the highest degree probable. As was said in the Introduction to this book, all that science is really ever in a position to offer is a coherent body of evidence that has emerged from a large number of varied tests.

The evidence for human consciousness arises ultimately from our social intercourse, and therefore it does not allow us to postulate with any certainty the existence of consciousness in animals (see Sperry 1965); but evidence from those who have lived with animals intimately, whether with birds, dogs, lions, or primates, suggests strongly that some degree of consciousness exists, at least in the warm-blooded vertebrates (Thorpe 1965). As already suggested, it is probable that consciousness, like any other human character, evolved slowly, and it may indeed appear in its most simple form at much lower levels of life than has been supposed. If consciousness is a function of brain, and the two are certainly concomitant, then we can postulate its evolution to coincide at least with the evolution of the vertebrate central nervous system. This is, in fact, the simplest and therefore the most acceptable hypothesis, though at present it cannot be tested.

But man has something more than mere consciousness; he also has self-awareness, for, while the animal knows, only man knows that he knows. Here, we are on even more difficult ground, and indeed we have no evidence and no clue to the history of this heightened consciousness. For the present, we must stick to our interpretation of the fall of man (see 10.8). With that in mind, we may see with Dobzhansky (1962) and others that self-awareness is man's distinctive mental character, a character which, linked with imagination, has raised him to the status of lord of creation. Hallowell describes the adaptive value of self-awareness as follows:

The attribute of self-awareness, which involves man's capacity to discriminate himself as an object in a world of objects other than himself, is as central to our understanding of the prerequisites of man's social and cultural mode of adjustment as it is for the psychodynamics of the individual. A human social order implies a mode of existence that has meaning for the individual at the level of self-awareness. A human social order, for example, is always a moral order. If the individual did not have the capacity for identifying the conduct that is his own and, through self-reflection, appraising it with reference to values and social sanctions, how would a moral order function in human terms? If I cannot assume moral responsibility for my conduct, how can guilt or shame arise? What conflict can there be between impulse and standards if I am unaware of values or sanctions? It is man's capacity for and development of self-awareness that makes such unconscious psychological mechanisms as repression, rationalization, and so on of adaptive importance for the individual. They would have no function otherwise. They allow the individual to function without full self-knowledge [1953, p. 614].

Hallowell also points out that the development of self-awareness is dependent on the projection of the internal experience in socially meaningful terms. Only speech, in fact, can reveal to an individual his self-objectification; speech is necessary for self-awareness (as Sperry 1965 has suggested), and self-awareness is necessary for the moral order of human society. While some self-awareness may exist in apparently moral animals like dogs, its full development is surely confined to man.

With the evolution of modern man, therefore, a new loneliness comes into his life; his separate nature is revealed to him by the evolution of new mental processes. As Eiseley (1958, p. 125) has put it, "for the first time in four billion years a living creature has contemplated himself and heard with a sudden, unaccountable loneliness, the whisper of the wind in the night reeds." Man looked at his environment and knew himself to be no part of it; he was alone, and he was divided from the source of his being (see Frontispiece).

11.12 *Human evolution*

IN THE FIRST CHAPTER of this book evolution was described as a homeostatic adjustment in a living system in response to environmental change, which can be the outcome only of such adjustment and nothing more. We have seen throughout our account of man's adaptations to a changing environment that this adjustment, whether at a physiological, anatomical, or social level, is made by shifts in the mean of variable characters. We have seen how the amount of stability found in the occurrence of bodily characters and behavior is maintained by the evolution of factors which, like exogamy, induce variability or, like ritual, instill stability into the dynamic living process.

We have seen how the primitive mammal—already a remarkable and immensely complex evolutionary product—became adapted to arboreal life. We have observed that the beginnings of erect posture occurred in the forest and have noted the concomitant changes in limb structure, in hand and foot. We have seen how primates were pre-adapted for plains life by their diet and posture either as quadrupeds or as bipeds, and we have tried to elucidate how they further adapted once they entered their new environment.

Perhaps the most essential humanizing adaptation was the increasing importance of society as a mechanism for survival; society and culture are what have saved us from extinction and made us men, just as we in turn create our society. In the words that Gordon Child chose as a title for his famous book, "man makes himself." And that is the curious feature of human evolution; somehow, man himself seems to be involved in the creative process, up to the present unconsciously, perhaps in the future consciously.

But what we have recounted is no more than a rough sketch of our subject. We know so little that we have been able only to glimpse a process of great duration and immense complexity. We might be forgiven for doubting that anything less than a miracle was needed to produce, by a process of adjustment from some strings of amino acids, a Mozart or an Einstein. But, although we have treated only part of this story, in only a very superficial way, we have not found any serious inadequacies in the hypothesis that man shows a particular kind of adaptation to his environment through his independence of it and is indeed the outcome of processes of natural selection.

Yet there are some problems to be acknowledged before we close. One concerns the limits of science, and another concerns the limits of our understanding. There are some special difficulties that are encountered when we attempt to apply the scientific method to human problems (Campbell 1964), difficulties arising from the special relationship between the observer and the observed. We know that perception is far more greatly influenced by previous experience than by the nature of the object that is perceived. Posthypnotic suggestion can completely destroy the reliability of our perceptions, and, at a more everyday level, it can easily be demonstrated that people tend to perceive what they expect to perceive rather than what is before them. The frailty of human perception is notorious, and it is particularly subject to aberration when the subject and object already have some relationship, real or imagined. For that reason, our interpretation of the evidence relating to human evolution may be subject to prejudice of which we know nothing. The dispassionate intellect exists only as an ideal, and an approach to it is made increasingly difficult as the subject and object are more closely involved with each other. The difficulties are particularly intense when we attempt to study our own behavior and culture; they are well demonstrated by the different schools of psychoanalysis. A perfectly objective analysis of human behavior could not be made by any human being.

In this context it is also well to recall that we are in the power of the *zeitgeist,* the contemporary way of looking at the world and at man—another important kind of aberration that destroys the clear focus of our science. This book, like almost every other, is a product of the times, with an emphasis that is typically slanted. The distortions in human studies are inbuilt and unavoidable. It is clear, however, that any approach to the truth can result only from the accumulation and record of human experience of every kind.

Finally, we must recognize the limits of our understanding, if only to indicate the most exciting directions for future research. The evolution of life and the evolution of consciousness each presents a problem that biologists have not yet solved. These two problems probably have something in common, but, in view of the subject of this book, we shall confine ourselves to the second only. If, like Hinshelwood (1959), we accept the existence of consciousness and mind—and few are likely to deny it today—we can account for it in two ways:

1. The potentiality for life and consciousness exists in every atom (of carbon, hydrogen, oxygen, nitrogen, etc.), and these properties are revealed to us as the atoms are combined into organic molecules of greater and greater complexity. In other words, the fundamental particles have a mental component that is only apparent when they constitute appropriate structures. Thorpe (1965, p. 26) maintains, however, that this suggestion will not stand because it means that an

unbelievable degree of potential organization was in fact present in the randomly moving atoms of the gases of the primordial nebulae: a potentiality for both organic and mental synthesis of vast complexity.

2. An alternative explanation lies in the idea of emergence, the idea that at some stages in the process of evolution a completely new and, in principle, unpredictable quality may appear. Since physics and chemistry know nothing of mind in matter, we must confront this possibility. The only alternative, it seems, is to accept the first possibility—and allow biology to modify physics.

The final solutions to these problems, which have been squarely faced by Thorpe (1965), we cannot foresee, though they may come somewhat nearer in our lifetime. But let us not suppose that the ultimate truth is at all simple. A simplification of any hypothesis or data is always a loss of truth, and we are guilty of such simplification at every turn. We would do well in closing to recall a comment by Whitehead:

> The aim of science is to seek the simplest explanation of complex facts. We are apt to fall into the error of thinking that the facts are simple because simplicity is the goal of our quest. The guiding motto in the life of every natural philosopher should be, seek simplicity and distrust it [1920, p. 163].

SUGGESTIONS FOR FURTHER READING

For a useful discussion of some of the problems mentioned in the early part of this chapter see D. R. Pilbeam and E. L. Simons, "Some Problems of Hominid Classification," *Amer. Sci.* 53 (1965): 237–59. For an account of the differentiation of modern man see W. W. Howells, "The Distribution of Man," *Scient. Amer.* 203 (1960): 112–27.

One of the outstanding characters of *Homo sapiens* is the intensive development of effectance motivation—of man's self-feeding curiosity. The origins of human tension and creativity have been discussed by J. E. Pfeiffer, "The Apish Origins of Human Tension," *Harper's Magazine,* 227 (July 1963): 55–60.

For a symposium describing research on the neural correlates of consciousness and bringing the whole field of the mind-body problem into scientific focus see J. C. Eccles, *Brain and Conscious Experience* (Heidelberg: Springer-Verlag, 1965).

Appendix

FOSSIL EVIDENCE FOR HUMAN EVOLUTION:
SOME IMPORTANT FOSSIL REMAINS OF EARLY MAN

Country	Locality	Remains	Approximate Age in Years B.P.*
HOMO SAPIENS			
Europe:			
Belgium	Spy, Province de Namur	† Parts of 2 male skulls and tibial fragment	35,000– 70,000
Britain	Swanscombe, Kent	Occipital and parietal bones	150,000–250,000
Czechoslovakia	Predmosti, Moravia	29 skeletons	c. 26,000
France	Cro-Magnon, Dordogne	Five adult skeletons	20,000– 30,000
	Fontéchevade, Charente	Frontal bone of 1 individual; calotte of second	70,000–150,000
	La Chapelle-aux-Saints, Correze	† Male skull and nearly complete skeleton	35,000– 45,000
	La Ferrassie, Dordogne	† Parts of 6 individuals, 1 nearly complete (male)	35,000– 55,000
	La Quina, Charente	† Parts of female skull and skeletal fragments	35,000– 55,000
	Montmaurin, Haute-Garonne	† Mandible and teeth	c. 150,000
Germany	Ehringsdorf, nr. Weimar	† Parts of female cranium and 2 mandibles plus remains of child's skeleton	60,000–120,000
	Neandertal nr. Dusseldorf	† Parts of male skull and skeleton	35,000– 70,000
	Steinheim nr. Stuttgart	Female cranium	150,000–200,000
Gibraltar	Forbes Quarry	† Female cranium	35,000– 70,000
Greece	Petralona	† Cranium	35,000– 70,000
Italy	[Monte] Circeo, Latina, south of Rome	† Cranium of male individual; part of mandible of another	35,000– 70,000
	Saccopastore nr. Rome	† Female cranium and parts of male skull	60,000–100,000

FOSSIL EVIDENCE FOR HUMAN EVOLUTION (cont'd)

Country	Locality	Remains	Approximate Age in Years B.P.*
Yugoslavia	Krapina, nr. Zagreb	† Fragmentary remains of c. 13 individuals	30,000– 45,000
Asia:	Amud	† Almost complete skull and skeleton	35,000– 50,000
	Galilee	† Parts of cranium and fragments of other individuals	c. 70,000
Israel	Mount Carmel: Cave of Mugharet es-Skhul	† Parts of at least ten individuals	35,000– 40,000
	Cave of Mugharet et-Tabun	÷ Skull and skeleton of female, mandible; fragments	40,000– 45,000
Iraq	Shanidar, N. Iraq	† Parts of six adult individuals and one child	45,000– 70,000
Java	Ngandong (Solo)	÷ Eleven calvariae and two tibiae	c. 20,000
Sarawak	Niah Cave	Cranium	c. 40,000
Africa:			
South Africa	Florisbad	Calotte with facial bones	c. 35,000
	Hopefield (Saldanha)	† Calotte	c. 55,000
Kenya	Kanjera	Fragments of 4 crania	c. 60,000
Morocco	Jebel Irhoud	† Two crania	c. 40,000
Sudan	Singa	Cranium	c. 23,000
Zambia	Broken Hill	† Cranium and skeletal fragments	c. 40,000
HOMO ERECTUS			
Algeria	Ternifine	Parietal and 3 mandibles	c. 350,000
China	Chenchiawo	Calotte, maxilla, and mandible	c. 600,000
	Choukoutien	Skulls and teeth of 14 individuals	300,000–400,000
Germany	Mauer (Heidelberg)	Mandible	c. 500,000
Hungary	Vértesszöllös	Cranial and mandibular fragments	c. 350,000
Java	Sangiran	Calvaria and parietal (1937–38)	c. 500,000
	Sangiran	Part calvaria and maxilla; 3 mandibular fragments (1936 and 1941)	c. 700,000
	Trinil	Calotte and femur	c. 500,000
	Modjokerto	Immature skull	c. 700,000
South Africa	Swartkrans	2 imperfect mandibles	c. 500,000
Tanzania	Olduvai (upper Bed II)	Cranium	500,000
	Olduvai (lower Bed II)	Mandible	c. 1,000,000
AUSTRALOPITHECUS AFRICANUS			
Chad	Yayo	Part cranium	c. 500,000
South Africa	Makapansgat	Calvaria, mandible and many other fragments	} c. 1,000,000 Precise age uncertain
	Sterkfontein	Two nearly complete crania and many others including pelvis fragments and mandibles	
	Taung	Child's cranium and mandible	
Tanzania	Olduvai (Bed I)	Parts of 2 crania and other fragments	1.5–1.8 million

FOSSIL EVIDENCE FOR HUMAN EVOLUTION (*cont'd*)

Country	Locality	Remains	Approximate Age in Years B.P.*
AUSTRALOPITHECUS ROBUSTUS			
South Africa	Kromdraai	Part cranium, mandibular and skeletal fragments	c. 500,000 or older
	Swartkrans	Cranium and many cranial and skeletal fragments	(precise age uncertain)
Tanzania	Olduvai (Bed I)	Cranium	c. 1.7 million
	Peninj	Mandible	c. 700,000
RAMAPITHECUS PUNJABICUS			
India	Siwalik	Mandibular and maxillary fragments	Miocene—Pliocene boundary
Kenya	Fort Ternan	Maxillary fragment	c. 14 million

* For further data see Oakley (1966) upon which many of these dates were based.
† Large-jawed forms of *Homo sapiens* (by implication when jaws not present).
The most important sites are shown on the map of the Old World, Figure 11.4, p. 345.
For a full catalog of fossil Hominidae see Oakley and Campbell (1967).

Note. The science of chronology is in a state of rapid development. Many of the dates given may require revision in the near future. Those about which there is most doubt belong to the species *Homo erectus*.

References

Amoroso, E. C.
  1952   Placentation. *In* A. S. Parkes (ed.), *Marshall's Physiology of Reproduction* 2: 127–311. 3d ed. London and New York, Longmans, Green & Co.
Andrew, R. J.
  1965   The origins of facial expressions. *Scient. Amer.* 213: 88–94.
Arambourg, C., and Hoffstetter, R.
  1963   *Le Gisement de Ternifine*, Vol. 1. Mem. Inst. Paléont. Hum., No. 32.
Ashton, E. H., and Zuckerman, S.
  1951   Some cranial indices of *Plesianthropus* and other primates. *Amer. J. Phys. Anthrop.* 9: 283–96.
Beach, F. A.
  1947   Evolutionary changes in the physiological control of mating behavior in Mammals. *Psych. Rev.* 54: 297–315.
Benedek, Therese
  1952   *Psychosexual Functions in Women.* New York, Ronald Press Co.
Biegert, J.
  1963   The evaluation of characteristics of the skull, hands, and feet for primate taxonomy. *In* S. L. Washburn (ed.), *Classification and Human Evolution*, pp. 116–45. Viking Fund Publs. Anthrop., No. 37. Chicago, Aldine Publishing Co.
Birch, L. C.
  1957   The meaning of competition. *Amer. Nat.* 91: 5–18.
Bishop, W. W.
  1964   More fossil primates and other Miocene mammals from northeast Uganda. *Nature, London* 203: 1327–31.
Black, D. R., Chardin, T. de, Young, C. C., and Pei, W. C.
  1933   *Fossil Man in China: The Choukoutien Cave Deposits, with a Synopsis of Our Present Knowledge.* Mem. Geol. Surv. China, Ser. A, No. 11.

BONIN, G. VON
1963   The Evolution of the Human Brain. Chicago, University of Chicago Press.
BONIN, G. VON, and BAILEY, P.
1961   Pattern of the cerebral isocortex. *Primatologia*, Vol. 2, Part 2, chap. 10.
BROOM, R., and ROBINSON, J. T.
1952   *Swartkrans Ape-Man*, Paranthropus crassidens. Transvaal Mus. Mem., No. 6. Pretoria.
BROOM, R., ROBINSON, J. T., and SCHEPERS, G. W. H.
1950   *Sterkfontein Ape-Man*, Plesianthropus. Transvaal Mus. Mem., No. 4. Pretoria.
BROOM, R., and SCHEPERS, G.
1946   *The South African Fossil Ape-Men, the Australopithecinae*, Transvaal Mus. Mem., No. 2. Pretoria.
BURTON, M.
1962   *Systematic Dictionary of Mammals of the World*, London, Museum Press Ltd.
CAMPBELL, B. G.
1963   Quantitative taxonomy and human evolution. *In* S. L. WASHBURN (ed), *Classification and Human Evolution*, pp. 50–74. Viking Fund Publs. Anthrop. No. 37. Chicago, Aldine Publishing Co.
1964   Science and human evolution, *Nature, London* 203: 448–51.
CANNON, W. B.
1932   *The Wisdom of the Body*. London, Kegan Paul.
CARPENTER, C. R.
1940   *A Field Study in Siam of the Behavior and Social Relations of the gibbon*. Comp. Psychol. Monogr., No. 16, p. 5. Republished 1964 in C. R. CARPENTER *Naturalistic Behavior of Nonhuman Primates*, University Park, Pennsylvania; The Pennsylvania State University Press.
CHANCE, M. R. A.
1961   The nature and special features of the instinctive social bond of primates. *In* S. L. WASHBURN (ed.), *The Social Life of Early Man*, pp. 17–33. Viking Fund Publs. Anthrop., No. 31. Chicago, Aldine Publishing Co.
CLARK, J. D.
1963   The evolution of culture in Africa. *Amer. Nat.* 97: 15–28.
CLARK, W. E. LE GROS
1947   Observations on the anatomy of the fossil Australopithecinae. *J. Anat.* (London) 81: 300–33.
1950   New palaeontological evidence bearing on the evolution of the Hominoidea. *Quart. J. Geol. Soc. London* 105: 225–64.
1955   The os innominatum of the recent Pongidae with special reference to that of the Australopithecinae. *Amer. J. Phys. Anthrop.* 13: 19–27.

1962. *The Antecedents of Man.* 2d ed. Edinburgh, University of Edinburgh Press.

1964 *Fossil Evidence for Human Evolution.* 2d ed. Chicago, University of Chicago Press.

CLARK, W. E. LE GROS, and LEAKEY, L. S. B.

1951 *The Miocene Hominoidea of East Africa.* London, British Museum (Nat. Hist.).

COLBERT, E. H.

1955 *Evolution of the Vertebrates.* New York. John Wiley & Sons.

DART, R. A.

1949 Innominate fragments of *Australopithecus prometheus. Amer. J. Phys. Anthrop.* 7: 301–38.

1957 *The Osteodontokeratic Culture of* Australopithecus prometheus. Transvaal Mus. Mem., No. 10. Pretoria.

1958 A further adolescent australopithecine ilium from Makapansgat, *Amer. J. Phys. Anthrop.* 16: 473–79.

1963 Carnivorous propensity of baboons. *Symp. Zool. Soc. London* 10: 49–56.

DARWIN, C.

1859 *On the Origin of Species by Means of Natural Selection. . . .* London, John Murray.

DAVIS, P. R.

1964 Hominid fossils from Bed 1 Olduvai Gorge: a tibia and fibula. *Nature, London* 201: 967–68.

DAVIS, P. R., and J. NAPIER.

1963 A reconstruction of the skull of *Proconsul africanus* (R.S. 51). *Folia Primat.* 1: 20–28.

DAY, M. H., and NAPIER, J. R.

1964 Hominid fossils from Bed 1 Olduvai Gorge: fossil foot bones. *Nature, London* 201: 969–70.

DE BEER, G. R.

1954 *Embryos and Ancestors.* Rev. ed. Oxford, Oxford University Press.

DEVORE, I.

1963 A comparison of the ecology and behavior of monkeys and apes. *In* S. L. WASHBURN (ed.), *Classification and Human Evolution,* pp. 301–19. Viking Fund Publs. Anthrop., No. 37. Chicago, Aldine Publishing Co.

DEVORE, I., and WASHBURN, S. L.

1963 Baboon ecology and human evolution. *In* F. CLARK HOWELL and F. BOURLIÉRE (eds.), *African Ecology and Human Evolution,* pp. 335–67. Viking Fund Publs. Anthrop., No. 36. Chicago, Aldine Publishing Co.

DOBZHANSKY, T.

1940 *Genetics and the Origin of Species.* New York, Columbia University Press.

1962   *Mankind Evolving.* New Haven, Conn., and London, Yale University Press.

1963   Cultural direction of human evolution: a summation. *Hum. Biol.* 35: 311–16.

DOBZHANSKY, T., and MONTAGU, M. F. A.

1947   Natural selection and the mental capacity of mankind. *Science,* 105: 587–90.

DUBOIS, E.

1894   Pithecanthropus erectus, *eine Menschenahnliche Uebergangsform von Java.* Batavia.

1926   On the principal characters of the femur of *Pithecanthropus erectus. Proc. Kon. Acad. Wet. Amsterdam.* 29: 730–43.

1932   The distinct organization of *Pithecanthropus* of which the femur bears evidence now confirmed from other individuals of the same species. *Proc. Kon. Acad. Wet. Amsterdam.* 35: 716–22. (also 37: 139–45 and 38: 850–52.)

DUBRUL, E. L.

1958   *Evolution of the Speech Apparatus.* Springfield, Ill., Charles C Thomas.

DUBRUL, E. L., and SICHER, H.

1954   *The Adaptive Chin.* Springfield, Ill., Charles C Thomas.

ECKSTEIN, P., and ZUCKERMAN, S.

1956   The oestrous cycle in the Mammalia. *In* A. S. PARKS (ed.), *Marshall's Physiology of Reproduction,* 1, Part 1, pp. 226–396. 3d ed. London and New York, Longmans Green & Co.

EISELEY, L.

1958   *The Immense Journey.* London, Victor Gollancz.

ERICKSON, G. E.

1963   Brachiation in New World monkeys and in anthropoid apes. *Symp. Zool. Soc. London* 10: 135–164.

ETKIN, W.

1963   Social behavioral factors in the emergence of man, *Hum. Biol.* 35: 299–310.

EVERNDEN, J. F., and CURTIS, G. H.

1965   The potassium-argon dating of late Cenozoic rocks in East Africa and Italy. *Curr. Anthrop.* 6: 343–85.

FORD, C. S., and BEACH, F. A.

1951   *Patterns of Sexual Behavior.* New York, Harper & Bros. Reprinted 1965; London, Methuen.

FREEDMAN, L. Z., and ROE, A.

1958   Evolution and human behavior. *In* A. ROE and G. G. SIMPSON (eds.), *Behavior and Evolution,* pp. 455–79. New Haven, Conn., Yale University Press.

FRISCH, K. VON

1950   *Bees, Their Vision, Chemical Senses and Language.* Ithaca, N.Y., Cornell University Press.

GARN, S. M.
1961   *Human Races.* Springfield, Ill., Charles C Thomas.
GARN, S. M., and LEWIS, A. B.
1963   Phylogenetic and intraspecific variations in tooth sequence polymorphism. *Symp. Soc. Study Hum. Biol.* 5: 53–73.
GESCHWIND, N.
1964   The development of the brain and the evolution of language. *In* C. I. J. M. STUART (ed.), *Report of the 15th Annual R.T.M. on Linguistic and Language Studies,* pp. 155–69. Monogr. Ser. Languages and Linguistics, No. 17.
GOODALL, J.
1965   Chimpanzees of the Gombe Stream Reserve. *In* I. DEVORE (ed.), *Primate Behavior,* pp. 425–73. New York, Holt, Rinehart and Winston.
GOODHART, C. B.
1960   The evolutionary significance of human hair patterns and skin colouring. *Adv. Sci.* 17: 53–59.
GREGORY, W. K.
1928   Were the ancestors of man primitive brachiators? *Proc. Amer. Phil. Soc.* 67: 129–50.
HALDANE, J. B. S.
1956   The argument from animals to men: an examination of its validity for anthropology. *J. Roy. Anthrop. Inst.* 86: 1–14.
HALL, K. R. L.
1963a   Tool-using performances as indicators of behavioral adaptability. *Curr. Anthrop.* 4: 479–94.
1963b   Variations in the ecology of the Chacma baboon, *Papio ursinus. Symp. Zool. Soc. London* 10: 1–28.
HALLOWELL, A. I.
1953   Culture, personality, and society. *In* A. L. KROEBER (ed.), *Anthropology Today,* pp. 597–620. Chicago, University of Chicago Press.
HARDY, MARY
1934   Observations on the innervation of the macula sacculi in man. *Anat. Rec.* 59: 403–18.
HEDIGER, H.
1961   The evolution of territorial behavior. *In* S. L. WASHBURN (ed.), *The Social Life of Early Man,* pp. 34–37. Viking Fund Publs. Anthrop., No. 31. Chicago, Aldine Publishing Co.
HERRICK, C. J.
1946   Progressive evolution. *Science* 104: 469.
1956   *The Evolution of Human Nature.* New York, Harper & Bros.
HILL, J. P.
1932   The developmental history of the primates. *Phil. Trans. Roy. Soc. B.* 221: 45–178.

HINSHELWOOD, C.
1959   The internal and external worlds. *Proc. Roy. Soc. A.* 253: 442–49.

HOCKETT, C. F., and ASCHER, R.
1964   The human revolution. *Curr. Anthrop.* 5: 135–68.

HOWELL, F. CLARK
1960   European and northwest African Middle Pleistocene hominids. *Curr. Anthrop.* 1: 195–232.

HUBEL, D. H.
1963   The visual cortex of the brain. *Amer. Sci.* 209: 54–62.

HUXLEY, J. S.
1958   Cultural process and evolution. *In* A. ROE and G. G. SIMPSON (eds.), *Behavior and Evolution,* pp. 437–54. New Haven, Conn., Yale University Press.

IMANISCHI, K.
1960   Social organization of sub-human primates in their natural habitat. *Curr. Anthrop.* 1: 393–407.

INGE, W. R.
1922   *Outspoken Essays.* 2d ser. London, Longmans, Green & Co.

ITANI, J. S.
1965   Social organization of Japanese monkeys. *Animals* 5: 410–17.

JERISON, H. J.
1955   Brain to body ratios and the evolution of intelligence. *Science,* 121: 447–49.

KAWAI, M.
1965   Japanese monkeys and the origin of culture. *Animals* 5: 450–55.

KEESING, F. M.
1958   *Cultural Anthropology.* New York, Rinehart.

KINSEY, A. C., and Staff of the Institute for Sex Research, Indiana University.
1953   *Sexual Behavior in the Human Female.* Philadelphia, W. B. Saunders Co.

KOHLER, W.
1925   *The Mentality of Apes.* New York and London, Kegan Paul.

KOHTS, N.
1935   *Infant Ape and Human Child.* Moscow, Sci. Mem. Mus. Darwin.

KORTLANDT, A.
1965   Comment on the essential morphological basis for human culture. *Curr. Anthrop.* 6: 320–25.

KRANTZ, G. S.
1963 . The functional significance of the mastoid process in man. *Amer. J. Phys. Anthrop.* 21: 591–93.

KROEBER, A. L., and KLUCKHOHN, C.
1952   *Culture: A Critical Review of Concepts and Definitions.* Pap. Peabody Mus. No. 47.

KUMMER, H., and KURT, F.
1963   Social units of a free-living population of hamadryas baboons. *Folia Primat.* 1: 4–19.

KUYPERS, H. G. J. M.
1964   The descending pathways to the spinal cord, their anatomy and function. *In* J. C. ECCLES and J. P. SCHADE (eds.), *Progress in Brain Research* 2: 178–202.

KUYPERS, H. G. J. M., SZWARCBART, M. K., MISHKIN, M., and ROSVOLD, H. E.
1965   Occipitotemporal corticocortical connection in the rhesus monkey. *Exp. Neurology* 11: 245–62.

LANCASTER, J. B., and LEE, R. B.
1965   The annual reproductive cycle in monkeys and apes. *In* I. DEVORE (ed.), *Primate Behavior,* pp. 486–513. New York, Holt, Rinehart and Winston.

LEACH, E.
1966   Ritualization in man in relation to conceptual and social development. *Phil. Trans. Roy. Soc.* B. 251: 247.

LEAKEY, L. S. B.
1959   A new fossil skull from Olduvai. *Nature, London,* 184: 491–93.
1960   Recent Discoveries at Olduvai Gorge, *Nature, London* 188: 1050–52.

LEAKEY, L. S. B., TOBIAS, P. V., and NAPIER, J. R.
1964   A new species of the genus *Homo* from Olduvai Gorge. *Nature, London* 202: 3–9.

LERNER, I. M.
1954   *Genetic Homeostasis.* London, Oliver and Boyd.

LEWIS, G. E.
1934   Preliminary notice of new man-like apes from India. *Amer. J. Sci.* 27: 161–79.

LOWE, C. VAN RIET
1954   The cave hearths. *S. Afr. Arch. Bull.* 33: 25–29.

MAGOUN, H. W.
1960   Concepts of brain function. *In* SOL TAX (ed.), *The Evolution of Man,* pp. 187–209. Chicago, University of Chicago Press.

MALTHUS, T. R.
1798   *An Essay on the Principle of Population.* London.

MARTIN, C. J.
1902   Thermal adjustment and respiratory exchange in Monotremes and Marsupials—a study in the development of homoeothermism. *Phil. Trans. Roy. Soc. London,* B. 195: 1–37.

MASON, A. S.
1960   *Health and Hormones.* London, Penguin Books.

MAYR, E.
1963   *Animal Species and Evolution.* Cambridge, Mass., Harvard University Press; London, Oxford University Press.

McCown, T., and Keith, A.
1939   *The Stone Age of Mount Carmel,* Vol. 2. Oxford, Oxford University Press.
Mednick, L. W.
1955   The evolution of the human ilium. *Amer. J. Phys. Anthrop.* 13: 203–16.
Mettler, F. A.
1956   *Culture and the Structural Evolution of the Neural System.* New York, Amer. Mus. Nat. Hist. Also in M. F. Ashley Montagu (ed.), *Culture and the Evolution of Man,* pp. 155–201. New York, Oxford University Press, 1962.
Miller, G. S.
1931   The primate basis of human sexual behavior. *Quart. Rev. Biol.* 6: 379–410.
Mills, J. R. E.
1963   Occlusion and malocclusion of the teeth of primates. *Symp. Soc. Study Hum. Biol.* 5: 29–51.
Montagna, W.
1965   The skin. *Scient. Amer.* 212: 56–66.
Montagu, M. F. Ashley
1962   Time, morphology and neotony in the evolution of man. *In* M. F. Ashley Montagu (ed.), *Culture and the Evolution of Man,* pp. 324–42. New York, Oxford University Press.
Morton, D. J.
1922   Evolution of the human foot. *Amer. J. Phys. Anthrop.* Part I, 5: 305–306; Part II, 7: 1–52.
1927   Human origin. *Amer. J. Phys. Anthrop.* 10: 173–203.
1964   *The Human Foot.* New York, Haffner Publishing Co.
Moss, M. L., and Young, R. W.
1960   A functional approach to craniology. *Amer. J. Phys. Anthrop.* 18: 281–92.
Napier, J. R.
1960   Studies of the hands of living primates. *Proc. Zool. Soc. London* 134: 647–57.
1961   Prehensibility and opposability in the hands of primates. *Symp. Zool. Soc. London* 5: 115–32.
1962   The evolution of the hand. *Scient. Amer.* 207: 56–62.
1963a   Locomotor functions of hominids. *In* S. L. Washburn (ed.), *Classification and Human Evolution,* pp. 178–89. Viking Fund Publs. Anthrop., No. 37. Chicago, Aldine Publishing Co.
1963b   Brachiation and brachiators. *Symp. Zool. Soc. London* 10: 183–94.
1964   The evolution of bipedal walking in the hominids. *Arch. Biol.* (Liége) 75 (suppl.): 673–708.
Napier, J. R., and Davis, P. R.
1959   *The Forelimb Skeleton and Associated Remains of* Proconsul Africanus. London, British Museum (Nat. Hist.).

NAPIER, J. R., and NAPIER, P. H.
   1967   *Handbook of Living Primates.* London and New York, Academic Press.
NOBACK, C. R., and MOSKOWITZ, N.
   1963   The primate nervous system: functional and structural aspects in phylogeny. *In* J. BUETTNER-JANUSCH (ed.), *Evolutionary and Genetic Biology of Primates* 1: 131–177. New York, Academic Press.
OAKLEY, K. P.
   1951   A definition of man. *Penguin Science News* 20: 69–81. Also *in* M. F. ASHLEY MONTAGU (ed.), *Culture and the Evolution of Man,* pp. 3–12. New York, Oxford University Press, 1962.
   1961   On man's use of fire, with comments on toolmaking and hunting. *In* S. L. WASHBURN (ed.), *The Social Life of Early Man,* pp. 176–93. Viking Fund Publs. Anthrop., No. 31. Chicago, Aldine Publishing Co.
   1963   *Man the Toolmaker.* 5th ed. London, British Museum (Nat. Hist.).
   1966   *Frameworks for dating fossil man.* 2d. ed. London, Weidenfeld and Nicholson; Chicago, Aldine Publishing Co.
OAKLEY, K. P., and CAMPBELL, B. G.
   1967   *Catalogue of Fossil Hominids, Vol. 1, Africa.* London, British Museum (Natural History). Vols. 2 and 3 in preparation.
OPPENHEIMER, A.
   1964   Tool use and crowded teeth in Australopithecinae, *Curr. Anthrop.* 5: 419–21.
OVEY, C.
   1964   *The Swanscombe Skull.* Occ. Pap. Roy. Anthrop. Inst. 20. London.
OXNARD, C. E.
   1963   Locomotor adaptations in the primate forelimb. *Symp. Zool. Soc. London* 10: 165–82.
PENFIELD, W., and RASMUSSEN, T. B.
   1957   *The Cerebral Cortex of Man.* New York, Macmillan Co.
PENFIELD, W., and ROBERTS, L.
   1959   *Speech and Brain Mechanisms.* Princeton, N.J., Princeton University Press.
PFEIFFER, J.
   1955   *The Human Brain.* New York, Harper & Bros.
PILBEAM, D. R., and SIMONS, E. L.
   1965   Some problems of hominid classification. *Amer. Sci.* 53: 237–59.
POCOCK, R. I.
   1925   The external characters of the catarrhine monkeys and apes. *Proc. Zool. Soc. London* 1925: 1479–1579.
POLYAK, S.
   1957   *The Vertebrate Visual System.* Chicago, University of Chicago Press.

RASMUSSEN, T. B., and PENFIELD, W.
1947   Further studies of the sensory and motor cerebral cortex in man. *Fed. Proc. Amer. Soc. expt. Biol.* 6: 452–560.

RENSCH, B.
1956   Increase of learning capability with increase in brain size. *Amer. Nat.* 90: 81–95.
1959   Trends toward progress of brains and sense organs. *Cold Spring Harbor Symp. Quant. Biol.* 24: 291–303.

ROBINSON, J. T.
1953   Telanthropus and its phylogenetic significance. *Amer. J. Phys. Anthrop.* 11: 445–502.
1956   *The Dentition of the Australopithecinae.* Transvaal Mus. Mem., No. 9. Pretoria.
1963   Australopithecines: culture and phylogeny. *Amer. J. Phys. Anthrop.* 21: 595–605.
1965   Homo "habilis" and the australopithecines. *Nature, London* 205: 121–24.

ROBINSON, J. T., and MASON, R. J.
1957   Occurrence of stone artifacts with australopithecines at Sterkfontein. *Nature, London* 180: 521–24.

ROE, A.
1963   Psychological definitions of man. *In* S. L. WASHBURN (ed.), *Classification and Human Evolution*, pp. 320–31. Viking Fund Publs. Anthrop., No. 37. Chicago, Aldine Publishing Co.

ROMER, A.
1945   *Vertebrate Paleontology.* Chicago, University of Chicago Press.
1956   *The Osteology of Reptiles.* Chicago, University of Chicago Press.
1962   *The Vertebrate Body.* Philadelphia and London, W. B. Saunders Co.

ROSENBLUETH, A., WIENER, N., and BIGELOW, J.
1943   Behavior: purpose and teleology, *Philos. Sci.*, 10: 18–24.

SADE, D. S.
1964   Seasonal cycle in size of testes of free-ranging *Macaca mulatta. Folia Primat.* 2: 171–80.

SAHLINS, M. D.
1959   The social life of monkeys, apes and primitive man, *Hum. Biol.* 31: 54–73.

SCHALLER, G. B.
1963   *The Mountain Gorilla: Ecology and Behavior.* Chicago, University of Chicago Press.

SCHENKEL, R.
1947   Ausdrucks-studien an wölfen. *Behavior* 1: 81-129.

SCHLOSSER, M.
1911   Beiträge zur kenntnis der oligozänen land-säugetiere aus dem fayum: Ägypten. *Beitrage Paleont. Geol. Oesterreich-Ungarns* 24: 51–167 (Plate I).

SCHULTZ, A. H.

1924   Growth studies on primates bearing upon man's evolution. *Amer. J. Phys. Anthrop.* 7: 149–64.

1930   The skeleton of the trunk and limbs of higher primates. *Hum. Biol.* 2: 303–438.

1935   Eruption and decay of teeth in primates. *Amer. J. Phys. Anthrop.* 19: 489–581.

1936   Characters common to higher primates and characters specific for man. *Quart. Rev. Biol.* 11: 259–83, 425–55.

1937   Proportions of long bones in man and apes. *Hum. Biol.* 9: 281–328.

1941   Length of spinal regions in primates. *Amer. J. Phys. Anthrop.* 24: 1–22.

1942   Conditions for balancing the head in primates. *Amer. J. Phys. Anthrop.* 29: 483–97.

1948   The number of young at birth and the number of nipples in primates. *Amer. J. Phys. Anthrop.* 6: 1–23.

1950   Man and the catarrhine primates. *Cold Spring Harbor Symp. Quant. Biol.* 15: 35–53.

1953   Relative thickness of bones in primates. *Amer. J. Phys. Anthrop.* 11: 277–311.

1955   The position of the occipital condyles and of the face relative to the skull base in primates. *Amer. J. Phys. Anthrop.* 13: 97–120.

1956   Post-embryonic age changes. *Primatologia* 1: 887–964.

1960   Einige Beobachtungen und Masse am Skelett von *Oreopithecus. Z. Morph. Anthrop.* 50: 136–49.

1961   Some factors influencing the social life of primates in general and early man in particular. *In* S. L. WASHBURN (ed.), *The Social Life of Early Man,* pp. 58–90. Viking Fund Publs. Anthrop., No. 31. Chicago, Aldine Publishing Co.

1963a   The foot skeleton in primates. *Symp. Zool. Soc. London* 10: 199–206.

1963b   Age changes, sex differences, and variability as factors in the classification of primates. *In* S. L. WASHBURN (ed.), *Classification and Human Evolution,* pp. 85–115. Viking Fund Publs. Anthrop., No. 37. Chicago, Aldine Publishing Co.

SHOCK, N. W.

1951   Growth curves. *In* S. S. STEVENS (ed.), *Handbook of Experimental Psychology,* pp. 330–46. New York, John Wiley & Sons.

SIVERTSEN, E.

1941   On the biology of the harp seal. *Hvalradets Skrifter* 26: 1–166.

SIMONS, E. L.

1964   On the mandible of *Ramapithecus. Proc. Nat. Acad. Sci. U.S.A.* 51: 528–36.

1965   New fossil apes from Egypt and the initial differentiation of the Hominoidea. *Nature, London* 205: 135–39.

SIMONS, E. L., and PILBEAM, D. R.
1965   Preliminary revision of the Dryopithecinae (Pongidae, Anthropoidea). *Folia Primat.* 3: 81–152.
SIMPSON, G. G.
1935   The first mammals. *Quart. Rev. Biol.* 10: 154–180.
1949   *The Meaning of Evolution.* New Haven, Conn., Yale University Press.
SPERRY, R. W.
1955   On the neural basis of the conditioned response. *Brit. J. An. Behaviour* 3: 41–44.
1965   Hemispheric interaction and the mind-brain problem. *In* J. C. ECCLES (ed.), *Brain and Conscious Experience.* Heidelberg, Springer-Verlag.
SPUHLER, J. N.
1959   Somatic paths to culture. *Hum. Biol.* 31: 1–13.
STEWART, T. D.
1962   Neanderthal cervical vertebrae. *Bibliotheca primatol.,* Fasc. 1: 130–54.
STRAUS, W. L.
1936   The thoracic and abdominal viscera of the primates. *Proc. Amer. Phil. Soc.* 76: 1.
1949   The riddle of man's ancestry. *Quart. Rev. Biol.* 24: 200–23.
1963   The classification of Oreopithecus. *In* S. L. WASHBURN (ed.), *Classification and Human Evolution,* pp. 146–77. Viking Fund Publs. Anthrop., No. 37. Chicago, Aldine Publishing Co.
STRAUS, W. L., and CAVE, A. J. E.
1957   Pathology and posture of Neanderthal man. *Quart. Rev. Biol.* 32: 348–63.
TANNER, J. M.
1962   *Growth at Adolescence.* 2d. ed. Oxford, Blackwell Scientific Publications.
TESTUT, L.
1928   *Traité d'Anatomie humaine.* 8th ed. Paris, Doin & Co.
THOMPSON, D. W.
1942   *On Growth and Form.* New ed. Cambridge, Cambridge University Press.
THORPE, W. H.
1965   *Science, Man and Morals.* London, Methuen & Co.
TOBIAS, P. V.
1963   Cranial capacity of *Zinjanthropus* and other australopithecines. *Nature, London* 197: 743–46.
1967   *Olduvai Gorge 1951–1961.* Vol. 2. Cambridge, Cambridge University Press.
TOBIAS, P. V., and VON KOENIGSWALD, G. H. R.
1964   A comparison between the Olduvai hominines and those of

Java and some implications for hominid phylogeny. *Nature, London* 204: 515–18.

TOBIAS, P. V., *et al.*
1965   New discoveries in Tanganyika: their bearing on hominid evolution. *Curr. Anthrop.* 6: 391–411.

TYLOR, E. B.
1871   *Primitive Culture.* London, John Murray.

VAN VALEN, L., and SLOAN, R. E.
1965   The earliest primates. *Science* 150: 743–45.

WALLS, G. L.
1963   *The Vertebrate Eye and Its Adaptive Radiation.* New York, London, Haffner Publishing Co.

WASHBURN, S. L.
1950   The analysis of primate evolution with particular reference to the origin of man. *Cold Spring Harbor Symp. Quant. Biol.* 15: 57–78.
1957   Ischial callosities as sleeping adaptations. *Amer. J. Phys. Anthrop.* 15: 269–76.
1963a   The study of race. *Amer. Anthrop.* 65: 521–31.
1963b   Behavior and human evolution. *In* S. L. WASHBURN (ed.), *Classification and Human Evolution,* pp. 190–203. Viking Fund Publs. Anthrop., No. 37. Chicago, Aldine Publishing Co.

WASHBURN, S. L., and DeVORE, I.
1961   Social behavior of baboons and early man. *In* S. L. WASHBURN (ed.), *Social Life of Early Man,* pp. 91–105. Viking Fund Publs. Anthrop., No. 31. Chicago, Aldine Publishing Co.

WASHBURN, S. L., and HAMBURG, D. A.
1965   The implications of primate research. *In* I. DeVORE (ed.), *Primate Behavior,* pp. 607–22. New York, Holt, Rinehart and Winston.

WEIDENREICH, F.
1938   Discovery of the femur and humerus of *Sinanthropus. Nature, London* 141: 614–17.
1939–41 The brain and its rôle in the phylogenetic transformation of the human skull. *Trans. Amer. Phil. Soc.* 31: 321–442.
1945   *Giant Early Man from Java and South China.* Anthrop. Pap. Amer. Mus. Nat. Hist., No. 40, Part 1.

WEINER, J. S.
1954   Nose shape and climate. *Amer. J. Phys. Anthrop.* 12: 615–18.

WHITE, L. A.
1959   The concept of culture. *Amer. Anthrop.* 61: 227–51.

WHITE, R. W.
1959   Motivation reconsidered: the concept of competence. *Psych. Rev.* 66: 297–333.

WHITEHEAD, A. N.
1920   *The Concept of Nature.* Cambridge, Cambridge University Press.

WHYTE, L. L.
1965   *Internal Factors in Evolution.* London, Tavistock Publications.

Woo, J. K.
1965 Preliminary report on a skull of *Sinanthropus lantianensis* of Lantian, Shensi. *Scientia sinica* 14: 1032–36.

Woollard, H. H.
1927 The retina of primates. *Proc. Zool. Soc. London* 1927: 1–17.

Wynne-Edwards, V. C.
1965 Self-regulating systems in populations of animals. *Science* 147: 1543–48.

Ziegler, A. C.
1946 Brachiating adaptations of chimpanzee upper limb musculature. *Amer. J. Phys. Anthrop.* 22: 15–32.

Zuckerman, S.
1930 The menstrual cycle of the primates. *Proc. Zool. Soc. London* 1930: 691–754.

Glossary

Italicized words appearing in the definitions are cross-references to other entries in the Glossary.

ABDUCTOR: Term applied to muscles that move a part of the body away from the middle line of the body. (Compare ADDUCTOR.)

ACETABULUM: A cup-shaped depression on the external surface of the *innominate bone* into which the head of the *femur* fits. (See Fig. 5.3.)

ACHILLES TENDON: Tendon of the heel that joins the *gastrocnemius* and *soleus* muscles to the *calcaneus* or heel bone. (See Fig. 5.15.)

ACROMIOCLAVICULAR JOINT: *Articulation* of *acromion* and *clavicle*. (See Fig. 6.2.)

ACROMION: The outer end of the spine of the *scapula* that projects over the *glenoid fossa:* it *articulates* with the *clavicle* at the *acromioclavicular joint*. (See Fig. 6.2.)

ADAPTATION (adj. ADAPTIVE): A *character* or set of *characters* of a *deme* selected by the *environment* that by its existence improves the chance of survival of the deme. Adaptations also allow exploitation of the *environment*.

ADDUCTOR: Term applied to muscles that move a part of the body toward the middle line of the body. (Compare ABDUCTOR.)

ADRENALIN: A *hormone* produced by the adrenal *glands* under conditions of stress or fear.

ALLANTOIS: A *fetal* membrane that in egg-laying *vertebrates* lies close to the shell and forms an *organ* of *respiration;* in *mammals* it contributes to the formation of the *placenta*.

AMINO-ACID: An organic compound based on a carbon chain or ring with amine (NH_2) and carboxyl (COOH) groups of atoms. Amino-acids are all synthesized by green plants, and some are synthesized by animals; in the case of man some eight out of about twenty must be obtained "ready made" and cannot be synthesized. *Proteins* are synthesized from amino-acids.

AMNION: The membrane that forms the fluid-filled sac in which the embryo grows.

AMNIOTE EGG: An egg containing an *embryo* provided with an *amnion*.

ANATOMY: The science of the *morphology* and structure of *organisms*.

ANESTRUS (adj., ANESTROUS): A period of sexual quiescence between the mating seasons of *mammals;* a condition not regularly found in man except following *parturition.*

ANTERIOR: The front of, or front part of, any object or *organism.*

ANTERIOR INFERIOR ILIAC SPINE: A small protuberance of bone on the *anterior* edge of the *ilium* to which is attached the *rectus femoris* muscle, which flexes the thigh. (See Fig. 5.8.)

ANTERIOR SUPERIOR ILIAC SPINE: A small protuberance of bone on the *anterior* edge of the *ilium* to which are attached the *oblique abdominal muscles.* (See Fig. 5.3.)

ANTHROPOCENTRIC: A view of nature that places man in the center and examines the world from man's point of view.

ANTHROPOIDEA (adj., ANTHROPOID): A *suborder* of the *order Primates* containing the monkeys, apes and men.

ANTIBODIES: *Proteins* in the blood of *mammals* that are formed in response to *antigens* and protect the body from their toxic action.

ANTIGEN: A substance which is foreign to the body of an animal and usually toxic to it. It is capable of stimulating the formation of an *antibody.*

APOCRINE: The term applied to *glands* in the skin that *secrete* the odorous components of sweat.

ARBOREAL: Refers to trees; tree-living.

ARCHIPALLIUM: The older part of the *cortex* of the *cerebral hemispheres,* distinguished from the *neopallium,* which evolved more recently. (See Fig. 8.5.)

ARCHOSAURIA: The dinosaurs, the great ruling reptiles (like *Tyrranosaurus*) which dominated the earth during *Cretaceous* times before the great *radiation* of the *mammals.* (See Fig. 4.5.)

AREOLA (pl., AREOLAE): A ring of pigmented skin surrounding the nipple.

ARTICULATION (adj., ARTICULAR): A joint or connection between two bones allowing movement.

ARTIFACTS: Objects formed by the purposeful activity of animals, especially man.

ARTIODACTYLS: The even-toed *ungulates*—an order of *mammals* including pigs, sheep, and cattle.

ASSOCIATION CORTEX: That part of the outer layer of the *cerebral hemispheres* believed to function as a result of the connection there of two or more other areas of the *cortex* concerned with sensory or motor activity.

ASTRAGALUS: See TALUS.

AUDITORY CORTEX: That part of the outer layer of the *cerebral hemispheres* believed to be responsible for the reception and onward transmission of auditory input to the brain.

AUSTRALOPITHECUS: A genus of fossil *Hominidae* first discovered in South Africa in 1924 and so named by Raymond Dart in 1925. It contains two species, *A. africanus* and *A. robustus*.

AXILLARY: Relative to the armpit.

AXILOSPINAL ANGLE: The angle between the *spine* of the *scapula* and the *lateral* margin of that bone.

AXONS: Nerve fibers.

BACULUM: A small rod-shaped bone which serves to stiffen the *penis* of many nonhuman *primates*.

BASAL METABOLIC RATE: The rate of heat production in an individual at the lowest level of body activity in the waking state.

BEHAVIOR: The totality of motor activity of an animal.

BICEPS: Refers here to the muscle that flexes the forearm in relation to the upper arm. (See Fig. 6.10.) Originating on the *scapula,* it is *inserted* upon the *bicipital tuberosity* of the *radius*.

BICIPITAL TUBEROSITY: A small protuberance upon the shaft of the *radius* where the *biceps* muscle is *inserted*. (See Fig. 6.10.)

BICUSPID: Having two *cusps*.

BILOPHODONT: Having the *cusps* of the tooth arranged to form two ridges with a valley between, characteristic of *Cercopithecoidea* among the *primates*. (See Fig. 7.13.)

BIOLOGICAL EFFICIENCY: The efficiency of a species in converting food materials into *biomass*.

BIOLOGY: The branch of science that deals with living *organisms*.

BIOMASS: The total mass of living substance that constitutes a particular species.

BIPEDALISM: The act of locomotion on two feet.

BRACHIATION: The act of locomotion by means of the arms.

BRACHYCEPHALIC: Having a head that is relatively short and broad. (Compare DOLICHOCEPHALIC.)

BRAINSTEM: That part of the base of the brain which leads to the *spinal cord*.

BROCA'S AREA: An area on the *cerebral cortex* that Broca discovered to be in some way responsible for speech. (See Fig. 10.4.)

CALCANEUS: The heel bone. (See Fig. 5.15.)

CALOTTE: The bones of the roof of the skull.

CALVARIA (pl., CALVARIAE): The *neurocranium* without the facial bones.

CANTILEVER: A beam supported from one end.

CARNIVORA: An order of flesh-eating *mammals,* including lions, cats, and dogs.

CARNIVORE: An animal living exclusively or almost exclusively on other animals. (Compare HERBIVORE.)

CARPAL BONES: The small bones of the wrist. (See Fig. 6.16.)

CARTILAGE: A skeletal tissue of *vertebrates* distinct from bone, consisting of a resilient translucent matrix containing fibres.

CATARRHINA: An alternative term for the *Cercopithecoidea*.

CEBOIDEA (adj., CEBOID): The *superfamily* of *primates* found in Central and South America, containing 13 *genera* and known as New World monkeys. (See Table 3.2.)

CECUM: A short and blind-ended branch of the intestine, found in certain *herbivorous* mammals, that has evolved to facilitate the digestion of cellulose.

CENTER OF GRAVITY: A point, the support of which allows a body to remain balanced in any position.

CENTRAL NERVOUS SYSTEM (*CNS*): That part of the nervous system of animals which includes the brain and *spinal cord*.

CENTRUM: The central mass of a *vertebra* of the *spine* that transmits the weight of the body in man and sustains other compressive forces in *quadrupeds*.

CERCOPITHECOIDEA (adj., CERCOPITHECOID): A *superfamily* of *primates* found in the Old World, containing 13 *genera* and known as Old World monkeys. (See Table 3.2.)

CEREBELLUM: The *posterior* part of the brain, lying, in man, beneath the *occipital* lobe of the *cerebral hemispheres* and attached to the *brainstem*.

CEREBRAL CORTEX: The outer layer of the *cerebral hemispheres* or *cerebrum*. (See Fig. 8.19.)

CEREBRAL HEMISPHERES: The two parts of the *cerebrum* connected by the *corpus callosum*. (See Fig. 8.11.)

CEREBRUM: The principal and most *anterior* portion of the human brain, divided into two hemispheres. (See Fig. 8.8.)

CERVICAL REGION: The neck region of the *spine*.

CETACEANS: The *mammals* that have evolved *adaptations* to a marine *environment*, including whales, porpoises, and dolphins.

CHARACTER: Refers here to a particular attribute of an animal.

CHEMORECEPTOR: A sensory *organ* of the nervous system that is stimulated by certain chemical substances (e.g., an *organ* of taste or smell.)

CHIRIDIA: Complex *organs* that terminate the limbs, e.g., paws, hands, or feet.

CHROMOSOME (adj., CHROMOSOMAL): A thread-shaped structure, numbers of which occur in the nucleus of every plant and animal cell. Chromosomes consist largely of *DNA* and carry the *genetic* code of the individual or *gamete*.

CHRONOLOGY: The science of the study of time, age, and sequence.

CLAN: A unilateral (one-line) descent group of large size.

CLASS: In biology, this is a taxonomic rank. (See TAXONOMY.)

CLAVICLE: The collarbone, which forms part of the *pectoral girdle* and connects the *scapula* and forelimb to the *sternum*. (See Fig. 6.2.)

CLITORIS: A small cylindrical *organ* situated at the anterior end of the *labia* in female *primates*. Its stimulation effects erection and erotic response under appropriate conditions. (See Fig. 9.2.)

COCCYX: A small bone at the end of the vertebral column consisting of a few much reduced *vertebrae*, present only in primates without tails. (See Fig. 5.3.)

COCHLEA: A cone-shaped cavity in the ear region of the skull consisting of a spinal canal containing the *organ of Corti.*

COITUS: Sexual intercourse.

COMPARATIVE ANATOMY: The study and comparison of the form and structure of different animals.

COMPOUND GIRDER: A beam or girder constructed of smaller units with spaces between them.

CONCEPT: A mental abstraction from experience involving classification of that experience.

CONCEPTUAL MEMORY: That part of the memory which records concepts as an analysis and classification of experience.

CONDITIONING: A kind of learning from which the resulting behavior pattern becomes fully automatic and involves no conscious thought processes.

CONE: A sensory *organ* of the nervous system stimulated by light and able to distinguish differences in wave frequency; it is found in the *retina* of animals able to see color.

CONTACT RECEPTOR: A sensory *organ* of the nervous system stimulated by contact with objects, including *organs* sensitive to touch and taste.

COPULATION: Sexual union between male and female individuals; *coitus.*

CORACOID PROCESS: A beak-like projection of the *scapula* upon which is *inserted* the *biceps* muscle. (See Figs. 6.6 and 6.10.)

CORONOID PROCESS: A small prominence on the *mandibular ramus* in which the *temporalis* muscle is inserted. (See Fig. 7.2).

CORPUS CALLOSUM: A mass of nerve fibers running across the *cerebrum* between the two *cerebral hemispheres.* (See Figs. 8.9 and 8.11.)

CORPUS LUTEUM (pl., CORPORA LUTEA): A small yellowish ductless *gland* that develops in the *ovary* immediately after *ovulation.* Its most important product is the *hormone progesterone.* If pregnancy does not occur, the *gland* rapidly degenerates.

CORTEX (adj., CORTICAL): The outer layer or mantle of an *organ*—used here to describe the important outer layer of the *cerebrum.*

CORTICOSPINAL FIBERS: Nerve fibers connecting the *cerebral cortex* and the *spinal cord.*

CRANIUM (adj., CRANIAL): The skull, excluding the mandible.

CRETACEOUS: A *period* of the earth's history believed to have lasted from about 135–63 million years ago. (See Table 2.1.)

CRURAL JOINT: The ankle, the joint of the hind leg. (See Fig. 5:15.)

CULTURE: The totality of *behavior* patterns of a social group of animals that are passed between generations by learning; socially determined *behavior* learned by imitation and instruction.

CUSP: A protuberance on the grinding surface of a tooth.

DECIDUATE: Here applied to a *placenta;* the term indicates that when the *placenta* is shed, it brings with it the outer layers of the *endometrium* with which it is intimately associated.

DELTOID: A muscle of the upper arm, with its *origin* in the *clavicle* and *scapula* and its *insertion* in the shaft of the *humerus.* (See Fig. 6.3.)

DEME: A local interbreeding population; a group of individuals so situated that any two of them have equal probability of mating with each other and producing offspring (Mayr 1963).

DENTAL ARCADE: The curved line formed by the teeth in the *maxilla* and *mandible;* the dental arch.

DENTITION: The teeth as a whole.

DEOXYRIBONUCLEIC ACID (DNA): A chemical substance that constitutes *chromosomes* and carries the genetic code, the *genotype,* of each individual within every cell.

DEVELOPMENTAL HOMEOSTASIS: The capacity of the developmental pathways to produce a normal *phenotype* in spite of developmental or environmental disturbances (Mayr 1963).

DIASTEMA (pl., DIASTEMATA): The gap formed in each jaw to receive the canine tooth of the opposite jaw, found in animals with canines much larger than their other teeth.

DIGASTRIC MUSCLES: Muscles that lower the jaw and stabilize the *hyoid bone.* Their *origin* lies near the *mastoid process* at the base of the skull, and they are *inserted* into the lower border of the *symphyseal* region of the *mandible.* (See Fig. 10.3.)

DIGITS: Fingers or toes.

DIPHYODONTISM: The property of producing two sets of teeth during an individual's life—the milk teeth, or deciduous teeth, and the permanent teeth.

DIPLOË: A sponge-like bony structure separating and joining the two layers of compact bone (the *inner* and *outer table*) of the *cranium.*

DISCRIMINATION: The act of perceiving slight differences.

DISTAL: The part of the body farthest from the middle line, or from the trunk; referring to the extremities of the body. (Compare PROXIMAL.)

DISTANCE RECEPTOR: A sensory organ of the nervous system stimulated by physical disturbances emitted by objects at a distance (e.g., light, sound, scent).

DNA: See DEOXYRIBONUCLEIC ACID.

DOLICHOCEPHALIC: Having a head that is relatively long and narrow. (Compare BRACHYCEPHALIC.)

DORSAL: Relating to the back; the opposite of *ventral.*

DRYOPITHECINAE: A *subfamily* of the *Pongidae* containing fossil apes of different *genera,* including *Dryopithecus* and *Gigantopithecus.*

DRYOPITHECUS: A fossil *genus* of the subfamily *Dryopithecinae* (of the *family Pongidae*) containing the important *subgenus Proconsul* and many *species.*

ECCRINE: The name of *glands* of the skin that secrete sweat.

ECOLOGICAL NICHE: The particular part of the whole animate and inanimate *environment* that is occupied by a particular *species* or *subspecies.*

ECOLOGY: The science of the mutual relations of different *organisms* and their *environments.*

EFFECTANCE MOTIVATION: The spontaneous exploratory activity of mammals that does not satisfy drives of hunger, sex, or self-preservation.

EFFECTOR: An organ that receives nerve impulses and reacts by movement or *secretion* (e.g., a muscle or a *gland*).

EMBRYO (adj., EMBRYONIC): Term applied to organisms during early stages of *ontogeny* while dependent on maternal food supplies; within the egg or during the early stages of gestation. (See also FETUS).

ENDOCAST: A cast of the interior of the *cranial* cavity.

ENDOCRINE: Describes a system and its components which control bodily activity by chemical, as distinct from nervous, means. The chemicals produced are termed *hormones,* and the *glands* that produce them are termed "ductless glands."

ENDOGAMY: Inbreeding; the selection of a mate from within a small group by another member of that group. (Compare EXOGAMY.)

ENDOMETRIUM: The sponge-like *vascular* lining of the *mammalian uterus,* into which the *placenta* penetrates.

ENTROPY: The phenomenon of randomness, which, according to the second law of thermodynamics, in any closed system can only increase, never decrease.

ENVIRONMENT: The total surroundings of an individual.

EPIDERMIS: The outer layers of the skin.

EPIGAMIC: Relating to sexual reproduction or to *copulation,* and serving to attract or stimulate individuals of the opposite sex during courtship.

EPIGLOTTIS: A small plate of *cartilage* at the root of the tongue that folds back over the aperture of the *larynx,* covering it during the act of swallowing. (See Fig. 10.2.)

EPITHELIOCHORIAL PLACENTA: A *placenta* in which the maternal and *fetal* bloodstreams are separated by both maternal and *fetal tissues.* (Compare HEMOCHORIAL PLACENTA, and see Fig. 9.1.)

EPOCH: A span of time; geological term referring to certain subdivisions in the earth's *chronology.* (See Table 2.1).

ERECTOR SPINAE: Muscles of the back that help maintain the erect spine in man. They find their *origin* on the *sacrum* and *ilium* and are *inserted* into the ribs and *vertebrae.*

ESOPHAGUS: Part of the digestive tract between the *pharynx* and the stomach.

ESTROGEN: A group of *hormones,* mainly produced in the *ovary,* which induce *estrus* and *ovulation* in a mature female individual. During growth, the increasing production of estrogen brings about the development of *secondary sexual characters* and *menarche.*

ESTROUS CYCLE: The series of *uterine, ovarian,* and other changes that occur in mammals and are responsible for *copulation,* pregnancy, etc.

ESTRUS: The stage of the *estrous cycle* around *ovulation,* when the female animal is receptive to and encourages males in *copulation.*

EVOLUTION: Cumulative change in the characteristics of populations of *organisms,* occurring in the course of successive generations related by descent.

EXOGAMY: Outbreeding; the selection of a mate from outside a small group of individuals. (Compare ENDOGAMY.)

EXPERIENTIAL MEMORY: That part of the memory which records experience in temporal sequence.

EXTENSOR: A muscle the contraction of which tends to straighten the bones about a joint. (Compare FLEXOR.)

EXTERNAL PTERYGOIDS: See LATERAL PTERYGOIDS.

EXTRAPYRAMIDAL SYSTEM: Descending nerve tracts that do not enter the "pyramids" of the *medulla;* a more direct system of tracts than the *pyramidal system.* (See Fig. 3.7.)

FALLOPIAN TUBES: Two tubes leading from the two *ovaries* to the *uterus.* The eggs are shed into the open end of these tubes and so pass into the *uterus.*

FAMILY: Usually refers to a group of individuals related by blood and/or marriage including at least one adult male, one adult female, and one or more young, though it cannot be strictly defined. The term is also a taxonomic rank. (See TAXONOMY.)

FEMUR (pl., FEMORA): The *proximal* bone of the leg, the thighbone. The head of the *femur* fits into the *acetabulum.* (See Fig. 5.13.)

FENESTRA OVALIS: A small opening, sealed by a *membrane,* through which vibration is transmitted from the *middle ear* to the *cochlea.*

FETUS (adj., FETAL): The unborn young of a *viviparous* animal after it has taken form in the *uterus.*

FIBULA (pl., FIBULAE): One of the two *distal* bones of the leg. (See also TIBIA.)

FITNESS: In an evolutionary context, this term refers to the possibility of survival of a *deme* over a long period of time in a changing environment.

FLEXOR: A muscle the action of which is to flex a joint. (Compare EXTENSOR.)

FOLLICLE, OVARIAN: or Graafian follicle—a *vesicular* body in the *ovary* containing the egg.

FOLLICLE, HAIR: Pit within mammalian skin surrounding and supporting the hair root.

FOLLICLE-STIMULATING HORMONE (FSH): A hormone produced by the *anterior pituitary gland* that stimulates the *ovarian follicles,* inducing their maturation and the liberation of *estrogen.*

FOSSA: Refers here to certain recognized hollows in bones, such as the fossa iliaca shown in Fig. 5.3.

FOSSIL MAN: Descriptive of fossil bones, skulls, etc., of great age, belonging to early man and other early *hominids.* Some of the most important specimens are listed in the Appendix of this book.

FOVEA CENTRALIS: A small pit in the surface of the *retina* where the *photoreceptor* cells are not overlaid by nerve fibers and blood capillaries, an area of the *retinal* surface permitting optimum optical *discrimination* (also called "yellow spot").

FRONTAL BONE: The bone of the skull that rises above and behind the *orbits* and forms the *anterior* part of the *neurocranium*.

FRONTAL LOBES: The *anterior* lobes of the *cerebral hemispheres*. (See Fig. 8.8.)

FSH: See FOLLICLE-STIMULATING HORMONE

FUNCTION: In *biology,* the activity of a biological mechanism.

FUNCTIONAL COMPLEX: A group of *anatomical* and *physiological* characters that jointly bring about a particular necessary and integrated activity in an animal.

GAMETE: The germ cells or sex cells that are produced by male and female sexually reproducing *organisms;* gametes of each sex must fuse together to initiate the growth of a new individual.

GANGLION: An aggregation of nerve cells.

GASTROCNEMIUS: A muscle of the calf of the leg that has its *origin* in the *distal* end of the *femur* and its insertion by the *achilles tendon* into the *calcaneus.* (See Fig. 5.15.)

GENE (adj., GENETIC): A unit of the material of inheritance.

GENE POOL: The totality of *genes* of a given population existing at a given time (Mayr 1963).

GENETIC DRIFT: Changes in the *gene pool* not due to *selection, mutation,* or immigration.

GENETIC HOMEOSTASIS: The property of a population of balancing its *genetic* composition so as to resist sudden changes (Mayr 1963).

GENIAL TUBERCLE: A very small protuberance of bone on the inner surface of the *symphyseal* region of the *mandible* in which are *inserted* the *geniohyoid muscles* that anchor the tongue to the *mandible.*

GENIOHYOID MUSCLE: A muscle that supports the tongue, has its *origin* in the *genial tubercles* of the *mandible* and its *insertion* in the *hyoid bone.* (See Fig. 10.2.)

GENOTYPE: The totality of *genetic* factors that make up the *genetic* constitution of an individual.

GENUS (pl. GENERA): An important taxonomic rank including a group of species which have more in common with each other than they have with other similar groups. (See TAXONOMY.)

GESTATION: The period of pregnancy during which the *embryo* (and *fetus*) develops and grows. It begins with *implantation* and ends with *parturition.*

GLAND: An *organ* producing a *secretion,* either onto the surface (as sweat glands) or into a cavity (as digestive glands) or into the bloodstream (the *endocrine* glands).

GLANS PENIS: The conical expansion that forms the end of the *penis;* it is very sensitive to mechanical stimulation.

GLENOID CAVITY: A socket formed by two *articular* depressions on the edge of the *scapula* into which the head of the *humerus* fits. (See Fig. 6.2.)

GLUTEUS MAXIMUS: A muscle that effects *abduction* of the thigh in nonhuman primates but is an *extensor* in man; it has its *origin* at the *posterior* end of the *iliac* crest and is *inserted* upon the upper part of the shaft of the *femur*. (See Fig. 5.8.)

GLUTEUS MEDIUS: A muscle that effects *abduction* of the thigh; it has its *origin* on the outer surface of the *ilium* and is *inserted* upon the *greater trochanter* of the *femur*. (See Fig. 5.11.)

GLUTEUS MINIMUS: A muscle that effects *abduction* of the thigh; it has its *origin* on the outer surface of the *ilium* and is *inserted* upon the *greater trochanter* of the *femur*. (See Fig. 5.11.)

GONADS: *Organs* that act both as *endocrine* glands and in the generation of *gametes;* in the male the testes, in the female the *ovaries*.

GORILLA: A living *genus* of apes confined to one *species* in central Africa— *Gorilla gorilla*. There are two subspecies, the lowland gorilla of West Africa and the mountain gorilla of the east-central region, on the Congo-Uganda frontier.

GREATER TROCHANTER: A large bony prominence near the upper end of the *femur* in which are *inserted* the *gluteus medius* and *gluteus minimus* muscles. (See Fig. 5.13.)

HALLUX: The great toe; the first *digit* of the *pes*.

HAND-AXES: Stone artifacts of a *particular* shape and with certain functions first produced in the Middle *Pleistocene epoch*. (See Fig. 11.3.)

HEMOCHORIAL PLACENTA: A *placenta* in which the maternal and *fetal* blood-streams are separated only by *fetal* tissues; the maternal tissues have disintegrated. (Compare EPITHELIOCHORIAL PLACENTA, and see Fig. 9.2.)

HERBIVORE: An animal feeding exclusively on vegetable matter. (Compare CARNIVORE.)

HETERODONT: Having teeth of varying shapes; a characteristic, typical of *mammals*, that facilitates *mastication*. (Compare HOMODONT.)

HETEROSIS: The *selective* superiority of individuals with dissimilar paired *genes*.

HOMEOSTASIS (adj., HOMEOSTATIC): The maintenance of a dynamic equilibrium in living processes; the self-regulating property of *organic* systems.

HOMINIDAE (adj., HOMINID): The *family* of *primates* including man and fossil *species* related to him. Three *genera* are now recognized: *Ramapithecus, Australopithecus*, and *Homo*. (See Table 3.3.)

HOMINOIDEA (adj., HOMINOID): A *super-family* of the *primates* containing the *families* of apes and men.

HOMO: A *genus* of the family *Hominidae* containing two *species: Homo sapiens*, which includes man, and *Homo erectus*, which is known only from fossils. Its earliest members probably date from about 1 million years ago.

HOMO ERECTUS: A *species* of the *genus Homo* known only from fossils and probably extant from about 1 million to about 250,000 years ago.

HOMO HABILIS: A name referring to a group of fossils discovered by Dr. and Mrs. Leakey at Olduvai. The *species* is not included in Table 3.3

because the author believes that these specimens are better classified either as *Australopithecus africanus* or as *Homo erectus*.

HOMO SAPIENS: The most recent *species* of the genus *Homo*, which includes man. It is believed to date from about 250,000 years ago.

HOMODONT: Having teeth of similar shape; a characteristic of lower vertebrates. (Compare HETERODONT.)

HOMOIOTHERMY: The property, characteristic of birds and *mammals*, of maintaining the body at a constant temperature by means of a complex *homeostatic* mechanism.

HORMONE: A chemical substance formed in one part of the body by a ductless *gland* and carried by the blood to another part, which it stimulates to functional activity. The chemical messenger of the *endocrine* system.

HUMERUS (pl., HUMERI): The bone of the upper arm, *articulating* with the *scapula* above and the *radius* and *ulna* at its *distal* end. (See Fig. 6.10.)

HYLOBATINAE: A *subfamily* of the *Pongidae* including the smaller *genera* of apes that are today found in Asia. There are two living *genera*, the gibbon (*Hylobates*) and the siamang (*Symphalangus*).

HYOID: A small bone to which the tongue is anchored at its base. (See Figs. 10.2 and 10.3.)

HYPERTROPHY: Increase in size of a part or *organ*.

HYPOCONULID: The fifth *cusp* of a lower molar tooth.

HYPOTHALAMUS: A small mass of nervous tissue at the base of the brain. (See Fig. 8.11.)

HYPOTHESIS: A supposition advanced as a basis for reasoning or argument or as a guide to experimental investigation; a tentative theory.

ILIAC PILLAR: A thickening of the *ilium* that helps to resist the compression of the bone produced between the *acetabulum* and the *origin* of the muscles that flex the thigh.

ILIUM (adj., ILIAC): The hipbone, a large flat bone that forms part of the *pelvis*. (See Fig. 5.3.)

IMPLANTATION: The entry of the fertile egg of *mammals* into the *endometrial* lining of the *uterus;* it is the beginning of pregnancy.

INCEST: *Copulation* with an individual within a forbidden group of close kin.

INDEX OF CEPHALIZATION: An index that relates the weight of the brain to the weight of the body. Index $= \dfrac{\text{Brain weight}}{\text{Body weight}^{0.66}}$

INFERIOR: Lower, in relation to another structure. (Compare SUPERIOR.)

INNATE BEHAVIOR: Behavior which arises spontaneously in individuals without learning. Sometimes referred to as "unlearned," such behavior is difficult to detect, and can only be identified by rearing an animal away from its kind but in an otherwise natural environment.

INNER EAR: That part of the ear which contains the *mechanoreceptors* for sound, balance, and movement.

INNER TABLE: The layer of compact bone that forms the inner surface of the *neurocranium*.

INNOMINATE BONE: The structure of bone formed by the fusion of the *ilium,* *ischium,* and *pubis* in the adult and constituting the *lateral* part of the *pelvis.* The two innominate bones articulate with each other anteriorly and with the *sacrum posteriorly.* Also called *os coxae.*

INSECTIVORA: An order of *mammals* that contains small insect-eating creatures now living (such as the shrew in Fig. 3.1) as well as certain very primitive forms.

INSERTION: Refers here to the less movable of the two points of attachment of a muscle. (Compare ORIGIN.)

INSTINCT: Sometimes defined as an unlearned behavior pattern, sometimes as a conditioned behavior pattern, and sometimes as a psychological drive.

INSTITUTION: An established form of cultural group *behavior.*

INTERMEMBRAL INDEX: An index relating the different lengths of the hindlimbs and forelimbs. Index $= \dfrac{\text{length of } humerus + radius}{\text{length of } femur + tibia} \times 100.$

INTERNAL ENVIRONMENT: The *environment* of the body cells, consisting primarily of a complex fluid maintained constant in composition and temperature by a wide range of *homeostatic* mechanisms.

INTERNAL FERTILIZATION: The fertilization of the egg within the body of the female rather than in water; an important adaptation of *terrestrial vertebrates* to dry land.

INTERNAL PTERYGOIDS: See MEDIAL PTERYGOIDS.

INTERNUNCIAL NEURON: A nerve cell that relays impulses from the descending nerve fibers to the *motor neuron,* which effects muscular contraction.

INTEROSSEUS MEMBRANE: Refers here to the *ligamentous membrane* connecting the *ulna* to the *radius* and transmitting forces of tension between them.

INTERSPINOUS LIGAMENTS: *Ligaments* connecting the *spinous processes* of the *vertebrae* and transmitting tension between them.

INTERVERTEBRAL DISC: A disc interposed between the bodies of adjacent *vertebrae,* consisting of an outer fibrous part and an inner gelatinous mass.

INTROMISSION: A term usually applied to the insertion of the *penis* within the *vagina.*

ISCHIAL CALLOSITIES: A thickening of the outer layer of the skin overlying the *ischial tuberosities,* found in Old World monkeys. (See Fig. 9.2)

ISCHIAL SPINE: A small bony protuberance on the *posterior* margin of the *ischium* in which *originate* the muscles that form the floor of the abdomen. (See Fig. 5.3.)

ISCHIAL TUBEROSITY: A rough bony projection at the lower end of the body of the *ischium.* (See Fig. 5.8.)

ISCHIUM (adj., ISCHIAL): One of the three bones of the *innominate bone.* In adult *mammals* it is joined to the *ilium* and *pubis.* (See Fig. 5.3.)

ISOIMMUNIZATION: The development of an *antibody* as a result of *antigens* introduced from another individual; for example, *antibodies* may pass from the *fetal* to the maternal blood streams during pregnancy and cause isoimmunization of the mother.

LABIA: Refers here to the two pairs of lips, the *labia majora* and *labia minora*, which protect the *clitoris, urethra,* and *vagina.*

LACTATION: The production of milk by *mammals* from the *mammae* or breasts following *parturition.*

LARYNX: The organ of voice production in man; the upper part of the respiratory tract between the *pharynx* and the *trachea.* (See Fig. 10.2.)

LATERAL: On the side; to the side of the midline. (Compare MEDIAL.)

LATERAL GENICULATE BODY: A swelling at the angle of each optic nerve tract, at the base of the brain, to the side of the midline. (See Fig. 3.9.)

LATERAL PTERYGOIDS: Also known as external pterygoids, these paired muscles have their *origin* in the *sphenoid bone* at the base of the skull and are *inserted* into the *mandible.* Contracted together, they move the *mandible* forward. (See Fig. 7.4.)

LATISSIMUS DORSI: These broad muscles of the back have their *origin* in the *thoracic* and *lumbar vertebrae, sacrum,* and *iliac crest,* and are *inserted* into the *humerus.* They *adduct,* rotate, and extend the forelimb. (See Fig. 6.3.)

LAW: A politically formulated rule supported by sanctions.

LEMNISCAL SYSTEM: A system of *nerve tracts* making a relatively direct link between the *peripheral* sensory nerve cells and the *cerebral cortex.* (See Fig. 3.8.)

LESSER TROCHANTER: A bony prominence near the upper end of the *femur,* in which are *inserted* some of the muscles that flex the thigh.

LH: See LUTEINIZING HORMONE.

LIGAMENT (adj., LIGAMENTOUS): A strong band of fibres connecting two bones at a joint, to restrict movement and prevent dislocation.

LIMB GIRDLE: A complex structure of bone that connects the limbs and spine and transmits forces of compression between them. (See PECTORAL GIRDLE and PELVIC GIRDLE.)

LINGUAL: Adjective referring to the tongue.

LOAD ARM: That part of a beam which lies between the pivot and the point at which the load is applied. (See Fig. 7.6.)

LOAD LINE: Line of action of forces through a structure.

LUMBAR REGION: The third region of the spine, consisting of *vertebrae* to which ribs are not *articulated;* the lower back, between *thorax* and *pelvic girdle.*

LUNATE SULCUS: A furrow on the surface of the *cerebral hemispheres,* readily identifiable in *primates,* which forms a boundary to the *visual cortex;* sometimes termed *simian sulcus.* (See Fig. 8.5.)

LUTEINIZING HORMONE (LH): A hormone *secreted* by the *anterior pituitary gland;* its prime function is to stimulate development of the *corpus luteum.*

MALAR BONE: One of the bones of the face lying below the *orbit*. (See Fig. 8.1.)

MAMMAE: Milk-secreting *glands* of *mammals;* breasts.

MAMMALIA: A class of *vertebrate* animals the majority of which are characterized by *homoiothermy, mastication, viviparity,* and the secretion of milk for the nourishment of their young. They are divided into three *subclasses, Placentalia, Marsupialia,* and *Monotremata.*

MANDIBLE (adj., MANDIBULAR): The bone of the lower jaw that bears the lower *dentition.* (See Fig. 8.1.)

MANDIBULAR CONDYLES: Bony eminences on each side of the *mandible* that fit into a groove in the base of the skull and about which the jaw pivots. (See Fig. 7.2.)

MANDIBULAR CORPUS: The horizontal part of the *mandible* that carries the teeth. (See Fig. 7.2.)

MANDIBULAR RAMUS: That part of the *mandible* which carries no teeth and to which the masticatory muscles are attached; in higher *primates* it is formed at right angles to the *mandibular corpus.*

MANDIBULAR TORUS: A thickening in the *symphyseal* region of the *mandibular corpus* on the inner side, which helps to strengthen it. (See Fig. 7.9.)

MANUBRIUM: The upper segment of the *sternum.* (See Fig. 6.2.)

MANUS: The hand; in animals, the forepaw or front foot.

MARSUPIALIA: A *subclass* of *mammals* (including the opossum and kangaroo) living in America and Australia in which a *placenta* of a peculiar kind is developed, with the young born in a very undeveloped state. After birth they continue growth in a pouch containing the milk glands.

MASSETER: Paired muscles of *mastication;* each *originates* upon the *zygomatic arch* and is *inserted* upon the outer surface of the *ramus* and *coronoid process* of the *mandible.* (See Figs. 7.2 and 7.3.)

MASTICATION: The breakdown of foodstuffs by the dentition, involving cutting, chewing, grinding, tearing, etc.

MASTOID PROCESS: A bony prominence at each side of the base of the skull behind the ear. It carries the insertion of the *sternomastoid muscle.* (See Fig. 4.15.)

MATERIAL CULTURE: The totality of *artifacts* produced by a population of social animals.

MAXILLA: The bone of the face constituting the upper jaw. (See Fig. 8.1.)

MECHANORECEPTOR: Sensory *organ* of the nervous system that is stimulated by pressure or movement; e.g., organs of touch, hearing, balance, etc.

MEDIAL: At the middle line—the line that divides a bilaterally symmetrical organism into two halves that are mirror images.

MEDIAL PTERYGOIDS: Also known as internal pterygoids, these paired muscles have their *origin* in the base of the skull (at the *sphenoid* and *maxilla* bones) and are *inserted* in the inner surface of the *mandibular ramus;* they close the jaw. (See Fig. 7.3.)

MEDULLA (adj., MEDULLAR): The center of a structure or *organ.*

MEGANTHROPUS: A *genus* of the family *Hominidae,* not now believed to be distinct from the *genus Homo.* The name was given to a *mandibular* fragment discovered in Java in 1941.

MELANIN: A dark brown or black pigment.

MELANOCYTES: Special cells, the function of which is to produce *melanin;* they are normally present in the skin of *primates.*

MEMBRANE (adj., MEMBRANOUS): Fine sheet-like tissue lining parts of the body.

MENARCHE: The establishment during growth of the *menstrual cycle* in higher *primates,* as shown by *menstruation.*

MENSTRUAL CYCLE: A form of the *estrous cycle* found in man and some *primates,* characterized by a regular discharge of blood from the *uterus.*

MENSTRUATION: The regular discharge of blood from the *uterus* characteristic of some *primates;* it occurs more or less monthly and is an event in the *estrous cycle.*

MENTIFACTS: Assumptions, ideas, values, intentions (Huxley 1958).

MESOZOIC: A geological *era,* including the *Cretaceous, Jurassic,* and *Triassic epochs* (See Table 2.1).

METACARPUS (adj., METACARPAL): Small bones of the *manus* between the *carpal* bones and fingers, common to all *primates.* (See Fig. 6.16.)

METATARSUS (adj., METATARSAL): Small bones of the *pes* between the *tarsal* and toe bones common to all *primates.* (See Fig. 5.15.)

MIDDLE EAR: Small cavity in the bones of the skull through which sound vibrations are transmitted by small bones, between the eardrum and the *fenestra ovalis.*

MIOCENE: A geological *epoch* of the *Tertiary period,* believed to have lasted from about 25 million to 13 million years ago.

MOBILITY: The ability to be moved by an outside force. Compare (MOTILITY)

MOMENT OF BENDING: A moment (rotational force) tending to cause a beam to bend; a product of the magnitude of the force upon the beam and the perpendicular distance between the point and the line of action of the force.

MONOTREMATA: A *subclass* of *mammals* confined to Australia and New Guinea, clearly distinguished from other *mammals,* since they lay eggs and possess many other reptilian features.

MORPHOLOGICAL STATUS: An estimate, based on *morphology,* of the position of an *organism* in its relation to other *organisms.*

MORPHOLOGY: The science of the form and configuration of animals.

MORTALITY RATE: The death rate, usually calculated as the number of deaths per annum per 1000 of the population.

MOTILITY: The ability to move actively, peculiar to animals. (Compare MOBILITY.)

MOTOR CORTEX: A part of the *cerebral cortex* that has been discovered to function as a transmitter and receiver of nerve impulses associated with muscular contraction.

MOTOR GYRUS: A prominent rounded elevation on the surface of the *cerebral hemispheres* that includes the *motor cortex.*

MOTOR NEURON: A *neuron* whose *axon* connects to a muscle fibre and which transmits impulses from the *central nervous system* to effect muscular contraction.

MUCOPERIOSTEUM: The fine *membranous* lining of bone characteristic of the roof of the mouth and the interior of the nose, which, in the latter, carries the *olfactory* receptors.

MUSCULATURE: The arrangement of muscles on the skeleton of an animal.

MUTAGENIC: Having the property of inducing *mutation.*

MUTATION: Refers in *biology* to a sudden and relatively permanent change in a particular *gene* or in *chromosomal* structure.

MUZZLE: That part of the face containing the nasal cavity, the *turbinal bones,* and *olfactory* organ; the protruding nose, typical of dogs.

MYOTOMES: Muscles lying to the side of the spine that, on contraction, cause *lateral* curvature of the spine; characteristic of lower *vertebrates,* fish, etc.

NATURAL SELECTION: The principal mechanism of *evolutionary* change described by Darwin in 1859; the mechanism whereby those individuals best *adapted* to the environment contribute more offspring to succeeding generations than do the remainder, so that if their characteristics are inherited, the composition of the population is changed.

NEANDERTAL: A valley in western Germany famous for the discovery in a limestone cave in 1856 of the first fossil man, clearly distinct from modern man, to be identified as such.

NEGATIVE FEEDBACK: A concept that refers to the mechanism of *homeostasis,* whereby changes in one direction effect adjustment in an opposite direction.

NEOPALLIUM: The *phylogenetically* more recent part of the *cerebral hemispheres* that has evolved since the older *archipallium* and overlaid it in man. (See Fig. 8.5.)

NEOTENY: An *evolutionary* change in which young states of development of early forms persist into the maturity of later forms by the evolution of earlier sexual maturation or the retarded development of individual structures.

NERVE PATHWAYS: See NERVE TRACTS.

NERVE TRACTS: Bundles of nerve fibers connecting different points of the nervous system.

NEUROCRANIUM: That part of the skull which encloses the brain; the brain box, excluding the jaws and facial bones.

NEURONS: Nerve cells; special cells the function of which is to transmit electrical impulses along very long extremities—the nerve fibers or *axons.*

NUBILITY: The stage in the growth of a girl at which eggs are regularly produced; the beginning of the reproductive span of life.

NUCHAL: Adjective referring to the neck region at the back of the skull;

the nuchal area on the *occipital* bone is where the nuchal muscles are inserted. (See Fig. 4.14.)

NUCHAL CREST: A bony crest that develops on the skull of some *primates* at the boundary of the *nuchal* area and serves to increase the actual area of attachment of the *nuchal* muscles upon the *occipital* bone.

OBLIQUE ABDOMINAL MUSCLES: Muscles forming the sidewalls of the abdominal cavity; they have their origin in the lower ribs and their insertion in the crest of the ilium.

OCCIPITAL: Adjective referring to the back of the head, and in particular to the bone that forms the back of the skull. (See Fig. 8.1.)

OCCIPITAL CONDYLES: A pair of rounded *articular* surfaces on the *occipital* bone at the base of the skull that form the joint between the skull and the first *cervical vertebra*. (See Fig. 7.10.)

OCCIPITAL LOBE: That part of the *cerebral hemispheres* which lies at the back of the head. (See Fig. 8.8.)

OCCLUSAL PLANE: The plane of *occlusion* of the teeth; the plane on which the teeth meet when the jaw is closed. (See Fig. 7.5.)

OCCLUSION: The way in which the dentitions of the upper and lower jaws come together when the jaws are closed.

OLFACTORY APPARATUS: The totality of structures that contribute to the sense of smell.

OLFACTORY BULBS: The two small bulb-like extremities of the olfactory region of the brain that receive the olfactory nerves from the nose. (See Fig. 8.5.)

OLIGOCENE: A geological *epoch* of the *Tertiary* period, believed to have lasted from about 36 to 25 million years ago.

ONTOGENY: The course of development and growth during the life of an individual. (Compare PHYLOGENY.)

OPTIC CHIASMA: The structures formed beneath the forebrain by nerve fibers from the right eye crossing to the left side of the brain and vice versa. (See Fig. 3.9.)

ORBIT: A cavity in the skull surrounded by a ring of bone that contains and protects the eyeball.

ORDER: A taxonomic rank; see TAXONOMY.

OREOPITHECUS: A *genus* of the *Hominoidea* from the *Pliocene epoch,* not clearly related to either *Hominidae* or *Pongidae.*

ORGAN: Any part of an animal that forms a structural or functional unit.

ORGAN OF CORTI: The auditory *receptor.*

ORGANISM: An individual living thing.

ORGASM: The culmination of *copulation,* characterized by the pleasurable release of nervous tension, by muscular contraction, and ejaculation of semen by the male.

ORIENTED: Past participle of verb "to orient," which describes the direction in which an object lies.

ORIGIN: Refers here to the less movable of the two points of attachment of a muscle. (Compare INSERTION.)

ORTHOGENESIS: *Evolution* of lineages following a predetermined pathway not subject to natural selection.

OS CALCIS: See CALCANEUS.

OS COXAE: See INNOMINATE BONE.

OS PENIS: See BACULUM.

OSTEOLOGY: The science of the skeleton and its structure; the study of bones.

OUTER EAR: That part of the ear which is visible externally and consists of a flap of skin upon *cartilage.*

OUTER TABLE: The layer of compact bone that forms the outer surface of the *neurocranium.*

OVARIAN FOLLICLE: See FOLLICLE, OVARIAN.

OVARY: The *gonad* of female animals that produces eggs and, in *mammals, hormones.*

OVIDUCT: The duct that carries the eggs from the *ovary* to the exterior; in *mammals* it consists of three parts, the *fallopian tube,* the *uterus,* and the *vagina.*

OVULATION: The discharge of a ripe egg from the *ovarian follicle* into the opening of the *fallopian tubes.*

PALMAR: Relating to the palms of the hands and feet; the *volar* areas of the *chiridia.*

PAN: The chimpanzee, a well-known *genus* of the family *Pongidae* found in equatorial Africa. There are two *subspecies,* the normal and the pygmy form.

PAPILLA: A small projection on the skin.

PAPIO: The baboon—a well-known *genus* of the Old World monkeys, the *Cercopithecoidea;* the baboon is a common *quadrupedal,* ground-living form found throughout Africa.

PARABOLIC GIRDER: A girder or beam of parabolic form used in the construction of *cantilevers* of certain types.

PARIETAL BONE: The bone that forms the side of the *neurocranium;* the parietal bones meet at the midline on top of the skull and are elsewhere fused, in adults, with the *occipital, temporal,* and *frontal bones.* (See Fig. 8.1.)

PARIETAL LOBE: Those parts of the *cerebral hemispheres* which lie approximately under the *parietal bones* of the skull, between the *frontal* and *occipital lobes.* (See Fig. 8.8.)

PARTURITION: Giving birth, childbirth.

PATELLA: The kneecap; a small disc of bone lying over the knee joint that transmits the tension developed by the *quadriceps* muscle to the *tibia.*

PECTORAL GIRDLE: The structure of bones that suspends the body between the forelimbs in quadrupeds and that suspends the arms from the body in man; in *primates,* it consists of two bones on each side, the *clavicle* and the *scapula.*

PECTORALIS MAJOR: A muscle that has its *origin* in the *clavicle, sternum,* and ribs and its *insertion* in the *humerus*. It *adducts* and rotates the arm. (See Fig. 6.2.)

PEDOMORPHOSIS: See NEOTENY.

PELVIC CANAL: The central opening of the bony ring of the *pelvis* through which the young must pass at birth to reach the external world.

PELVIC GIRDLE: The structure of bones that transmits the weight of the body to the hindlimbs. Unlike the *pectoral girdle,* it is fused to the spine, where the *sacral vertebrae* themselves are fused together. (See PELVIS.)

PELVIS (pl., PELVES; adj., PELVIC): A bony structure consisting of the two *innominate bones* fused together *anteriorly* and to the *sacrum posteriorly,* forming a basin-like ring of bone in man. (See also PELVIC GIRDLE.)

PENTADACTYLY: The possession of five *digits* on *manus* and *pes.*

PENIS: The male sex organ evolved as an organ of internal fertilization containing erectile tissues and, in most primates, a small bone, the *baculum.*

PERCEPT: The mental product of perception, a mental construct quite distinct from the thing perceived.

PERIOD: Refers here to certain major subdivisions in the earth's *chronology.* (See Table 2.1).

PERIPHERAL: The opposite of central; applied to the surface of an *organ* or the body of an animal.

PERISSODACTYLS: The odd-toed *ungulates,* an *order* of *mammals* including the rhinoceros and horse.

PES: The foot; in animals the hind paw or hind foot.

PHALANGEAL FORMULA: A simple formula indicating the order of length of the *digits.*

PHALANGES: See PHALANX.

PHALANX (pl., PHALANGES): The small bones of the *digits peripheral* to the *metacarpals* and *metatarsals*—the finger and toe bones.

PHARYNX: The throat, the joint opening of the *esophagus* and *trachea.* (See Fig. 10.2)

PHENOTYPE: The sum of the characters manifest in an *organism,* to be contrasted with the *genotype*; the phenotype is formed by the interaction of the fertilized egg and its *environment,* in the process called growth.

PHONATION: The act of making speech sounds.

PHOTORECEPTOR: The sensory organ of the nervous system that is stimulated by electromagnetic waves of certain frequencies (380–760 $m\mu$), the nerve impulses from which are interpreted in the brain as light.

PHYLOGENY (adj., PHYLOGENETIC): The *evolutionary* lineage of *organisms;* their *evolutionary* history.

PHYSIOLOGY: The science of organic function, of the processes of *organisms* that constitute their life.

PIRIFORM LOBE: A lobe of the *archipallium* associated with the analysis of *olfactory input.* (See Fig. 8.5, *A.*)

PITHECANTHROPUS: A generic name given to certain hominid fossils now usually classified as *Homo erectus.*

PITOCIN: A *hormone* produced by the *posterior pituitary gland*, responsible for muscular contractions of the *uterus*.

PITUITARY BODY: A compound *gland* lying beneath the base of the brain close to the *hypothalamus*; it has been described as the "master" gland of the *endocrine system*. (See Fig. 8.11.)

PLACENTA: An *organ* peculiar to *mammals* consisting of *embryonic* tissues evolved to absorb nourishment from the wall of the *uterus* and there to discharge waste products; it is connected to the *fetus* by the umbilical cord and produces *hormones* that keep the *uterus,* and indeed the mother, adapted to the state of pregnancy.

PLACENTALIA: A *subclass* of *mammals* with world-wide distribution, in which a *placenta* is formed from the *fetal allantois* for the nourishment of the *fetus*. This most widespread *subclass* includes *primates, ungulates,* and many other *orders*. (See Fig. 2.1.)

PLANTAR LIGAMENTS: The *ligaments* of the sole of the foot that maintain the arched form of the foot bones.

PLANTIGRADE FOOT: A foot in which the whole *ventral* surface comes into contact with the ground, which may be compared with digitigrade, in which only the *ventral* surfaces of the *digits* are used, as in the dog or cat.

PLASTICITY: Refers here to the plasticity of the *phenotype* during *ontogeny*; its variable response to differences in *environment* in spite of constancy in the *genotype*—a more obvious character of plants than of animals.

PLATYRRHINA: An alternative term for the *Ceboidea,* or New World monkeys.

PLEISTOCENE: A geological *epoch* of the *Quaternary* period, believed to have lasted from about 3 million to 10,000 years ago.

PLIOCENE: A geological *epoch* of the *Tertiary* period, believed to have lasted from about 13 million to 3 million years ago.

POLLEX: The first *digit* of the *manus,* the thumb.

PONGIDAE (adj., PONGID): The *family* of *primates* including living apes such as gorilla, chimpanzee, and gibbon, and many fossil forms. (See Table 3.3.)

PONGO: The orangutan, a *genus* of the *family Pongidae* confined to Sumatra and Borneo.

POSTERIOR: Behind or after; back part of any organism.

POWER ARM: That part of a beam which lies between the pivot and the point at which (muscular) forces are exerted. (See Fig. 7.6.)

PRECISION GRIP: A grip, characteristic of the human hand, in which the tip of the thumb can be opposed to the tips of the other fingers to give a precise yet firm grip. (See Fig. 6.15.)

PREFRONTAL AREA: The most *anterior* part of the *cerebral cortex,* so named because it lies to the front of the "frontal area" on the *frontal lobes*. (See Fig. 8.8.)

PRIMATES: An *order* of the *class Mammalia,* characterized by *arboreal adaptations* and including man himself.

PROCONSUL: A *subgenus* of the *subfamily Dryopithecinae* (of the *family*

Pongidae), known from the *Miocene* lake beds of Rusinga in Kenya. Three *species* have been described.

PROGESTERONE: A *hormone* that is *secreted* mainly by the *corpus luteum* and that prepares the *endometrium* for *implantation* and brings about many of the changes associated with pregnancy.

PROGNATHISM: With jaws projecting beyond the rest of the face.

PROLACTIN: A *hormone secreted* by the *anterior pituitary,* responsible for the onset of milk production after *parturition.*

PRONATION: Position, or rotation toward the position, of the forelimb so that the *manus* is twisted through 90 degrees relative to the elbow, the *radius* and *ulna* being crossed. (Compare SUPINATION.)

PRONOGRADE: Walking with the *palmar* surface of the *manus* or *pes* downward.

PROPLIOPITHECUS: A *genus* of fossil ape at present classified in the *subfamily Hylobatinae,* from the *Oligocene epoch* in Egypt.

PROPRIOCEPTORS: A sensory *organ* of the nervous system that is found in muscles as well as other parts of the body and detects stretch or contraction.

PROSIMII (adj. PROSIMIAN): A *suborder* of the *order Primates* containing various Old World *genera,* including the tree shrews, lemurs, lorises, and tarsiers.

PROTEIN: A very complex organic compound containing chains of *amino-acid* molecules; proteins occur in infinite variety and are the basis of most living substance.

PROXIMAL: Part of the body farthest from the trunk or from the middle line. (Compare DISTAL.)

PSYCHOLOGY: The science of conscious life, of mental and emotional processes.

PTERYGOID MUSCLES: Muscles controlling movement of the lower jaw. (See LATERAL PTERYGOIDS and MEDIAL PTERYGOIDS.)

PTYALIN: A digestive chemical present in the saliva of some *mammals,* including man, which brings about the breakdown of starch into sugar.

PUBIC SYMPHYSIS: The *anterior* area of union of the two *innominate bones* —the two pubic bones. Fusion at this point is completed in man only at full maturity. (See Fig. 5.3.)

PUBIS: A bone that, with the *ilium* and *ischium,* forms the *innominate bone*; it is the most *anterior* of the three. (See Fig. 5.5.)

PULVINAR: The most *posterior* part of the *thalamus;* it is significantly larger in higher *primates* than in lower forms.

PYRAMIDAL SYSTEMS: Descending *nerve tracts* that are interrupted by *synapses* and form relatively indirect links between the *cerebrum* and the muscles. (See Fig. 3.7.)

QUADRUPEDALISM: The act of locomotion upon four feet.

QUATERNARY: The most recent geological period, believed to date from about 3 million years ago and containing the *Pleistocene* epoch, as well as recent time.

RADIATION: Refers here to *evolutionary* radiation of a variety of *species* from a single *species,* all bearing a proportion of characters in common.

RADIUS (pl., RADII): The *lateral* and shorter of the two bones of the forearm. (See Fig. 6.10.)

RAMAPITHECUS: A *genus* of fossil apes from the *Pliocene* and/or *Miocene* epochs in northern India and Kenya, classified in the *family Hominidae.* There is only one *species* known, *R. punjabicus.*

RAMUS (adj., RAMAL): Literally a branch; here commonly applied to the vertical part of the *mandible* upon which is *inserted* the musculature and which bears no teeth.

RECEPTORS: A term applied to *organs* of the nervous system with a sensory function.

RECTUS ABDOMINIS: A muscle of the abdominal wall *originating* on the *pubic* bone and *inserted* upon the *sternum* and lower ribs, which maintains tension between *pelvis* and *thorax.* (See Fig. 4.17.)

RECTUS FEMORIS: One of four *extensors* of the knee joint, this muscle has its *origin* in the *anterior inferior iliac spine* and upper margin of the *acetabulum,* and its *insertion* through the *patella* to the *tibia.*

REFERENT: An object referred to, an external object that is perceived.

REFLEXES: An involuntary reaction on the part of an *organism* to a particular stimulus; reflexes may be *innate* or conditioned by learning.

REPTILES: A class of *vertebrates,* usually *terrestrial,* dominant in the *Mesozoic era.* They evolved from amphibians, and in turn *mammals* evolved from them. Examples include alligators, lizards, and snakes.

RESPIRATION: Refers here to the inhalation of air for the absorption of oxygen into the bloodstream, and its exhalation, together with carbon dioxide, by the lungs.

RETICULAR SYSTEM: An indirect and *phylogenetically* old system of ascending *nerve tracts* forming a relay of *neurons* between the sensory *neurons* and the *thalamus* and *cortex.* (See Fig. 3.8.)

RETINA (adj., RETINAL): Part of the eye containing nerve *receptors* (*rods* and *cones*) sensitive to light. (See Fig. 3.9.) These receptors form a dense layer on the inner surface of the eyeball.

RHINAL SULCUS: A *sulcus* on each *cerebral hemisphere* that separates the *archipallium* and *neopallium.* (See Fig. 8.5.)

RHINARIUM: The moistened, hairless, tactile-sensitive skin that surrounds the nostrils of many mammals, seen typically in the dog.

RHINENCEPHALON: The *olfactory* brain; that part of the brain concerned with olfaction, the sense of smell.

RHODESIAN MAN: A fossil skull and other bones discovered in a mine at Broken Hill, Zambia, in 1921.

RITES DE PASSAGE: Rituals connected with important points in the development of individuals as members of society.

RODENT: An *order* of *mammals* characterized by teeth evolved for gnawing; it is the largest *order,* with 350 *genera,* including rats, mice, squirrels, and porcupines.

RODS: A sensory cell of the nervous system stimulated by light, especially of very small intensities. (See CONES and RETINA.)

SACCULUS: A sensory *organ* that, with the *utricle,* is sensitive to the direction of gravity and changes in that direction; part of the *inner ear.* (See Fig. 8.7.)

SACRUM (adj., SACRAL): A single curved bone that is part of the *pelvis,* formed in man by the fusion of five sacral *vertebrae.* (See Fig. 5.3.)

SADDLE JOINT: A joint with a saddle-shaped *articular* surface allowing movement in two planes as well as rotation.

SAGITTAL: The sagittal plane of an *organism* is that through the midline dividing the body into two symmetrical halves.

SAGITTAL CREST: A crest that develops along the *sagittal* line on top of the skull in certain *primates* and serves to increase the area of *origin* of the *temporal muscles.* (See Fig. 8.2).

SALTATION: Jumping; a mode of progression found among certain *prosimians,* usually with the spine erect.

SANCTION: A mechanism whereby society as a whole enforces *behavior* patterns upon individuals, for example by punishment.

SCAPULA (pl., SCAPULAE): A bone of the *pectoral girdle,* the shoulder blade. (See Figs. 6.2 and 6.3.)

SEBACEOUS GLANDS: Oil-producing *glands* of the skin.

SECONDARY SEXUAL CHARACTER: A *character* peculiar to males or females but without a function directly related to reproduction.

SECRETION (v., SECRETE): An activity, specialized in *gland*-cells, involving the passage of a substance produced by a cell from within it to the surrounding tissues.

SECTORIAL: Cutting; referring to teeth that have evolved a cutting edge.

SELECTION (adj., SELECTIVE): As used here, this term refers to *natural selection.*

SEMATIC: Acting as a signal to other animals.

SEMIBRACHIATION: A form of *arboreal* locomotion in which the forelimbs are extended above the head to grip the branches and propel the body through space; the hindlimbs are also often used to grip the branches below the body.

SEMICIRCULAR CANALS: Sensory *organs* of the *inner ear* evolved to detect the direction and acceleration of movement. (See Fig. 8.7.)

SENSORY CORTEX: See SOMATIC SENSORY CORTEX, VISUAL CORTEX, AUDITORY CORTEX.

SERRATUS ANTERIOR: Sometimes termed "serratus magnus," this muscle has its *origin* in the lower ribs and its *insertion* in the *scapula*; it rotates the *scapula* and pulls it forward. (See Fig. 6.3.)

SEXUAL DIMORPHISM: The characteristic difference between the sexes of a single *species.*

SIMIAN SHELF: A small bony shelf on the inner surface of the *symphyseal* region of the *mandible,* serving to strengthen it. (See Fig. 7.9.)

SIMIAN SULCUS: See LUNATE SULCUS.

SINANTHROPUS: A generic name given to certain hominid fossils now usually classified as *Homo erectus.*

SINUS: A hollow in a bone.

SOCIFACTS: Acts of cultural *behavior.*

SOFT PALATE: The back of the palate not directly supported by bone, which separates the back of the mouth from the nasal cavity.

SOLEUS: A muscle of the calf of the leg having its *origin* in the *proximal* parts of the *tibia* and *fibula* and its *insertion* by the *achilles tendon* into the *calcaneus.* (See Fig. 5.15.)

SOMATIC SENSORY CORTEX: That part of the *cortex* in which are located *neurons,* which receive and transmit the somesthetic input to the brain. (See Fig. 8.8.)

SOMESTHETIC: Refers to sense *receptors* of the skin (e.g., receptors of touch, temperature, and pain).

SOREX: A shrew, a *genus* of small animals of the *order Insectivora* found in both the Old and the New World. (See Fig. 3.1.)

SPECIALIZATION: In the context of *evolutionary* studies, a *character* evolved for a particular and limited function—the opposite of a generalized *character.*

SPECIES: The definition of the species is complex, but it may be summarized as a group of naturally or potentially interbreeding *demes* which are reproductively isolated from other such groups, surviving for a certain period of time. Part of the lineage that this species constitutes over a period of time may be designated by a different name after evolutionary change of such magnitude has occurred that populations from different geological time levels differ about as much as do contemporaneous species. (See Campbell 1964.)

SPERM: (pl., SPERMATOZOA): The male sex cell or *gamete.*

SPERMATOGENESIS: The generation of *sperms* that occurs in the *testes.*

SPHENOID BONE: A butterfly-shaped bone situated at the anterior part of the base of the skull, of which it forms the floor.

SPINAL CORD: The extension of the *central nervous system* within the vertebral column, and consisting of neurons and nerve tracts in the form of a hollow tube.

SPINE: Used here to connote the vertebral column or backbone.

SPINOUS PROCESS: Connotes the bony projection on the *dorsal* side of most *vertebrae.*

STATUS: Social position, or position in relation to related objects.

STERNOCLAVICULAR JOINT: *Articulation* of *sternum* and *clavicle.* (See Fig. 6.2.)

STERNOMASTOID: Paired muscles which effect rotation of the head and have their origin in the *sternum* and *clavicle,* their insertion in the *mastoid process* and *occipital bone.* (See Fig. 4.15).

STERNUM: The bone that *articulates* the ribs on the *ventral* side of the *thorax.* (See Fig. 6.2.)

SUBCLASS: A taxonomic rank. (See TAXONOMY.)

SUBFAMILY: A taxonomic rank. (See TAXONOMY.)

SUBGENUS: A taxonomic rank. (See TAXONOMY.)

SUBORDER: A taxonomic rank. (See TAXONOMY.)

SULCUS: A fissure; one of the grooves or furrows on the surface of the brain, especially the *cerebral hemispheres.*

SUPERFAMILY: A taxonomic rank. (See TAXONOMY.)

SUPERIOR: Higher, in relation to another structure. (Compare INFERIOR.)

SUPINATION: Position of the forelimb such that the *manus* lies in the same plane as the elbow joint so that the *radius* and *ulna* lie parallel. (Compare PRONATION.)

SUPRAORBITAL TORUS: A rounded thickening of the *frontal* bone along the upper edge of the *orbits,* evolved to carry some of the forces developed by a powerful masticatory apparatus.

SUPRASPINOUS LIGAMENTS: *Ligaments* connecting the *spinous processes* of the *vertebrae.*

SWEAT GLANDS: *Glands,* situated in the skin of *mammals,* that secrete the components of sweat. (See APOCRINE and ECCRINE.)

SYMBOL: An object, activity, or concept representing and standing as a substitute for something else.

SYMPHYSIS (adj., SYMPHYSEAL): A union of two bones (e.g., *pubic symphysis*).

SYNAPSE (pl., SYNAPSES): The point of contact of an *axon* and another *neuron* between which nerve impulses can pass; the connecting point between two nerve cells.

TALUS: The ankle bone (*astragalus*), which *articulates* with the *tibia* and *fibula* to form the ankle joint. (See Fig. 5.15.)

TARSUS (adj., TARSAL): The root of the *pes,* consisting of seven bones, including the *talus* and *calcaneus.* (See Fig. 5.15.)

TAXONOMY: The science of the classification of plants or animals which involves placing them in classes according to their relationships and ordering these classes in hierarchies. The conventional ranks used in this book are shown below in their hierarchical position:

Kingdom
  Phylum
    Class
      Sub-class
        Order
          Sub-order
            Super-family
              Family
                Sub-family
                  Genus
                    Sub-genus
                      Species
                        Sub-species

TEMPORAL BONE: A bone found on each side of the skull between the *occipital, parietal,* and *frontal* bones. (See Fig. 8.1.)

TEMPORAL LINE: A slight depression, visible on the skull, which delineates the area of *origin* of the *temporalis* muscle. (See Fig. 8.1.)

TEMPORAL LOBE: A lobe of the *cerebral hemispheres* lying low down on each side of the brain. (See Fig. 8.8.)

TEMPORAL MUSCLE: See TEMPORALIS.

TEMPORALIS: The largest of the muscles that close the jaws; it has its *origin* on the sides and roof of the skull and its *insertion* in the *coronoid process* of the *mandible.* (See Figs. 7.2 and 7.3.)

TERRESTRIAL: Refers to the earth; living on the ground.

TERTIARY: A geological *period* believed to have lasted from about 63 million to 3 million years ago characterized by the *radiation* of the *Mammalia.*

TESTIS: The *gonad* of male animals that produces *sperm,* and, in *mammals,* the male sex *hormones.*

THALAMUS: A large egg-shaped mass of tissue within the brain that serves as a relay for sensory stimuli to the *cortex.* (See Fig. 8.11.)

THORAX (adj., THORACIC): The chest; the upper part of the trunk between neck and abdomen containing a basket-like structure of ribs and *sternum.* (See Fig. 5.4.)

TIBIA (pl., TIBIAE): A bone of the calf that carries all the weight transmitted down the hind legs in higher *primates.* (See Fig. 5.15.)

TOOL: An *artifact* that may be considered as an extension of the manipulative *organs.*

TRACHEA: The windpipe or breathing tube running from the *epiglottis,* through the neck, to the point where it divides into two branches that lead to the lungs. (See Fig. 10.2.)

TRAPEZIUS: A muscle of the neck and shoulder with its *origin* in the *nuchal* area of the skull, the *cervical vertebrae* and *thoracic vertebrae,* and its *insertion* in the *scapula.* (See Fig. 6.3.)

TRICEPS BRACHII: A muscle that extends the forearm; it has its *origin* in the *scapula* and head of the *humerus* and its *insertion* on the *ulna* at the elbow. (See Fig. 6.10.)

TROCHLEA: The grooved surface at the lower end of the *humerus* that *articulates* as a hinge joint with the *ulna.* (See Fig. 6.8.)

TURBINAL BONES: The fine bones of the nose that carry the nasal *mucoperiosteum.*

ULNA (pl., ULNAE): The *medial* and larger of the two bones of the forearm. (See Fig. 6.10.)

UNGULATES: A group of *mammals* including two *orders* of plains-living *species,* the *Perissodactyla* and *Artiodactyla.*

URETHRA: Tube leading from the urinary bladder of mammals to the exterior; in female humans it opens within the vulva, in males by the *penis.*

UTERUS: The womb, a hollow muscular organ evolved from the *oviduct* in which the fertilized egg develops into a *fetus.* (See Fig. 2.4.)

UTRICLE: A *membranous* fluid-filled sac lying in the *inner ear*, which functions with the *sacculus* to detect the direction of gravity and movement. (See Fig. 8.7.)

VAGINA: The lowest part of the *oviduct* in *mammals* which joins the *uterus* to the exterior. Evolved to receive the *penis* in *copulation*.

VARIATION: Naturally occurring differences between individuals of a single *species* that are due to differences in *genotype*.

VASCULAR: Containing blood vessels.

VENTRAL: Relating to the belly or abdomen; opposite of *dorsal*.

VERSATILITY: Applied here to the flexibility of *behavior* that results from evolved learning and perception.

VERTEBRA: Complex structure of bone, a number of which form the backbone in *vertebrates;* beside constituting the main structural components of the body, the vertebrae also protect the *spinal cord*.

VERTEBRATES: The most important *subphylum* (major group) of the animal kingdom; containing all animals with backbones, including fish, reptiles, birds, and *mammals*.

VESICULAR: Sack-like; a small cellular structure like a vessel or sack, often containing fluid.

VESTIGIAL CHARACTER: A rudimentary structure in an animal corresponding to a fully formed structure in an earlier or related form, sometimes assumed to have lost its function.

VIBRISSA (pl., VIBRISSAE): A long hair, such as a whisker, with sensory nerve endings at its base, evolved as a highly sensitive detector of mechanical stimulus.

VISUAL CORTEX: That part of the *cerebral cortex* involved in the reception and analysis of nerve impulses from the eyes.

VIVIPARITY: (adj., VIVIPAROUS): The ability to give birth to living young, as contrasted with laying eggs.

VOLAR PADS: The hairless pads with special skin found on the friction surfaces of the *manus* and *pes* in *primates* as well as on the tails of some New World monkeys.

WORD MEMORY: That part of the memory which records words and the motor patterns for speech and writing.

ZINJANTHROPUS: A *genus* of the family *Hominidae*, not now believed to be distinct from the *genus Australopithecus*. The name was given to a skull discovered in Tanzania in 1959.

ZYGOMATIC ARCH: An arch of bone from the cheek to the ear region, called the cheekbone, carrying the *origin* of the *masseter* muscle. (See Fig. 7.2.)

Index

a

Acetabulum, 113, 117, 118, 126
Achilles tendon, 128
Acromion process, 143, 146
Adam and Eve, 318, 320
Adaptability, 11, 12
Adaptation, 11, 24, 328 f., 352–356, 360
Adaptation, arboreal, 64
    cultural, 286 f., 356–361
Adaptedness, 12
Aggression, 272–274, 304, 360
Agriculture, 292
Alexander the Great, 25
Alimentary canal, 198
Alouatta, 63
Altmann, S. A., 325
America, 241, 351
Amino-acids, 174
Amniote egg, 42
Amoroso, E. C., 247, 248, 370
Amphibians, 86, 87
Amphioxus, 168
Amud, 345, 368
Analysis, visual, 77, 224
Anatomy, comparative, 3
Ancestor worship, 317
Andrew, R. J., 238, 311, 370
Anestrus, 253
Anterior inferior iliac spine, 113, 116, 117
Anterior superior iliac spine, 113, 117
Anthropoidea, 62, 64

Antibodies, 248
Anxiety, 320
Aotus, 63
Apes, 60 f.
    black, *see* Cynopithecus
    early man, *see* Australopithecus
    fossil, *see* Dryopithecus
    great, *see* Pongidae
Appendix, vermiform, 200
Arambourg, C., 370
Archipallium, 216, 223, 224
Areolae, 242, 255
Artifacts, 288–289
Ascher, R., 203, 208, 307, 308, 375
Ashton, E. H., 100, 234, 370
Asiatics, *see* Man
Astragalus, *see* Talus
Ateles, 63, 68, 152
Australia, 241
Australians, 206, 273, 351, 352
Australopithecus, 63, 70, 79–83, 97, 100,
    105, 119, 121, 123–125, 128,
    130, 135, 145, 146, 151, 152,
    163–165, 173, 182, 184, 186,
    190, 192–195, 197, 198, 201,
    202, 205–208, 211, 212, 231,
    233–235, 262, 326, 329 f., 369
Axilospinal angle, 146

b

Baboon, desert, *see* Hamadryas baboon

Baboon (cont'd)
  savanna, see Papio
Baculum, 255, 256
Bailey, P., 224, 228, 371
Balance, 58, 98–100, 103, 131, 221, 222
Baldness, 239
Barnicot, N. A., 208
Bats, 56
Beach, F. A., 257, 258, 260, 370, 373
Beard, 239, 240
Behavior, 5, 19, 49, 171, 200–208
  See also Sexual behavior
Bending moment, 89, 185
Benedek, Therese, 254, 370
Bicipital tuberosity, 153, 154
Biegert, J., 158, 159, 167, 186, 218, 370
Bigelow, J., 379
Biomass, 25
Bipedalism, 115 f., 203, 333
Birch, L. C., 15, 370
Birds, 21, 176, 277
Bird song, 21, 22
Birth canal, 117, 119, 250, 251
  rate, 250
Bishop, W. W., 331, 370
Bison, 88, 90
Black, D. R., 205, 370
Body hair, see Hair, body
  structure, 86 f.
  temperature, 35–39
  See also Thermoregulation
Bolas, 203, 340
Bonin, G. von, 215, 224, 228, 371
Boulière, F., 208
Brachiation, 65–68, 93, 142 f., 333
  modified, 66
  semi-, 65, 93, 149
  true, 68
Brachyteles, 63
Brachycephaly, 235
Brain, 27, 50, 51, 98–100, 169, 210, 215 f., 223 f., 265, 296–298
  case, 230–235
  size, 165, 230–234
  stem, 52, 225
Breasts, 255, 264
Breeding season, 275, 276
Bride-price, 278
Bridges, 88
Broca's area, 311–312
Broken Hill, 345, 368

Broom, R., 121, 125, 145, 146, 151, 152, 371
Browridges, see Supraorbital torus
Burton, M., 54, 56, 371
Bushmen, 124, 125, 173, 205, 258, 273, 354, 355
Buttocks, 258, 264

C

Cacajao, 63, 239
Calcaneus, 128
Callicebus, 63
Callimico, 63
Callithrix, 63, 249, 250
Call system, 306, 307
Campbell, B. G., 85, 338, 364, 371, 378
Canada, 207
Canines, 183, 188, 190–194, 261, 262
Cannon, W. B., 16, 17, 27, 371
Cantilever, 88
Capillaries, 38
Capuchin, see Cebus
Carboniferous, 36
Carnivores, 42, 161, 171, 202, 227, 294
Carpal bones, 154, 162
  vibrissae, 157, 158
Carpenter, C. R., 276, 285, 371
Cat, 214
Catarrhina, see Monkeys
Cave, A. J. E., 97, 123, 125, 381
Cave bear, 205
Cave dwellings, 205, 348
Cave of Hearths, 205
Ceboidea, see Monkeys
Cebus, 63, 255
Cecum, 198–200
Cellulose, 198
Center of gravity, 90, 91
Centrum, 89, 94
Cercocebus, 63, 215
Cercopithecoidea, see Monkeys
Cercopithecus, 63, 69, 89, 98, 149, 187, 239, 240
Cerebellum, 52, 225, 228–230
Cerebrum, cerebral hemispheres, 50, 52, 223–230
Cervical region, see Neck
Cetacea, see Whales
Chance, M. R. A., 272, 371

Chardin, T. de, 370
Cheek pouches, 199
Chenchiawo, 344, 345, 368
Chimpanzee, *see Pan*
Chin, 185–187, 308
China, 343, 344, 347
Chiridia, 133
Chiroptera, 56
Choukoutien, 146, 152, 203, 205, 345, 347, 368
Chronology, 36, 82, 344, 347, 348, 350, 352, 367–369
Circeo (Monte), 345, 368
Clan, 283
Clark, J. D., 164, 331, 371
Clark, W. E. le Gros, 1, 6, 59, 85, 89, 92, 100, 114, 115, 121, 124, 125, 137, 146, 151, 156, 167, 180, 191, 193, 195, 196, 208, 232, 234, 235, 236, 346, 347, 372
Classification, hominid, 63, 348, 351
  primate, 59 f.
Clavicle, 138–146
Claws, 58, 64–66, 131, 133, 157
Climate, 333
Clitoris, 254, 255, 258, 259
Clothes, 255, 359
Coccyx, 105
Cochlea, 221, 223
Coitus, *see* Copulation
Colbert, E. H., 169, 372
Colobinae, 199, 200
Colobus, 63, 65, 255
Common langur, *see Presbytis*
Communication, 170, 222, 223, 304–308, 358
Competition, 15
  intrauterine, 250
Computor, 50, 342
Concept, 292–300
Conceptual thought, 78, 295–297
Condylar position index, *see* Indices
Conflict, 273
Conscience, 319
Consciousness, 224, 313, 319–321, 361–363, 365
Consonants, 311
Controller, 26
Cooking, 207
Copulation, 42, 43, 253, 255, 257–260, 267, 275

Coracoid process, 146, 153
Corpus callosum, 225–228, 312
Corpus luteum, 45, 46, 47
Cortex, 216, 223–228, 297
  association, 216, 225, 227, 228, 293
  auditory, 223–225
  cerebral, 27, 50, 71, 171, 172, 223–228, 234, 257, 312, 341, 342
  motor, 165, 172, 225, 226, 229, 311
  sensory, 165, 225, 226, 229
  visual, 76, 78, 215, 216, 224, 225
Corticospinal fibers, 71
Cranial capacity, 230–234, 346, 347, 349
Cretaceous, 35, 36
Cro-Magnon, France, 81, 345, 352, 367
Culture, 266, 268, 270, 271, 286 f.
  material, 164, 289, 290
  modern, 359–361
Curtis, G. H., 164, 201, 329, 336, 339, 344, 373
Cusp, 194 f.
Cynopithecus, 63

d

D'Arcy Thompson, W., 88
Dart, R. A., 121, 124, 174, 202, 340, 372
Darwin, Charles, 89, 263, 372
Daubentonioidea, 62
Davis, P. R., 100, 128, 151, 157, 160, 167, 234, 372, 377
Day, M. H., 85, 131, 134, 135, 372
De Beer, G. R., 31, 372
Definitions, taxonomic, *Australopithecus,* 336
  Hominidae, 328
  Homo, 346
  Ramapithecus, 329
Deme, 11, 23
Dental arcade, 181, 185, 187 f.
Dentition, 187 f.
  bilophodont, 196, 197
  deciduous, 41
  heterodont, 40–41, 188
  homodont, 40–41, 188
  human, 187 f.
  permanent, 187 f.
Deoxyribonucleic acid (DNA), 12

Descent groups, 278, 280, 282, 283
Despecialization, 30
DeVore, I., 39, 172, 238, 261, 267, 272, 273, 275, 285, 372, 382
Diastema, 191–193
Diet, 165, 170–174, 194, 197, 200–208
Digestion, 176, 198–200
Digits, see Phalanges
Diphyodontism, 41
Diploë, 231
Discrimination, auditory, 222, 223
    visual, 77, 215
Dobzhansky, T., 10, 13, 23, 33, 286, 290, 351, 359, 362, 372, 373
Dogs, 190, 202, 304–307, 319
Dolichocephaly, 235
Dominance, cerebral, 311, 312
    sexual and social, see Sexual
Douc langur, see Pygathrix
Douroucouli, see Aotus
Dryopithecinae, 63, 79, 80, 182
Dryopithecus, 125, 126, 330, 331, 335
Dubois, E., 125, 373
DuBrul, E. L., 98, 185, 186, 187, 308, 310, 373

e

Ear, 210, 220–223
    inner, 221–223
    middle, 221
    outer, 221
Eccles, J. C., 366
Echinoderms, 31
Eckstein, P., 46, 373
Ecology, 200–208, 351
Educability, 290
Education, 268
Effector, 26
Effectance motivation, 49–51
Efficiency, reproductive, 249–250
Egg cell, 42–47
Ehringsdorf, 367
Eiseley, L., 361, 363, 373
Elbow, 149–153
Elephant, 232
Elephantulus, 219
Embryo, 42, 246–249
Emergence, 366
Endocast, 231, 232

Endocrine system, 43
Endogamy, 281–283
Endometrium, 43, 44, 46, 247–249
Environment, 12 f.
    external, 26
    internal, 17, 26
Environmental change, 28, 353
Enzymes, 176
    digestive, 41
Eocene, 36
Epigamic features, 239, 242, 255, 264
Epiglottis, 309, 310
Equilibria, 16 f.
    internal, 16–19
Erickson, G. E., 65, 111, 373
Erythrocebus, 63, 69
Eskimo, 48, 173
Estrous cycle, 43, 252, 275
Estrus, 44, 46, 252–255, 257, 267, 275, 279
Ethics, 318–321
Etkin, W., 290, 373
Evernden, J. F., 164, 201, 329, 336, 339, 344, 373
Evolution, 8 f.
    cultural, 290-292, 323, 359
    rate, 28, 207, 356
Exogamy, 281-284
Exploratory activity, see Effectance motivation
Expression, 304
    facial, 236-238
Extrapyramidal tracts, 71
Eyes, 58, 210, 214-218

f

Face, 217, 219, 235-245
Fallopian tubes, 43, 44
Family, 260, 262, 276-281
Famine, 14
Femur, 120, 125-128
Fenestra ovalis, 221
Fertilization, 42, 44, 46
Fetus, 46
Fibula, 127, 128
Fins, 86
Fire, 204-207
Fishes, 86
Fitness, biological, 11

Florisbad, 345, 368
Follicle, hair, 38, 238
  ovarian, 43, 46, 47
Fontéchevade, 367
Food, carrying, 164
  sharing, 164, 202, 203
Foot, 127-135
Forbes Quarry, 345, 367
Ford, C. S., 258, 260, 373
Ford, D., 285
Forelimbs, 138 f.
Foresight, 295-296
Fort Ternan, 345, 369
Fossil hominids, 80 f., 367-369
Fossil man, 80-83, 367-368
Fovea centralis, 215
Freedman, L. Z., 295, 320, 321, 373
Frisch, K. von, 19, 373
Frontal bone, 211, 213
  lobes, 216, 224–226, 228, 311–312
Fruit, 171
FSH, *see* Hormones, follicle-stimulating
Function, 5
Functional complex, 5, 35
Fur, 38, 92

Gizzard, 176
Glaciation, 205, 350
Glands, apocrine (scent), 239–242
  eccrine (sweat), 203, 242, 243
  sebaceous, 241, 242
Glans penis, 256
Glenoid cavity, 139, 142, 144, 145, 149
Gonads, 43–46, 256
Goodall, J., 164, 172, 288, 295, 374
Goodhart, C. B., 239, 255, 264, 374
Gorilla, 66, 79, 100, 112, 127, 130, 131,
    133, 134, 143, 147, 163, 180,
    186, 188, 211, 212, 218, 231,
    232, 234, 235, 241, 256, 259,
    261, 266, 273, 333
Great toe, *see* Hallux
Gregory, W. K., 333, 374
Grooming, 275
Growth, periods, 247
  rate, 48, 198–199, 247, 249, 263, 265–
    268
Guenon, *see* Cercopithecus
Gueraza, *see* Colobus
Guilt, 319
Gyrus, motor, *see* Cortex, motor

g

Gait, 123, 137
Galago, 65
Galilee, 368
Gametes, 10
Ganglion, 169
Garn, S. M., 198, 352, 354, 374
Gelada, *see* Theropithecus
Gene, 10 f.
Gene pool, 11
Genesis, Book of, 316, 318, 320
Genetic drift, 29
  variation, 11 f.
Genial tubercle, 176, 186
Geniculate body, 76, 77
Genitalia, 255–256
Genotype, 126
Geoldi's marmoset, *see* Callimico
Germ cells, *see* Gametes
Geschwend, N., 227, 374
Gestation, 43, 119, 246–249
Gibbons, *see* Hylobates
Gigantopithecus, 196

h

Hair, axillary, 239, 240
  body, 31, 38, 203, 236, 238–240, 243,
    263, 264
  facial, 239, 240, 264
  head, 238, 239–241, 264
  pubic, 239, 240, 255, 265
Haldane, J. B. S., 288, 374
Hall, K. R. L., 164, 280, 374
Hallowell, A. I., 362, 374
Hallux, 131, 133
Hamadryas baboon, 278–280, 339
Hamburg, D. A., 271, 382
Hand, gibbon, 159
  human, 161–165
  primate, 157–161, 172
Hand-axes, 165, 206, 341
Hardy, M., 222, 374
Harrison, G. A., 208
Hay, R. L., 201
Head, 97–104, 168 f., 209 f.
Hearing, 220-223
Heat, *see* Estrus

Heat loss, 38–39, 238
Hediger, H., 306, 374
Heidelberg, 186, 347
Hemispheres, dominant, *see* Dominance, cerebral
Herbivore, 171
Herrick, C. J., 25, 53, 74, 228, 300–302, 358, 374
Heterosis, 282
Hill, J. P., 374
Hindlimbs, 108 f.
Hinshelwood, C., 361, 365, 375
Hockett, C. F., 203, 208, 307, 308, 375
Hoffstetter, R., 370
Home base, 203, 205, 207
Homeostasis, 34
  developmental, 18, 182
  genetic, 23
  individual, 16
Hominidae, 63, 79–83, 194 f., 328 f.
Hominoidea, 62, 63, 64, 79, 151
Homo, 63, 70, 79–82, 97, 147, 156, 158, 185, 235, 330
  erectus, 63, 80–82, 98, 100, 123, 125, 135, 146, 151, 152, 165, 186, 188, 192, 193, 205, 206, 212, 217, 231, 234, 329, 340, 343, 344, 347, 348, 368
  habilis, 348
  sapiens, 30, 31, 63, 80-82, 97, 98, 123, 152, 157, 186, 206, 231, 273, 348 f., 367, 368
Homoiothermy, 35–39
Honeybee, 19, 304
Hopefield, 345, 368
Hormones, 43, 45
  estrogen, 45–47, 253, 257
  follicle-stimulating (FSH), 45, 47
  luteinizing (LH), 45, 47
  pitocin, 46
  progesterone, 45–47, 253
  prolactin, 46
Howell, ‧F. Clark, 208, 336, 344, 349, 375
Howells, W. W., 366
Howler, *see Alouatta*
Hubel, D. H., 77, 375
Human hand, *see* Hand
Humerus, 139–157
Hungary, 347
Hunger, 18

Hunting, 164, 173, 174, 202–204, 234, 280, 294, 307, 339, 340, 350
Huxley, J. S., 288, 375
Hylobates, 59, 68, 79, 93, 94, 97, 98, 104–105, 143, 147, 151, 152, 187, 218, 231, 247, 256, 263, 273, 276, 278
Hylobatinae, 63, 68, 79
Hyoid bone, 176, 309, 310
Hypothalamus, 26, 36, 39, 45, 50, 229

i

Iliac crest, 113
  pillar, 113, 121
  tubercle, 113, 121
Ilium, 110 f.
Imanischi, K., 276, 287, 375
Imitation, 21, 49
Immunization, 248
Implantation, 43, 46, 253
Inbreeding, *see* Endogamy
Incest, 267, 277, 282–284
Incisors, 179, 184, 188–190
India, 343
Indians, North American, 241, 351
Indices, brachial, 147, 152
  cephalization, 233
  condylar, 100, 235
  deltoid, 147
  hand, 159
  intermembral, 109–110, 147
  nasal, 219
  supraorbital height, 234, 235
Individualization, 260, 266, 321–324
Indri, 158, 160
Industrialization, 292, 360
Infanticide, 277
Inge, W. R., 25, 375
Initiation ceremonies, 268
Innominate bone, 110 f.
Insectivora, 55–56
Instinct, 21
Institution, social, 268, 281, 313–318
Instruction, 21
Intelligence, 22, 300–304, 322, 323, 357
Intelligent thought, 22
Interdependence, economic, 314, 317–318
Interosseus membrane, 154, 155

Interspinous ligaments, 89
Intervertebral discs, 89, 92
Intromission, 258, 259
Involution, 358
Iraq, 368
Ischial callosities, 115, 254
  spine, 113, 119
  tuberosities, 113, 117, 119
Ischium, 110 f.
Isoimmunization, 248
Israel, 368
Itani, J. S., 273, 375

j

Jackals, 202
Java, 80, 125, 343, 344, 347
Jaw, *see* Mandible
Jay, Phyllis, 285
Jebel Irhoud, 345, 368
Jerison, H. J., 233, 375
Joints, acromioclavicular, 138, 140
  crural, 128
  sternoclavicular, 139, 140
Jurassic, 36

k

Kangaroo, 34, 90, 91
Kanjera, 345, 352, 368
Kawai, M., 281, 287, 375
Keesing, F. M., 277, 287, 375
Keith, A., 123, 351, 377
Kinsey, A. C., 254, 375
Kinship, 282–284
Kluckhohn, C., 286, 375
Knowledge, 269–271
Koenigswald, G. H. R. von, 337, 343,
  344, 381
Köhler, W., 295, 375
Kohts, N., 237, 375
Kortlandt, A., 227, 294, 306, 319, 375
Krantz, G. S., 103, 375
Krapina, 186, 345, 368
Kroeber, A. L., 286, 375
Kromdraai, 135, 151, 152, 345, 369
Kummer, H., 278, 280, 376
Kurt, F., 278, 280, 376
Kuypers, H. G. J. M., 71, 77, 78, 376

l

Labia, 44, 255, 256
La Chapelle, 81, 123, 317, 345, 367
La Ferrassie, 135, 167
La Quina, 367
Lactation, 253
Lagomorpha, 198–200
Lagothrix, 63
Lancaster, J. B., 275, 285, 376
Lancelet, *see Amphioxus*
Laryngeal sacs, 186
Larynx, 186, 309–311
Law, 318
Leach, E. R., 315, 376
Leakey, L. S. B., 125, 135, 146, 151,
  173, 195, 331, 344, 346, 372, 376
Learning, 19 f., 49, 251, 271, 272, 300,
  301, 322
Lee, R. B., 275, 376
Leg, 125–128
Lemniscal system, 73, 74
Lemuriformes, 62
Lemuroidea, 60–62, 92, 127, 189, 190,
  194, 221, 248
Lemurs, *see* Lemuroidea
Leontocebus, 63, 239
Lerner, I. M., 23, 376
Lever, arm, 152–154
  foot, 128–130, 136
  mandible, 180, 181
Lewis, G. E., 198, 329, 330, 374, 376
Lienhardt, R. G., 325
Life span, 247, 265–271, 280, 356
Limbs, 64 f., 108–109
  fore, 138 f.
  hind, 90, 91, 108 f.
  proportions, 109–111
Lineage, evolutionary, 79
Linton, R., 285, 325
Lips, 172, 210, 236, 310
Lip-smacking, 311
Load line, foot, 129–132, 136
  head, 98–102
  leg, 127
Locomotion, 2, 64, 108 f.
Locomotor classification, 64 f.
Lorises, *see* Lorisioidea
Lorisiformes, 62

Lorisioidea, 62
Lowe, C. van Riet, 205, 376
Lumbar region, 93
Lymph, 17

m

Macaca, 63, 93, 96, 97, 112, 132, 143, 147, 150, 191, 197, 199, 216, 223, 231, 239, 247, 254, 281
Macaques, see Macaca
Magoun, H. M., 51, 376
Makapansgat, 146, 151, 345, 369
Malar bone, 211, 213
Malinowski, B., 325
Malthus, T. R., 8, 9, 376
Mammae, 48
Mammalia, 34, 176, 233
Mammals, Arctic, 17
    jaws of, 40 f., 176 f.
    meat, 173, 174, 203, 280
    See also Mammalia
Man, early, see Homo erectus
    modern, 100, 351 f.
    subspecies of modern, 352–354
Man-apes, see Australopithecus
Mandible, 176 f., 211, 261
    condyles, 177, 179–181
    corpus, 183
    human, 181 f.
    ramus, 179–181
    torus, 185–187
Mangabey, see Cercocebus
Manipulation, 78, 138 f., 293, 294, 297, 357
Manubrium, 139
Manus, 157–161
Marine organisms, 17
Markgraf, 331
Marmosets, see Callithrix
Marriage, 268–270, 278, 283
Marsupials, see Marsupialia
Marsupialia, 34
Martin, C. J., 39, 376
Mason, A. S., 46, 205, 376
Mason, R. J., 379
Mastication, 40, 176 f., 185
Masticatory apparatus, 170, 176 f., 207, 210–213
Mastoid process, 102, 211

Mauer, 345, 368
Maxillae, 177, 211, 213
Mayr, E., 18, 29, 33, 277, 376
McCown, T. D., 123, 351, 377
Mediating mechanisms, 26
Mednick, L. W., 121, 377
Meganthropus, 344
Melanesians, see Man, subspecies of modern
Melanocytes, 243
Memory, 50, 77, 203, 293, 297–300, 342
    conceptual, 299
    experimental, 298, 299
    word, 299, 300
Menarche, 247, 252, 260, 263, 266, 267, 269
Mendelian population, see Deme
Menopause, 270
Menstrual cycle, 46, 47, 252
Mentifacts, 289, 291
Mesopithecus, 192, 193, 281
Mesozoic, 36
Metabolic rate, 43
Metacarpals, 162–164
Metallurgy, 207, 292
Metatarsals, 128, 134, 135
Mettler, F. A., 377
Migrations, 206, 353
Milk, 48
Milk teeth, see Dentition
Miller, G. S., 277, 377
Mills, J. R. E., 197, 377
Miocene, 36, 82, 151, 157, 192, 201, 235, 281, 330, 332, 333
Mishkin, M., 376
Modjokerto, 345, 368
Molars, 179–181, 189, 191, 196–198, 212
Molarization, 194-197
Moles, 56
Monkeys, 60 f., 131, 159–161, 189 f., 233
    New World (Platyrrhina, Ceboidea), 62–68
    Old World (Catarrhina, Cercapithecoidea), 62, 79, 256, 261
Monotremata, 34
Monotremes, see Monotremata
Montagna, W., 238, 239, 377
Montagu, M. F. Ashley, 31, 290, 373, 377

Montmaurin, 345, 367
Morphology, 13
Mortality rate, 48
Morton, D. J., 132, 133, 137, 377
Moskowitz, N., 72, 73, 378
Moss, M. L., 231, 377
Mount Carmel, 123, 345, 368
Mouth, 169, 170
Mucoperiosteum, 218, 219
Mugharet Es-Skhul, 368
Mugharet Et-Tabun, 368
Muscles, 2
  abdominal, 89, 95, 115
  abductor, 120, 127
  abductor pollicis, 162
  adductor, 120, 122
  adductor pollicis, 162
  biceps brachii, 122, 153
  biceps femoris, 116–118
  deltoid, 141, 144
  digastric, 309, 310
  erector spinae, 117, 119
  extensor, 115, 125, 153
  facial, 236
  flexor, 115, 125, 153
  gastrocnemius, 128
  geniohyoid, 308
  gluteus, maximus, 116–118, 121
    medius, 121, 122
    minimus, 121, 122
  hamstring, 116
  latissimus dorsi, 141, 147, 148
  levator ani, 105
  masseter, 177, 178, 183, 213
  nuchal, 89, 98–104, 234
  oblique, 120, 122
  pectoralis major, 139, 140, 148
  pectorales, 147, 148
  pterygoids, external, 177
    internal, 177
    lateral, 177, 179, 185
    medial, 177, 178, 183
  rectus, abdominis, 105
    femoris, 115, 117
  serratus, anterior, 139, 142, 144
    magnus, 139, 141
  soleus, 128
  sterno-mastoid, 102–104
  subscapularis, 151
  temporalis, 177, 178, 183, 210–213
  tongue, 175, 176, 309

trapezius, 139, 141, 142, 144
triceps brachii, 153
Mustache, 239
Mutation, 13
Mutation rate, 29
Muzzle, 56, 58, 98–100, 210, 219
Myotomes, 86, 169
Myths, 316–318

n

Nails, finger, 58, 133, 134
Napier, J. R., 6, 65, 66, 85, 100, 121,
    123, 125, 131, 134, 135, 146,
    151, 157, 160, 162, 163, 165,
    167, 234, 333, 336, 372, 376,
    377, 378
Napier, P. H., 6, 85, 378
Nasal cavity, 219, 309
  index, *see* Indices
Nasalis, 63
Natural selection, 10 f., 238, 268
Neandertal, 80, 123, 128, 135, 157, 345,
    350, 367
Neck, 97–104
Neopallium, 216, 223, 224
Neoteny, 30
Nerve cells, *see* Neurons
Nerves, optic, 75, 76, 229
Nervous system, central, 70
Neurocranium, 210, 212, 213, 230–235
Neurons, internuncial, 71
  motor, 71
  relay, 71–74
  sensory, 73–74
Newt, 86
Ngandong, 345, 368
Niah, 345, 352, 368
Nipples, 242, 255
Noback, C. R., 72, 73, 378
Nose, 210, 218–220
Nubility, 266, 268
Nuchal area, 98–104
  crest, 101, 212
  muscles, *see* Muscles, nuchal

o

Oakley, K. P., 85, 204, 205, 287, 378

Occam's razor, 327
Occipital bone, 211
  condyle, 98–104, 187
  lobe, 216, 224, 225
Occlusal plane, 178-181
Olduvai, 128, 134, 135, 146, 151, 164, 165, 173, 184, 201, 206, 335, 344, 345–348, 368, 369
Olfactory apparatus, 58, 175
  bulbs, 216, 220, 223, 229
  lobes, 58
  sense, 171–175
Oligocene, 36, 331
Ontogeny, 247 f.
Opossum, 34, 39
Oppenheimer, O., 182, 378
Opposability, hallux, 133–136
  pollex, 158–164
Optic chiasma, 75, 76
Orang utan, see Pongo
Orbits, 213, 217, 235
Oreopithecidae, 63
Oreopithecus, 334
Organ of corti, 221
Orgasm, 258-260
Os calcis, see Calcaneus
Os coxae, 110 f.
Osman Hill, W. C., 85
Os penis, see Baculum
Outbreeding, see Exogamy
Ovaries, 43, 44, 47
Ovey, C., 349, 378
Oviduct, 43
Ovulation, 43, 47, 252, 267
Oxnard, C. E., 144, 145, 146, 147, 154, 378

P

Pagi Island langur, see Simias
Paleozoic, 36
Paleocene, 36, 55
Pan, 61, 66, 79, 93, 94, 97, 100, 118, 126, 132, 133, 147, 149–151, 156, 158, 160, 186, 192, 193, 199, 217, 218, 231, 234, 237, 247, 250, 253, 263, 294, 298
Panting, 38, 242
Pantotheres, 36, 40

Papilla, 157, 174
Papio, 63, 69, 94, 97, 120, 159, 174, 193, 231, 253, 261, 263, 267, 272, 273, 278–280, 311, 333, 339
Parental care, 48
Parietal bone, 210, 211
  lobes, 224–228, 293, 297
Parturition, 253
Patas monkey, see Erythrocebus
Paws, 157
Pectoral girdle, 86, 138–147
Pedomorphosis, see Neoteny
Pei, W. C., 370
Peking man, 80, 125, 146, 152, 205, 347
Pelvic canal, see Birth canal
  girdle, 86, 97
Pelvis, 93, 105, 110 f., 334
Penfield, W., 224, 226, 297–300, 311, 312, 378, 379
Peninj, 345, 369
Penis, 256
Pentadactyly, 58, 157
Percept, 292–294
Perception, 53, 77, 162, 203, 215, 292–304, 356, 357
Permian, 36
Pes, 127–135
Petralona, 345, 367
Pfeiffer, J., 342, 366, 378
Phalangeal formula, 131
Phalanges, 64–70, 131, 157–165
Pharynx, 175, 309, 310
Phenotype, 12 f.
Phonation, 310
Pigs, 190
Pilbeam, D. R., 329, 331, 334, 335, 338, 366, 378, 381
Piriform lobe, 216, 220, 223, 224
Pithecanthropus erectus, 343
Pithecia, 63
Pitocin, see Hormone
Pituitary gland, 45, 229
Placenta, 46, 246–249
Placentalia, 34, 35
Placentals, see Placentalia
Plasticity, 18
  developmental, 15
Platypus, 34, 39
Platyrrhina, see Monkeys
Pleistocene, 30, 36, 82, 173, 201–206, 220, 233, 258, 343

Pliocene, 36, 82, 182, 192, 201, 202, 281, 333, 334, 343
Pocock, R. I., 253, 256, 378
Pollex, 158–165
Polyak, S., 76, 85, 378
Polyandry, 277
Polygamy, 267
Polynesians, see Man
Pongidae, 63, 79, 189 f., 233
Ponginae, 63, 79
Pongo, 66, 79, 100, 146, 147, 151, 152, 158, 160, 218, 231, 234, 239, 247, 263, 273, 276
Posture, 86 f., 221, 222
  erect, 65, 70, 121
Preadaptation, 84, 85, 334, 335
Precision grip, 160–163
Prediction, 52, 203
Predmosti, 367
Prefrontal area, 225–227
Pregnancy, see Gestation
Premolars, 189, 191, 194–196, 212
Presbytis, 63, 65, 97, 125, 149–151, 193, 273
Primate, 55 f.
  chiridia, 133
  foot, 127–135
  hand, 157–161, 172
  jaw, 177 f.
  locomotion, 64 f.
  perception, see Perception
  troop, 271–276, 278–280
  See also Classification
Problem-solving, 52
Proboscis monkey, see Nasalis
Proconsul, 79–83, 125, 126, 146, 149–151, 156, 157, 191–193, 211, 235, 331, 332, 334
  africanus, 100, 151, 156, 160, 161, 234
  nyanzae, 151
Prognathism, 182, 210–213
Progress, biological, 24–28, 34 f.
  technological, 291, 292, 355–360
Pronation, 154, 155
Pronograde, 159
Propliopithecus, 331, 332
Proprioceptors, 73, 340
Prosimii, 62, 65, 194, 218
Ptilocerus, 114, 180, 195
Ptyalin, 41, 199

Puberty, 252, 264, 266
Pubic hair, 239–240, 255, 265
  symphysis, 94, 113
Pubis, 110 f.
Pulvinar, 228
Pygathrix, 63
Pygmies, 353
Pyramidal system, 71

q

Quadrupedalism, 65
Quaternary, 36

r

Radcliffe-Brown, A. R., 285
Radiation, cosmic, 14, 30
  evolutionary, 34, 55 f.
Radius, 147, 153–156
Ramapithecus punjabicus, 63, 70, 79–83, 121, 182, 192, 263, 329 f., 369
Rasmussen, T. B., 226, 378, 379
Rats, 22
Reason, 343
Receptor, 26, 169, 209 f.
  chemo-, 170, 210, 218–220
  contact, 170
  distance, 170
  heat, 39
  mechano-, 170, 220–223
  photo-, 170, 210, 214–218
  tactile (somasthetic), 134–135
Reflexes, conditioned, 303, 311
Religion, 314–318
Rensch, B., 22, 233, 301, 379
Reproductive behavior, see Sexual behavior
  economy, 42
  potential, 249, 250
  processes, 246 f.
  rate, 249, 250
Reptiles, 35, 43
  jaw, 40
Respiration rate, 38
Reticular system, 73, 74
Retina, 58, 76, 215
Rhinarium, 56, 218

Rhinencephalon, 171
Rhinopithecus, 63, 65
Rhodesian man, 128
Ribs, 95–97
Right-handedness, 312
Rites de passage, 268, 283
Ritual, 314–318
Roberts, L., 224, 297–300, 311, 312, 378
Robinson, J. T., 97, 121, 195, 205, 208, 234, 262, 330, 336, 338, 371, 379
Roe, A., 203, 295, 320, 321, 373, 379
Romer, A., 37, 40, 379
Rosenblueth, A., 5, 342, 379
Rosvold, H. E., 376
Rowe, A., 33
Ruminants, 198

S

Saccopastore, 368
Sacculus, 221, 222
Sacrum, 94, 95
Saddle joint, 162, 163
Sade, D. S., 276, 379
Sagittal crest, 101, 184, 211, 212, 261
Sahlins, M. D., 285, 379
Saimiri, 63
Saki, *see Pithecia*
Saliva, 41, 199
Salt, 17, 275
Saltation, 65
Sanction, 314, 318
Sangiran, 344, 345, 368
Savanna baboon, *see Papio*
Scapula, 138–147
Scent glands, 46, 242
Schaller, G. B., 172, 259, 379
Schenkel, R., 305, 379
Schepers, G. W. H., 151, 152, 371
Schlosser, M., 332, 379
Schultz, A. H., 93, 94, 95, 96, 100, 107, 109, 110, 112, 115, 117, 119, 120, 125, 126, 128, 147, 157, 159, 172, 197, 199, 247, 249, 261, 306, 380
Sciatic notch, 113, 119
Scrotum, 256

Secondary sexual character, 119, 260–265
Seeds, 171
Selection pressure, 15, 182
Self-consciousness, -awareness, 319–321, 362, 363
-discipline, 318–321
Sematic characters, 236–243, 255
Semi-circular canals, 221, 222
Sense organ, *see* Receptor
Sex, 246 f.
Sex hormones, *see* Hormones
Sexual behavior, 257–260, 275, 276, 281–283
dimorphism, 190, 191, 204, 260–265, 267, 334
dominance, 239, 261–265, 273–275
maturity, 247, 252–255, 260–263, 266–270
receptivity, 204, 257, 260
reproduction, 13, 246 f.
selection, 261–265
skin, 253–256, 275
Shanidar, 345, 368
Shivering, 38
Shock, N. W., 264, 380
Shoulder girdle, *see* Pelvic girdle
Shrews, *see Sorex*
elephant, *see Elephantulus*
marsh, 56
otter, 56
tree, *see Tupaia*
Siamangs, *see Symphalangus*
Sicher, H., 185, 186, 187, 373
Signaling, 304–308
Silurian, 36
Simian shelf, 185–187
Simias, 63
Simons, E. L., 183, 329, 330, 331, 334, 335, 338, 366, 378, 380, 381
Simpson, G. G., 26, 33, 40, 321, 342, 381
Singa, 345, 368
Sitting position, 91, 92, 115
Sinuses, 231
Sivertsen, E., 48, 380
Siwalik Hills, 345, 369
Skin, 210, 238–243
Skin color, 31, 243
Skull form, 178, 209 f.

Sloan, R. E., 57, 382
Small toe, 130–137
Smell, see Olfactory sense
Snakes, 176
Snub nosed langur, see Rhinopithecus
Social animals, 20, 304
  bonding, 280–285, 313–321
  institutions, see Institution
  organization, 266, 272
  primates, 271–276, 278–282
  structure, 203, 204, 271–276, 279–285, 339
  survivals, 276
Socifacts, 288, 289
Soft palate, 309, 310
Sorex, 55, 56
Sound, see Hearing
South Africa, 368, 369
Specialization, 30
  arboreal, 58, 64–69, 70–74
  terrestrial, 69–70
Speciation, 336
Speech, 203, 223, 289, 296, 307–313, 363
  areas, 228, 297, 311, 312
Spermatogenesis, 256
Sperry, R. W., 303, 312, 363, 381
Spider monkeys, see Ateles
Spinous processes, 89, 92, 95
Spuhler, J. N., 308, 381
Spy, 367
Squirrel Monkey, see Saimiri
Stature, 233, 262–264
Steatopygia, 258
Steinheim, 345, 348. 349, 351, 367
Sterkfontein, 125, 146, 151, 205, 329, 345. 369
Sternum, 89, 95, 139
Stewart, T. D., 381
Stomach, 198, 199
Straus, W. L., 97, 123, 125, 198, 200, 327, 334, 381
Subcutaneous fat, 39, 203. 238
Success, 25
Suckling, 252
Sulci, 226, 228
  central, 216, 229
  lunate (simian), 216, 224
  rhinal, 216, 223, 224
Sun tanning, 18

Superego, 319
Supination, 154, 155
Supraorbital torus, 178, 213, 218, 349
Supraspinous ligaments, 89
Swamp-apes, see Oreopithecidae
Swanscombe, 348–350, 367
Swartkrans, 125, 184, 345, 348, 368, 369
Sweating, 17
Sweat glands, 38
Symphalangus, 79
Symphysis, mandibular, 185
  pubic, 120
Szwarcbart, M. K., 376

t

Tail, 58, 65, 91, 92, 104–106
Talus, 128, 135
Tamarin, see Leontocebus
Tanner, J. M., 208, 269, 381
Tarsiers, see Tarsiiformes
Tarsiiformes, 60–62, 127
Tarsioidea, 62
Tarsal bones, 128
Tasmanians, 360
Taste, 174–176
  buds, 175, 210
Taung, 345, 369
Taxonomy, 338, 348, 351
  See also Definitions
Technology, 356–361
Teeth, 2, 40, 176, 236
  See also Dentition and Tooth
Telanthropus capensis, 329, 330
Temperature regulation, see Thermoregulation
Temporal bone, 210, 211
  line, 101, 177, 178, 211–213
  lobe, 77, 216, 223–225
Termites, 164, 295
Ternifine, 165, 345, 347, 368
Terrestrial adaptations, 69, 70
  bipedalism, 70
  quadrupedalism, 69
Territory, 272, 273, 282
Tertiary, 36
Testes, 256
Testut, L., 179, 381

Thalamus, 225, 228, 229
Thermoregulation, 27, 36, 221, 222, 239, 242, 243
Theropithecus, 63, 69
Thompson, W. D'Arcy, 381
Thorax, 92–97, 142
Thorpe, W. H., 362, 365, 366, 381
Threat, 273, 274
Thumb, *see* Pollex *and* Opposability
Tibia, 127, 128
Titi, *see Callicebus*
Tobias, P. V., 146, 231, 336, 337, 343, 344, 376, 381, 382
Tongue, 174–176, 210, 309, 310
Tool carrying, 164
  making, 205, 207, 289
  modification, 164
  using, 164
Tools, 182, 356–361
  bone, 165, 202, 203
  stone, 164, 165, 202, 203, 291, 340, 341
Tooth crowding, 182
  eruption, 197, 198
  occlusion, 196, 197
  structure, 187 f.
Totem, 317
Touch, *see* Receptor
Trachea, 309
Tradition, 316
Tree climbing, 57 f.
  shrew, *see Tupaia and Ptilocerus*
Triassic, 35, 36
Trinil, 345, 347, 368
Trochanter, 125
Trochlea, 149, 150, 152
Troop size, 273, 276, 278
Trunk, 93
Tupaia, 56, 60–62, 143, 157, 158, 215, 216, 223
Tupaioidea, 62, 98
Turbinal bones, 218
Tusks, 41, 190
Tylor, E. B., 287, 382

u

Uakari, *see Cacajao*
Ulna, 151–157

Ultraviolet rays, 243
Ungulates, 109, 139, 171
Unlearned behavior, 20
Uterus, 43, 44, 246–249, 256, 260
Utricle, 221, 222

v

Vagina, 44, 254, 256, 260
Van Valen, L., 57, 382
Variation, 9 f., 313
Versatility, 18
Vertebrae, 89
  cervical, 95
  coccygeal, 104–105
  lumbar, 93, 94
  thoracic, 93, 94
  sacral, 95, 96
Vertebral column, 89
Vértesszöllös, 205, 345, 347, 368
Vestigial characters, 200
Vibrissae, *see* Carpal vibrissae
Victoriapithecus, 281
Viscera, 105
Vision, 171, 214–218
  binocular, 74
  color, 58, 171
  stereoscopic, 57 f., 75, 215, 293
Visual fields, 75
  system, 26, 74
Vitamin D, 243
Viviparity, 42
Vocal cords, *see* Larynx
Volar (friction) pads, 133, 135, 136, 157, 158, 242
Vowels, 310

w

Walking, 118–123
Wallace, Alfred Russel, 8, 9
Walls, G. L., 382
Washburn, S. L., 93, 107, 117, 118, 172, 261, 267, 271, 279, 285, 354, 356, 372, 382
Weapons, 194, 261
Weidenreich, F., 94, 101, 125, 146, 188, 217, 344, 382

Weight, 261–263
Weiner, J. S., 208, 219, 382
Whalebone, 41
Whales, 88, 232
  killer, 202
  toothed, 41
White, L. A., 286, 382
White, R. W., 49, 382
Whitehead, A. N., 366, 382
Whyte, L. L., 14, 32, 382
Wiener, N., 379
Wisdom tooth, 197
Wolves, 202
Woo, J. K., 344, 383
Woollard, H. H., 215, 383
Woolly monkey, *see Lagothrix*
Woolly spider monkey, *see Brachyteles*
Worship, ancestor, 317
Writing, 300, 311
Wynne-Edwards, V. C., 272, 275, 383

y

Yayo, 345, 369
Yellow body, *see* Corpus luteum
Yellow spot, *see* Fovea centralis
Young, C. C., 370
Young, J. Z., 54, 85, 245
Young, R. W., 231, 377

z

Ziegler, A. C., 166, 383
Zinjanthropus, 336
Zuckerman, S., 46, 100, 234, 252, 370, 373, 383
Zygomatic arch, 177, 178, 213

Robert J. Braidwood and Gordon R. Willey, editors

COURSES TOWARD URBAN LIFE: Archeological Considerations of Some Cultural Alternates

Traces the history of man from primitive food-collecting societies to the threshold of the urban food-producing civilizations. "A rare and important achievement."—*American Anthropologist.* Robert J. Braidwood is Professor of Old World Archeology, University of Chicago, and Gordon R. Willey is Professor of New World Archeology, Harvard University. Viking Fund Publications in Anthropology No. 32. 384 pp.

Karl Butzer

ENVIRONMENT AND ARCHEOLOGY: An Introduction to Pleistocene Geography

An original and comprehensive introduction to the methods and techniques basic to Pleistocene research and their application in reconstructing physical environments and man-land relationships in prehistory. The author is Professor of Anthropology and Geography in the University of Chicago. 528 pp., 92 ills.

Sherwood L. Washburn, editor

SOCIAL LIFE OF EARLY MAN

The world's leading experts summarize what is known of prehistoric man's social relationships and behavior, demonstrating their complex roots in the evolutionary process. "As complete a presentation of all the factors of early humanness as can be found between two covers."—*American Behavioral Scientist.* The author is Professor of Anthropology in the University of California at Berkeley. Viking Fund Publications in Anthropology No. 31. 312 pp.

Robert A. Manners, editor

PROCESS AND PATTERN IN CULTURE: Essays in Honor of Julian H. Steward

Essays on culture change, cultural patterns and regularities, and socio-cultural integration, developing the main themes of Steward's contribution to anthropology. The editor is Professor of Anthropology, Brandeis University. 480 pp.

Stuart Piggott

ANCIENT EUROPE: From the Beginnings of Agriculture to Classical Antiquity

A readable and copiously illustrated introduction to the main lines of European prehistory, from the first agricultural communities (in about 7,000 B.C.) to the spread of Roman civilization, and from the shores of the Atlantic to the Urals and Caucasus. The author is Professor of Archeology in the University of Edinburgh. 256 pp.

J. S. Slotkin, editor

READINGS IN EARLY ANTHROPOLOGY

An enormous and enormously valuable body of source material setting forth the pre-scientific frameworks upon which modern anthropology is based and the changing views and historical antecedents of the scientific study of man, from Paul of Tarsus and other New Testament writers to the professionalization of all fields of anthropology in the mid-19th century. The author is late of the University of Chicago. Viking Fund Publications in Anthropology No. 40. 532 pp.

Jan Vansina

THE ORAL TRADITION:

A Study in Historical Methodology

This book explores the possibility of reconstructing the history of non-literate peoples from their oral traditions by combining the techniques of linguistic anthropology with those of social and cultural anthropology. "The most significant work written on the relation of oral traditions to history.... Indispensable, and should be read by all anthropologists."—*American Anthropologist*. The author is Professor of History, University of Wisconsin. 222 pp.

Max Gluckman

POLITICS, LAW AND RITUAL IN TRIBAL SOCIETY

An authoritative introduction to political anthropology, providing a survey of the role of law, ritual and divination in tribal societies. The author is Professor of Social Anthropology, Victoria University, Manchester. 352pp., 28 plates.

A. L. Kroeber

A ROSTER OF CIVILIZATIONS AND CULTURE

The last work of this distinguished scholar who, using the tools of his own science, describes and compares the major units of culture in an essay that is as important as the familiar and spectacular attempts of Spengler and Toynbee along similar lines. "A significant legacy to the profession."—*American Anthropologist.* The author is late of the University of California at Berkeley. Viking Fund Publications in Anthropology No. 33. 84 pp.

Raymond Firth and B. S. Yamey, editors

CAPITAL, SAVING AND CREDIT IN PEASANT SOCIETIES:

Studies from Asia, Oceania, the Caribbean, and Middle America

This book is a major effort to present what anthropologists have directly observed of the economic operations of the communities which they have so closely studied. Raymond Firth, Dept. of Anthropology, and B. S. Yamey, Professor of Economics, both in University of London. 393 pp.

UNESCO International Committee for Social Sciences Documentation

INTERNATIONAL BIBLIOGRAPHY OF SOCIAL AND CULTURAL ANTHROPOLOGY

The Bibliography lists and classifies all important published contributions, from all countries, in all languages, and whatever the form in which they appear. "Most scholarly and comprehensive." —*Sol Tax, Professor of Anthropology, University of Chicago.* Compiled by the UNESCO International Committee for Social Sciences Documentation.

James B. Hendry

THE SMALL WORLD OF KHANH HAU

A concentrated study of the economic structure, relationships and life of a Vietnamese river village, with a special view to its adaptability and resistance to economic change. The author is an economist with the International Bank for Development and Reconstruction, Washington, D.C. 352 pp.

Conrad M. Arensberg and Arthur H. Niehoff

INTRODUCING SOCIAL CHANGE:

A Manual for Americans Overseas

A guide to the understanding of other cultures, value systems and ways of approaching problems, designed for all Americans living and working overseas; a companion volume to *A Casebook of Social Change*. Conrad Arensberg is Professor of Anthropology in Columbia University, and Arthur Niehoff is Senior Scientist in George Washington University. 214pp.

Arthur H. Niehoff

A CASEBOOK OF SOCIAL CHANGE

A comprehensive book of readings on development problems, using the case history method to assess and evaluate actual efforts at innovation in underdeveloped countries; a companion volume to *Introducing Social Change*. 256 pages.